Gerhard Sch

THE DYNAMICS OF NUTRITION

Michael Reiners
May 22, 1989

2104 **THE DYNAMICS OF NUTRITION** by Gerhard **SCHMIDT**. Translated by G. Karnow.

Using the "wealth of suggestions, indications and guidelines of all kinds relating to nutrition" which "are interspersed throughout his (Steiner's) whole life's work", Dr. Schmidt has been able to construct a comprehensive guide to nutrition in the light of Spiritual Science. The author's main goal "has been to develop these fundamental conceptions of Rudolf Steiner's investigations into nutrition. We have attempted to weave into this picture the isolated elaborations, indications, and suggestions which can be found in his work."
243pp. 6x9" Softbound $10.50

Gerhard Schmidt, M.D.

THE DYNAMICS OF NUTRITION

**The Impulse of Rudolf Steiner's Spiritual Science
for a New Nutritional Hygiene**

An Introduction

BIO-DYNAMIC LITERATURE
Wyoming, Rhode Island 02898

Originally published in 1975 in German with the title *Dynamische Ernährungslehre, Band I*. The English translation, done by Gerald F. Karnow, M.D., has been made available through the Swiss publisher, Proteus-Verlag, CH-9000 St. Gallen. The Swiss edition was sponsored by the Consumers' Association for the promotion of bio-dynamic agriculture and nutritional hygiene in Switzerland.

ISBN 0–938250–00–0

Original cover design by Walter Roggenkamp, done in English by Maria Ladd-Motch

Printed in the United States of America

TABLE OF CONTENTS

INTRODUCTION   1

Chapter 1

BASIC QUESTIONS OF NUTRITION: THE EXPAN-   5
SION OF NUTRITIONAL RESEARCH THROUGH
RUDOLF STEINER'S SPIRITUAL SCIENCE
Nutrition as a Question of Consciousness 5; An Incomplete Image of
Man and Nature 6; Nutrition Today 6; Development of the Modern
Science of Nutrition 7; The Birth of the Science of Nutrition 9;
Dissatisfaction with the Materialistic Theories of Nutrition 10; The
Necessity for New Methods of Research 11; Natural Laws Apply Only to
the Inorganic World 12; The World of Formative Forces 13; Reality of
Soul and Spirit 13; Catabolic and Metabolic Processes in Man 14; The
Concepts of Human Health and Disease 14; The Task of Nutrition and
Dietetics 15; Changes and Limitations of Modern Scientific View Points
15; Persistance of Old Thought Habits 16; The New Image of Man 16; New
Standards of Quality 17; The Four Members of Man and the Four-fold
Stream of Nutrition 17; The Function of the Members of Man in
Nutrition 18; Nutrition Appropriate to Man 20.

Chapter 2

WHAT IS THE PURPOSE OF NUTRITION?   21
Scale and Thermometer in Nutritional Research 21; The Constitution of
Food Substances as Measure of Quality 22; The Law of Energy and Its
Limitations 22; The Biochemical Individuality of Man 24; Destruction
and Resurrection of Matter in Man 24; Nutrition as Resistance Against
Nature 24.

Chapter 3

GENERAL ASPECTS OF THE PHYSIOLOGY OF   27
NUTRITION
Man and the Realms of Nature in Nutrition 27; The Four Steps in Diges-
tion, Mouth Digestion 30; The Overcoming of Foreign Nature in
Nutrition 32; Stomach Digestion 34; Digestive Processes in the Small

Intestine 35; Rhythmic Events in the Intestine, Significance of the Spleen
37; The Rhythmic Organization, The 24-Hour Rhythm 39; Absorption 42;
Devitalization and Revitalization of Nourishment 44; The Humanization
of Nutrients, The Role of the Liver-Gall Activity 47; Effects of Cholesterol
49; Carbohydrate Metabolism 50; Warmth as Carrier of the Ego-
organization 51; Significance of Intestinal Peristalsis 54; Polarity of the
Human Configuration 56; Significance of Intestinal Flora 57; Aspects of
Protein and Fat Digestion, Fermentation of Carbohydrates 59; Quantity
and Quality 61; Substantiality and Force Activity 72; Origin and Goal of
Nutrition, Earthly and Cosmic Nutrition 75.

Chapter 4

SMELL AND TASTE: SPICES AND AROMATIC SUBSTANCES

81

Introductory Viewpoints 81; The Significance of Aroma 81; Taste
Processes, The Problem of Spices 88.

Chapter 5

RHYTHM IN NUTRITION

93

The 24-Hour Rhythm of the Liver 95; Results of Modern Rhythm
Research 97; The Significance of Rhythm for Human Health 99.

Chapter 6

TEMPERATURE IN NUTRITION

101

Introductory Viewpoints 101; Physiology of the Sense of Temperature
101; The Warmth-Man 102; Warmth Processes in Man, The Caloric
Theory 104; Handling Temperature in Nutrition 105; The Essence of
Warmth and Coldness 106; Modern Thermal Technology in Nutrition
107; Drying and Roasting 110.

Chapter 7

RAW AND COOKED FOODS

113

Bircher-Benner's Discovery of Raw Foods 113; Spiritual Scientific
Aspects 114; The Significance of Soup 117.

Chapter 8

FOODS-DIETARY SUBSTANCES—MEDICINAL SUB-   119
STANCES
Fundamental Aspects 119; Relationship of the Plant to Threefold Man 120; The Medicinal Plant 121; Food and Dietary Substances 122; Table Salt 122; The Mineral 124; Further Viewpoints 126; Poison Formation 127; Character of Food and Medicinal Substances 129.

Chapter 9

NUTRITION FROM THE REALM OF PLANTS, NUTRI-   131
TION FROM THE REALM OF ANIMALS
Origin of Modern Vegetarianism 131; Expansion Through Spiritual Science 133; Vegetarian or Animal Nutrition? 136; Education 137; Results of Modern Nutritional Science 138; Rationale Through Modern Spiritual Science 140; Meat Nutrition 141; Milk and Milk Products 143.

Chapter 10

NUTRITION AND SPIRITUAL LIFE   145
Historical Aspects 145; Aspects of Modern Nutritional Science, The Significance of Phosphorus 146; Salt-Silica-Uric Acid-Sugar 149; The Carrot as Root Food 151; Red Beets and Horse Radish 155; Potatoes and Alcohol 155; Coffee and Tea 156; Spiritual Scientific Considerations Freed of Dogmatism and Eccentricity 159.

Chapter 11

NUTRITION AND SOUL LIFE   161
The Problem 161; Results of Modern Behavioral Physiology 162; Spiritual Scientific Aspect 164; Instinct, Drive, and Craving 165; "Not the Food, but the Soul Nourishes" 167; Fasting, Curative Fasting, Asceticism 168; Contemporary Aspects 170; Transformation of Nutritional Habits 171; Hunger and Thirst 173; The Table Prayer 176; Interactions Between Physical Substance and the Soul-Spiritual of Man 177; The New Image of Man in Earthly and Cosmic Nutrition 179.

Chapter 12

COMMUNITY-BUILDING THROUGH THE MEAL   183

Nutrition as Community-building Force 183; Historical Aspects 183; The
Community-building Effect of Certain Substances and Dietary Customs
185; The "Bone of Contention Character" of Our Nutrition 187; The
Craving for Enjoyment as Uniting Factor 188; Collectivization of
Nutrition, Problems of Modern Community Food Supply 188.

Chapter 13

THE HISTORY OF HUMAN NUTRITION   191

Introductory Aspects 191; Origins of Nutrition 192; Origin of Milk
Nourishment and the Three Phases of Its Development 194; Origin of
Plant and Animal Nutrition in Lemurian and Atlantean Times 194;
Demeter 196; From Hoe to Plow 199; The "Neolithic Revolution" 202;
Nutrition in Historical Time 203; Spiritual Scientific Aspects, the Seven
States of Nutrition 204; Wine and Bread 208; Future Aspects of Nutrition,
Working with Nature as Completed and as Becoming 211.

Chapter 14

THE DEVELOPMENT OF NUTRITION IN THE AGE OF   215
TECHNOLOGY. CONTEMPORARY NUTRITIONAL
HYGIENE

The Mechanization of the World Image in the Mirror of Nutrition 215;
Nutrition and Dietetics at the Threshold of the New Age 216; Nutrition
as Social Question, The Influence of Technology on Nutrition 218;
Objectification of the Concept of Quality 220; Symptoms of the
Contemporary Nutritional Situation 222; The Responsibility of Each
Individual 224.

CONCLUSION   227

WORKS CITED   229

INTRODUCTION

More than half a century has passed since Rudolf Steiner, the founder of modern Spiritual Science, developed a new knowledge of man and the world. Out of his Spiritual Science grew not only an expansion of the art of healing, a contemporary pedagogy, a fructification of natural science, and the foundation of a new method of agriculture, but also an expanded and renewed science of nutrition and hygiene. Rudolf Steiner did not give a cohesive "course on nutrition" as he did for numerous other fields; nevertheless, a wealth of suggestions, indications, and guidelines of all kinds relating to nutrition are interspersed throughout his whole life's work. In addition, he gave a number of isolated lectures which concern themselves specifically with the question of nutrition.

More important than the isolated remarks on nutrition are the often new and completely original thoughts related to nutrition. As fragmentary as it may appear in isolation, Rudolf Steiner developed a new and reality-based conception of the field of nutrition. In doing so he related—as he always did—to the scientific conceptions of his time. He extended these, however, and posited the whole problem upon a secure foundation. He was able to do this because he was in a position to burst the chains of knowledge which fettered humanity of the last centuries, thereby preparing a free field for the spiritual investigation of man and the world. This new freedom enables us to throw light upon questions and problems with which he himself did not deal, and which may even have developed since his time.

Consequently, the primary goal of our presentation has been to develop these fundamental conceptions of Rudolf Steiner's investigations into nutrition. We have attempted to weave into this picture the isolated elaborations, indications, and suggestions which can be found in his work. Then we concerned ourselves with a number of problems which resulted from the modern viewpoint of nutrition, and the research of modern science, specifically insofar as they verify the view of Rudolf Steiner or at least move in

1

this direction. We have pointed out and also established connections with several pioneers in the field of nutrition, who, before or after Rudolf Steiner's death, also broke new ground. This latter attempt has had to remain fragmentary to stay within the limits of the goal of this book. In our presentation we have tried to approach Rudolf Steiner's method of working. Consequently, many a reader may feel the lack of an expected systematic presentation, and instead will find here and there a repetition. However, it appears to be more appropriate to this subject matter to present it in a developing and descriptive manner, thereby opening this or that aspect until we have succeeded here and there to penetrate to the core of the matter.

In this endeavor the author wishes to express his gratitude for having been able to refer to many excellent presentations of these questions from other sources. What may justify the present undertaking is the attempt to make an extensive and complete examination of the problem, something which until now has not been done.

In the present volume it has been our task to examine the fundamental and general aspects of nutrition. Therefore we begin with the questions about the meaning and reality of nutrition, a sketch of the physiology of nutrition including the problems of rhythm and fragrance as well as the fundamental aspects of taking foods from the mineral, plant, and animal realms. Furthermore, we concern ourselves with the relationship of nutrition to human soul and spiritual life, with a rational understanding of the evaluation of uncooked and cooked foods, and with the differentiation of foodstuffs into remedies, dietary foods, and delicacies. Finally, a contribution to the social significance of nutrition and its developmental history suggests possibilities for a contemporary nutritional hygiene.

The problem of nutrition is today without a doubt exceedingly important. Through the stimulation of Spiritual Science it has become even more relevant. Rudolf Steiner himself said that it is "just the everyday things that are most difficult to be included into the spiritual life,—because eating and drinking are included only when we are able to follow why, in order to fulfill man's role in the world, we have to ingest physical substances in a rhythmical manner and what relationship these physical substances have to the spiritual life."[1]

Therewith we have broached the theme which will lead us into the considerations of the first chapter. For the unprejudiced reader of this book it will probably become clear, only after reading it, that a healthy further development of humanity in our time demands that a new light of consciousness illumine our conception of nutrition.

Finally, a few words about the title of our book, *The Dynamics of Nutrition*. Rudolf Steiner has often indicated that the substances we take up with our nourishment serve much more to stimulate and unfold activities in the organism than to serve as material deposits. "The primary concern is not with an arrangement of quantities of substances in metabolism, but rather, whether with foodstuffs we take up in us in a proper manner the vitality of forces (Lebendigkeit der Kraft)."[2] This expresses what the content of the teaching of a dynamic nutrition should be. Friedrich Boas has, in his *Dynamische Botanik*, made the fundamental attempt to present "the plant not only as form, not only as function, but as a center of effects and forces in nature."[3] He thereby established connections to Goethe and Alexander von Humboldt, and also to Lessing, who said: "In Nature everything is connected with everything, everything interweaves, everything interacts with everything, everything changes into the other." To look at such natural interactions was also the method by which Rudolf Steiner approached the problems of agriculture and nutrition, for, "in nature, in the World-Being in general, everything interacts."[4] Therewith Lessing's expression is significantly extended: "This dynamic law is valid not only in nature, not only on the earth." Actually such interaction occurs "in the World-Being in general," that is, between the terrestial and extra-terrestial realms. The transformations occur not only with terrestial substances and forces, but also in the realm of the supersensible, the formative forces. This interaction is all-inclusive; it encompasses Earth and Cosmos.

Without this knowledge of the Spiritual Science of Rudolf Steiner, neither a modern agriculture nor a contemporary nutritional hygiene is conceivable. In this sense we deal here with a dynamic nutrition as a foundation for a new science of the interaction of nourishment with man. In its basic principles, as well as in many details, this has been developed by Rudolf Steiner. What remains, however, is to make the existing building blocks visible, and to put them together, to allow the impressive edifice to appear with increasing clarity.[5]

Chapter 1

BASIC QUESTIONS OF NUTRITION: THE EXPANSION OF NUTRITIONAL RESEARCH THROUGH RUDOLF STEINER'S SPIRITUAL SCIENCE

Nutrition as a Question of Consciousness

Anyone who concerns himself with what is happening in nutrition today will hardly be able to avoid encountering its problems. Only a century ago, human beings chose their nutrition out of a relatively certain instinctual feeling. They had no serious problems with food or digestion. This state of affairs has changed drastically. The security which was felt towards nature as a provider of nourishment, a trust in the foods, has been replaced by an increasing uncertainty, even a mistrust about whether the given or chosen nourishment corresponds to expectations or necessities. Modern man is not only concerned with the loss of instinct, not only with the loss of quality of food, but also with the feeling that the acquired knowledge cannot fully meet the demands of our time. The horizon of his consciousness needs to be expanded and deepened as he strives towards renewed certainty and the faculty of judgment. This is what the observer of the present encounters everywhere in the most manifold variations.

The situation in modern research in nutrition can also be considered a symptom of this development. What in the beginning of the century moved within well-defined limits has almost overstepped all bounds. The number of researchers and their publications is almost innumerable. The seemingly solved problems experience a continuing, uncontrollable expansion and complication. Details and specialization triumph to an unimaginable extent and threaten to exceed all bounds. It is practically impossible for one person to gain an overview. And yet, behind all this one can sense the same

5

discomfort, the same uncertainty, and the same fearful question: Do we still have man in our research? Can we really approach nature,—or do both men and nature disappear into vagueness?

An Incomplete Image of Man and Nature

Karl Marx, in the last century, believed to have solved the riddle of man and nature and their interrelationships when he wrote: "The force of work is nothing else than transformed material substance in man. Metabolism demands that nature become humanized, and man become naturalized." With such conceptions Theoretical Materialism could be established. From it originated the world-wide, but useless, socialist experiment of establishing a new political and economic order. With this the image of man could only rigidify and nature be obscured even further. Finally, one had to admit "that no image of nature as reality stands behind natural scientific medicine,"[1]— thus not behind the study of nutrition. Dorr wrote: "This means that the natural scientific data are all correct, but that the image of man based upon these data is still erroneous."[2] No image of nature—no image of man—a distressing result of modern science, and yet a true situation encouraging an exploration into new realms of knowledge.

The key to open the gate to such realms was already prepared by Goethe: "He who is not willing to get into his head the idea that spirit and matter, soul and body, thought and perception, will and movement, were, are, and will be necessary double ingredients of the universe, both demanding equal rights—which can therefore be considered God's representatives—he who cannot rise to this thought should have stopped thinking long ago." In other words, natural science without Spiritual Science can understand neither man nor nature.

Nutrition Today

A consideration of the present situation of nutrition reveals the following:
1. Increasing and varied food supplies in the civilized countries.
2. Deficient food supplies in the developing countries.
3. Changes of nutritional habits. Excessive nutrition and malnutrition, undernutrition and deficient nutrition.
4. As a consequence of this development, nutritionally related diseases are on the rise.
5. A growing uncertainty about the essentials of nutrition as an expression of a longing for a new consciousness and increased responsibility.
6. Admission of an inadequate image of man and nature.
This symptomatology, to be considered in detail later, is a consequence of

6

the nineteenth century world view. Let us attempt to clarify this point with a few details concerning the study of nutrition.

Development of the Modern Science of Nutrition

The development of modern nutritional research began in the middle of the last century. A significant change occurred between 1840 and 1860. While at first in France, Lavoisier, Magendie, and Claud Bernard initiated a physical and chemical approach to physiology, this change was highlighted in central Europe by the remarkable Johann Müller (1801-1858). Having studied Goethe's natural scientific works in his youth with enthusiasm, he continued to be impressed by these works until the end of his life. His *Physiologie des Menschen* (1834-1840) shows a turn towards observation and experiment and opened the gate towards a mechanistic interpretation of the life processes. This mechanistic interpretation was then continued and elaborated by his students Virchow, Helmholtz, and Dubois-Reymond. R. Shrylock is correct in remarking in his *Entwicklung der Modernen Medizin* that this change "led consequently to a scientific scepticism, or else total materialism." [3]

Ludwig Feuerbach died in the same year in which Dubois-Reymond died, 1872. He was the thinker who proclaimed the end of philosophy, and also coined the well-known expression, "Man is what he eats." Although he was in no way a researcher in the field of nutrition, this conviction emerged from his completely one-sided, materialistic way of thinking. Originally an adherent of Hegel's idealistic philosophy, he later designated Hegel's views as fantastic remnants of belief in a transcendental creator. With his book *Das Wesen des Christentums* (1871) he established his atheism and materialism by postulating that the material, sense-perceptible world constitutes the only reality. As supersensible as they may appear, our consciousness and thinking are only the product of our brain. Matter is not the product of the spirit; instead, spirit itself is only the highest product of matter.

These views were to provide the philosophical support for materialism. They provided a rationale for Marx's and Engel's teachings which established political (historical) materialism. At the same time, however, these views became part and parcel of natural scientific thinking. Significantly, the birth of the science of nutrition occurred during this time and was therefore dominated by views which considered matter to be the only constituent of man and world—matter, however, whose essence was understood by no one.

Carl Voit, considered by many the founder of the modern study of nutrition, clearly points to the time period mentioned previously in his epoch-making inaugural speech "Concerning theories of nutrition of animal

7

organisms" (1868): "In delimiting the state of knowledge of our field in the 1840's we have to say . . . that theories of nutrition had not gone beyond the first beginnings. Nobody was able to say why we ate this or that substance, or why one organism maintains itself with meat, and another with the apparently very different hay. . ."

It is evident that in the 40's of the last century, a powerful, irresistible development began, which was entirely based upon the materialistic world view. This world view then determined the origin and development of the entire modern science of nutrition. Also in 1840 Liebig published his epoch-making work, *The Application of Organic Chemistry to Agriculture and Physiology*. Voit, in his inaugural speech, referred to this work: "For the science of nutrition Liebig's ideas were for a long time the guiding ideas and everything added in modern times has only been possible because of his achievements."

In this context it seems significant that Rudolf Steiner, during lectures in October 1917, pointed out that the middle years of the 19th century, especially the 40's, were an important period in the spiritual development of the European and American people—"at that time the peak development of materialistic intellect had been achieved on earth."[4]

We must not overlook, however, that this development resulted in a multitude of essential insights into problems of nutrition. Without them there would be no knowledge of proteins, fats, carbohydrates, minerals, vitamins. There would be no knowledge of the nutritive value of our foods, such as grains, milk, vegetables, spices, etc. Hardly anything would be known about fragrant substances, digestion and excretion, and so on.

On the other hand, we must not forget that this scientific study of nutrition was preceded by an instinctive knowledge about nutrition, whose high spiritual wisdom provided humanity with a secure foundation for millenia. This wisdom had disappeared in the course of time and could not renew itself, because humanity had lost the old dream-like insights into the spiritual connections of man, nature, and the cosmos. Instead, man developed the conscious intellectual capacities. This could not justifiably use old sources. And so in the beginning of the present time there remained at most only a traditional and frequently misunderstood, distorted knowledge of such relationships. These were easily contradicted by such men as Lavoisier, Liebig, or Dubois-Reymond. They were justified in doing this, because these fragments had become useless, created more obstacles than advances, and were actually in many ways invalid for modern man.

Such old insights, however, continued to trickle over into the 19th century and even inspired Goethe to develop his natural scientific approach. Rudolf Steiner then built on these concepts and developed them further into modern Spiritual Science.

The movements which came from Eastern cultures out of such old sources were, on the other hand, not suited to bring about the fructifications of Occidental thinking which Spiritual Science made possible. Their spiritual sources were long exhausted and the danger of dogmatization and sect formation connected with their views were unable to counter the advance of natural science. Whatever role the Eastern movements may play today in the realm of nutrition, it is to be understood more out of the longing of modern man for a spiritual understanding of the processes of nutrition than as the ability of these movements to fulfill these longings in a manner appropriate to our time. We will not concern ourselves with these movements, since a science of nutrition, based on Spiritual Science, which we have designated here as "dynamic nutrition," is in no way connected with them.

It is very different with movements based upon modern consciousness whose founders have made many significant contributions to modern nutrition. Among many are Max Bircher-Benner, Bunge, Ragnar Berg, Are Waerland, Hindhede, and also in our time many important scientists and physicians, for example, Kollath, Kuhl, Zabel, Heupke, and others, who have pointed out significant defects in the one-sidedly materialistic conceptions of nutrition. Finally, we have to include those personalities in medicine and science who are pioneers of a study of nutrition and hygiene based on Spiritual Science and to whom we will refer subsequently. The author is not only grateful for many indications from these personalities, but also for confirmation of the certainty that an inclusive presentation of nutrition as presented here answers a pressing necessity.

The Birth of the Science of Nutrition

When, in 1847, the four great scientists, Helmholtz, Dubois-Reymond, Brucke, and Ludwig, met in Berlin in order to "put physiology on a physical-chemical foundation and onto the same level as physics," their meeting actually signified a turning point in the history of humanity.

In Liebig's "Chemical Letters" we have an excellent presentation of this turning point from the chemical point of view. Liebig could be considered the first great scientist of nutrition, a chemist who applied himself to research into nutrition, metabolic processes, etc. Thereby he applied chemical thinking to human and animal digestive processes. He was especially fascinated by the presence of certain minerals in the organisms and applied his discoveries to soil and agriculture, introducing mineral fertilization. The physiology of nutrition was thus built on a foundation of physical-chemical methods of research. In this way, the "law of conservation of energy," postulated by Mayer and Helmholtz, became the foundation of the physiology of metabolism and led to the establishment of quantitative research methods as well as to the establishment of the calorie in the application of the laws of thermo-dynamics to the living organism. On this basis Voit developed the doctrine of the average caloric intake for the adult human as being 3,000 calories, consisting of 500 g carbohydrates, 118 g protein, and 56 g fat. On this same basis Rubner established his "Isodynamic Law." ("One hundred grams of fat provide the same energy as 230 grams of carbohydrates or 230 grams of protein.")

It is necessary to point to these aspects concerning the birth of the science of nutrition in order to clarify what the 20th century inherited from the past. The powerful influences of Darwin and Hegel, of Marx and Lasalle, of Malthus and others, are part of this inheritance. Into this situation on August 14, 1872, during the meeting of German scientists and physicians, Dubois-Reymond spoke his famous words: "Ignoramus et Ignorabimus"—we know nothing and are unable to know anything. There are insurmountable limits to our knowledge of nature and the study of man.

Today, over one hundred years later, we can notice that defects have arisen in the boldly constructed edifice of the modern science of nutrition. It has become clear: our image of nature does not correspond to reality—our image of man is incomplete. This means that the study of nature, true to reality, requires a new image of man and nature. This is a cardinal question for the present, to which Rudolf Steiner first directed his attention when talking about nutrition. He first had to lay the basic foundation of a study of man which would also be valid for the rest of nature.

Dissatisfaction with the Materialistic Theories of Nutrition

Even prior to the turn of the century eminent scientists were dissatisfied with the prevalent materialistic interpretation of nutrition. Gustav von Bunge, physiologist and biochemist at the University of Basel (1885–1920), was one of the prominent scientists, who, out of an inner conviction, disagreed with the mechanistic interpretations of his contemporaries. His life's work, upon which much of modern nutrition is based, is still relevant today.[5]

In his lecture "Vitalism and Mechanism" (1866), he said: "The deepest, most immediate insight which we can have into our innermost being shows us qualities of the most varied kind, shows us processes, which are not at all like a mechanism." He is clearly pointing out that we are dealing with qualities as the essential of human nature, with processes and events whose dynamics are, as it were, perceived in their physical manifestation. And so he came to the conclusion: "The more thorough, more detailed, more complete we are in examining life, the more we come to the conclusion that events, which we believed we could explain physically and chemically, are

10

actually much more complicated, and for the time being escape every mechanical explanation. . . The attempt to derive life's manifestations from physical and chemical laws has been as unsuccessful in other fields as it has been in the physiology of metabolism."

It was not surprising, then, that he came into conflict with Dubois-Reymond, who defended the mechanistic theory with considerable vehemence. In no way did Bunge desire a return to the old "Vitalism." Rather, it was for him "thoughtlessness to expect that with the same senses we would ever discover anything different in living than in non-living nature." Bunge recognized clearly that with the means of obtaining knowledge which we apply to lifeless nature it would never be possible to explore the living.

This position is of fundamental importance and has been frequently verified since then. A. Gigon in his *Thoughts Concerning the Nutrition of Man* said: "It is certainly erroneous to imagine that a living organism could be understood according to the principles of mechanics. The organism has a much freer, more versatile play of forces."[6] W. Heitler is more precise in his formulation of his answer to the question: "Life = Physics + Chemistry?" He says: "The laws active in an organism are diametrically opposed in their actions to those active within dead matter. . . Clearly laws are active in an organism which are not found in dead matter, and which account for the fundamental difference between life and death."[7]

The Necessity for New Methods of Research

The consequences of this recognition by competent scientists are also highly significant for nutrition. They lead to insights which Rudolf Steiner expressed a half century ago: "The development of natural science since the 15th century took the world of the living . . . separated from it the essentially human element, threw it away, and . . . led natural science to the triumphs it has achieved."[8] But how could nutrition of man be understood if not even the living was comprehended, if not even consideration was given to the lack of comprehension of his soul and spiritual element?

Bunge was quite aware of these consequences. In his argument with Dubois-Reymond he wrote: "The core of the question has not even been touched by the previously mentioned authors (who had contradicted him)— namely the impossibility to explain psychic qualities mechanically. . ." But Bunge asked further: "And how does this little structure (the cell) become the carrier of psychological occurrences? Here the proudest physiology humbly bows and psychology becomes silent." He was not, however, satisfied with a merely negative position. Just because he recognized that the outer sense-observation, and the thought formation depending on it, is unable to get hold of the living, or soul-spiritual, he directed his attention to

11

the "inner-sense, to observe the conditions and events of self-consciousness." And this "inner sense," by means of which one can observe the soul, can "at once spread light over this darkness," for "nothing can hold up the triumphant progress of science," because there are no "insurmountable boundaries" to our "spiritual faculties."

Therewith an authority in the field of modern natural science has stated that Dubois-Reymond's "Ignorabismus" is fundamentally invalid and that there are no insurmountable boundaries to human cognition.

Rudolf Steiner's Spiritual Science begins just at this point. He developed a method of knowledge which links on to the natural scientific method of research and manner of thinking. However, "while natural science remains in the sensible with its research and way of thinking," the spiritual scientific method "considers the psychological work with nature as a kind of self-education of the soul, and applies what has been achieved in this self-education to super-sensible realms."[9] In this manner one not only attains a "self-development which is achieved through an experience of nature," but one also attains an experience of self, and a true self-knowledge. In this, the power of thought, which recognizes itself as a supersensible element by strengthening itself through training within itself, is an instrument of knowledge which opens a previously hidden world.

The method of attaining knowledge of the spiritual world content, developed and presented in detail by Rudolf Steiner, appears to fulfill a demand which Bunge may have expressed when he said: "The fact that physiology begins with the most complicated organism, the human being, can be justified, because the human organism is the only organism we can investigate without relying merely on our senses. Through self-observation we penetrate into man's innermost being with a method which supplements the pictures obtained by sense-derived knowledge." (*Physiology*, Vol. II)

It is in fact the concern of Spiritual Science to extend the knowledge of man beyond what can be known from the accepted and justified methods used today. This extension of knowledge is made possible by supersensible cognition and attempts to provide a complete image of man and the world. This is, then, not in conflict with the natural scientific world view. However, an approach to nutrition from the viewpoint of Spiritual Science will not merely result in an addition of further viewpoints or facts; rather, it will give fruitful indications for daily life. It will therefore be our constant concern to elaborate this new element of a spiritual-scientific nutritional hygiene.

Natural Laws Apply Only to the Inorganic World

Rudolf Steiner had recognized what other scientists such as Bunge, Gigon, and Heilter indicated, that all natural laws are valid only in the physical world, only for the world of lifeless minerals. The plant world as member of the organic realm is "only possible on the earth because there are earthly substances which are not completely subject to physical laws. Rather . . . they are able to subject themselves to a lawfulness which is contrary to the physical laws." The realm in which such lawfulness is active is called the etheric world. In this sense "one can understand the phenomena of the plant world only if one can perceive in it the interaction of the earthly-physical with the cosmic etheric."

The World of Formative Forces

In the same way we can also attain a true perception of living man, of his etheric body (body of formative forces). Here, too, the physical substances and forces, when taken up by man, first have to lose their physical characteristics if they are to be taken up by the etheric body. We point therewith not only to a fundamental characteristic of human digestion, which will be considered in detail later, but to the relationship of man to the plant world as a source of nutrition.

Reality of Soul and Spirit

Despite all attempts by behavioral psychologists and others to approach the reality of the soul and spirit, the goal has not been achieved. An example of such an unsuccessful attempt appears in a work by Schaefer and Novak in a discussion of *Biophysical Models of Man*: "Finally the human 'soul' or 'self-consciousness' originates here in a manner which cannot be analyzed in terms of biophysics."

Here, too, a new method had to be found so that insights into the reality of the soul-spiritual could be gained. In the path of training indicated above, man actually attains the state in which the first purely spiritual experience is the observation of his own Ego, independent of its connection with the physical body. Thus the first result of such a spiritual training is that the soul perceives itself in its own essence. Considered from this point of view, Spiritual Science confirms Bunge's postulate that the possibility of the activation of the inner sense of man places one's own being at the starting point of research and at the same time places the self into the center of one's being. Science without man is thereby contrasted with the method of Spiritual Science through which man again is placed into the center. Spiritual Science thereby fulfills a longing expressed by many scientists today, who, however, are not in a position to fulfill it. Instead we hear of the "untenable limitation of natural scientific thinking," in the face of which medicine is unable to solve its problems "if it does not rigorously start with the supposition that man is always its central object."[10] The spiritual scientific research method fulfills this demand completely. It can therefore bring about a valid insight into the soul-spiritual nature of man and its relationship to the physical body.

Without this perception it is not possible to obtain a clear understanding of the relationship between man and the world through nutrition. Therefore one of the most significant aspects of Rudolf Steiner's Spiritual Science is the discovery of the interaction between the natural and the soul-spiritual aspects of man.

Catabolic and Metabolic Processes in Man

In the first chapter of Rudolf Steiner and Ita Wegmann's *Fundamentals of Therapy* the following relationships are formulated: "The spirit unfolds itself within man not on the basis of metabolic activity, but rather upon catabolic activity. Where the spirit is active in man, there substance has to withdraw from its activity."[11] This expresses what modern physiology, without recognizing its importance, knows very well. The metabolic processes in the human organism have a completely different relationship to the inner activities than the catabolic processes. Metabolism is always an expression of life-activities, of the formative forces, as they manifest themselves in growth, regeneration and reproduction. Catabolism, on the other hand, is connected with a pushing back of these forces, with the opposite pole of growth and life, the death forces, and thereby also with the forces of consciousness. Thus Rudolf Steiner indicates that the origin of thinking within the etheric body depends not upon a continuation of the etheric activity, but rather a cessation of that activity. Soul life can therefore only unfold itself on the foundation of a pushing back, and the more prominent the manifestation of the soul life is in the physical body, the more intensively this element of destruction will be expressed there.

The Concepts of Human Health and Disease

Human health depends upon an unfolding of those etheric, formative forces which manifest their activity in growth and regeneration. "Therewith health is recognized as that condition which has its origin in the etheric organism." And as nutrition stimulates and maintains these growth and regenerative forces, it must play an important role in maintaining the health of man. In this sense nutrition counters the forces of death. If man cannot nourish himself anymore, death must occur. That is the death of "old age" which has become so rare today, but which is actually a "failure of nutrition."[12]

14

That this situation is not so obvious today is related to the fact that the metabolic life-processes are always countered by a catabolic process, a breakdown process, a pushing back of health, which is the necessary foundation of the soul life. This can only develop when a force opposing health is active. That is, in reality, the activity which causes disease. For "in the spirit and soul activities one has to search for the origins of disease." (*Fundamentals of Therapy*, Ch. II) The human soul, designated in Spiritual Science, according to an old expression, by the term "astral body," thus appears in this sense as the carrier of disease processes. For the actual forces of healing, on the other hand, we will have to seek in the etheric body, "so that healing, making healthy, means: to have the possibility to bring about activities in the etheric body which oppose the disease-provoking effects of the astral body."[13]

(margin handwritten notes: disease: astral / healing: etheric)

The Task of Nutrition and Dietetics

We can recognize therefore that nutrition serves to stimulate and unfold the health-giving forces of the etheric body. In this sense it is active against the death forces and has at the same time the task of preventing disease. If such disease-forming processes have gained the upper hand in any way, then nutrition has to be modified into a specific diet. Thus a regulated diet is used in illness to actively support the healing process, as a supplement to medication. In addition, the special diet plays an important role in convalescence, as a transition back to the everyday diet.

Also to be taken into consideration is the concern that the diet not interfere with a healthy soul life. This means that in man one must not only consider the maintenance and support of the growth and regenerative processes, but also the previously discussed catabolic processes which are necessary for the functioning of human consciousness.

We have now arrived at a decisive point in our considerations: Man does not only attain the generalized consciousness also found in the animal realm, but in addition, he carries within himself an Ego-consciousness; he penetrates his physical body with his individuality. Just this fact will be of the greatest significance for human nutrition, because we will have to ask ourselves the question: How can our nutrition be responsive also to this Ego-organization?

Changes and Limitations of Modern Scientific Viewpoints

While for many decades man was considered to be only a sort of higher ape, scientists recently began to talk about the "special case, man." The pathologist Dorr (Heidelberg) asks: "Are we not continually making two cardinal errors in 'humanizing' the animal, and 'animalizing' man? Are we

15

not completely lost when, not without pride, we admit that the medicine of our days is 'scientific'?"[14] When, for example, the French clinician, Jean Hamburger, in his book, *The Power and Impotence of Medicine* (1973), points to the very significant discovery of the "Immunological Individuality" of man, we have evidence of a fundamental change in the image of man. That "these signs of our individuality are found in every one of our cells" and also "that every one of the billions of cells forming our body carries our seal" is a truly epoch-making discovery.[15] It would have been more so if Rudolf Steiner, as a result of his spiritual research, had not already written in 1924: "Down to the smallest parts of his substance, man in his formation is the result of this Ego-organization." (*Fundamentals of Therapy*, Ch. V) This could only mean that the "Ego-organization" has to be in the position to mold human substance according to its "model" and also to liberate foods from the last traces of external nature. The consequences for human nutrition are incalculable, but we must realize that modern science is unable to perceive them so long as it is unable to grasp the significance of the spiritual reality of the results of its research.

the Antigens, surface [handwritten marginal note]

Persistence of Old Thought Habits

When a scientist comes to the realization that "the total mass of the human brain far exceeds the mass of even the most highly developed animals," and then further on admits that "a factor such as the spiritual is not explained by this model," then we have at once an admission of the impotence of a scientific method which is unable to grasp the reality of the spiritual.[16] In this connection a statement by Rudolf Steiner is exceptionally revealing: "when someone says, I believe . . . in a life force, a spirit if you will, when all his explorations and thoughts about nutrition are arranged in such a way that he only asks: how does what I discover in the laboratory relate in the same way to the human organism—without taking the laws of the spiritual life into consideration—then his conception of man could be considered valid, but his world view could not become fruitful."[17] In other words, thought habits, the rigid adherence to an allegedly exclusive scientific method, doom the modern scientist to such impotence that often the greatest discoveries cannot lead to the expected progress. For our presentation, however, such discoveries provide valuable support by frequently verifying the results of spiritual-scientific research.

The New Image of Man

The image of man which can be verified when we take into account the results of modern science, which emphasize the uniqueness of the human brain as instrument of consciousness, can clarify the recognition of the

16

significance of thinking in man and also confirm the statement of the spiritual scientist: "The whole body of man is formed so that its crowning point is the spiritual organ, the brain." But, "the structure of the human brain can only be understood when it is considered with reference to its task: to provide the bodily foundation for the thinking spirit."[18] Should we not here ask the questions: Of what should human food consist to serve this task? How should the human brain be nourished? What actually nourishes this brain?

Spiritual Science has given fundamental indications to answer such questions.

New Standards of Quality

Closely connected is another question: Of what should nutrition consist in order to take into account the Ego-organization, which is active down to the last cell in the human body? Here a new standard of quality has to be established, not only for foods, but also for their preparation. To this end the following has to be taken into consideration: "It is granted to nature to be nature outside of the human skin; within the human skin, what is nature changes from nature to something opposed to nature."[19] Such concepts as "natural nutrition," etc., which are very prevalent today, will have to be changed and expanded if they are to remain valid.

The Four Members of Man and the Four-Fold Stream of Nutrition

In his fourfoldness as physical, etheric, and astral body, taken hold of and formed by the Ego-organization, we have before us the human being with which nutrition has to concern itself.

On the other side, nutrition is confronted by the three realms of nature: the mineral, plant, and animal realms. Only through the mineral does man have to come to terms with the lifeless, as for example, with salt. In the plant he is already concerned with the living, permeated by etheric, formative forces. In plant foods he meets these formative forces in the most varied manner. With animal foods he also takes up the soul forces which the specific animal had internalized. He has to come to terms with the diverse "astralities" of the animals. Only in the earliest period of his life, as a newborn, does he take in food derived from man as mother's milk.

Thus his four-fold being confronts a four-fold stream of nutrition. Whether or not nutrition will further his health, energize his soul-forces, and serve as a foundation of his spiritual activities will depend on its quality, the extent to which it is assimilated, and also upon his constitution.

17

Feuerbach's expression, "Man is what he eats," is understandable when nourishment, initially physical substance, is considered from a materialistic point of view. Yet we must be aware that physical substances are only the outer aspects of the spiritual. Natural science established in the 19th century that matter and energy are different states of the same principle. It was, however, unable to get hold of the underlying spiritual, because it lacked the methods. It was also not capable of seeing that the laws of the conservation of energy, of the calorie, etc., are only valid for the physical world, and for man, only insofar as he has a physical body. Rudolf Steiner specifically referred to Feuerbach's phrase in one of his first open lectures on nutrition (1908). "We do not only eat what we see with our eyes; in a certain sense, we also eat the spiritual which hides behind the material." "Through nutrition we enter into a relationship with the spiritual, the substrate of the material."[20] Rudolf Steiner points out that in this sense Feuerbach's phrase has some validity, but it immediately raises further questions: What happens to food in man? What happens in man when he digests, absorbs, excretes? What is the relationship of the effects of natural laws in our environment to the diverse needs and forces of the human organization? To answer these questions one needs the image of man presented by Rudolf Steiner.

The Functions of the Members of Man in Nutrition

While Dubois-Reymond held that the effects of substances can explain life but not consciousness, Rudolf Steiner had to ask why a number of carbon, oxygen, hydrogen, and nitrogen atoms should ever position themselves so as to bring about life. Just as they cannot bring about consciousness, so, too, they cannot bring forth life. The life processes do not continue the natural processes; they oppose them. A living plant overcomes gravity and opens itself to extra-terrestrial forces. It has to overcome the physical. This means that the formation of protein, which breaks down into C-O-N-H, as carrier of life, does not depend on terrestrial, but rather extra-terrestrial forces. As we mentioned already, Rudolf Steiner called these forces "etheric, formative forces," and collectively (insofar as they are part of an organism), it is this body that makes up its etheric body or body of formative forces. The etheric body brings about the form of the organism and is active in all life processes: growth, reproduction, and also nutrition. It is the force which, "during life prevents physical substances and forces from going their own way," that is, it is a "fighter" against the physical substances and forces. We can therefore understand why substances in the living organism cannot remain as they are outside of the organism. When man ingests food he has to change it, break it down, transform it from the first moment of contact, so that he can make it his own. Modern physiology, too, has arrived at this conclusion.

18

In excretion, substances have become lifeless again, have again become part of the mineral world. Not until death occurs do substances act within us as they do in the mineral world, and then they bring about the decomposition of the physical body. During life they are subject to higher forces. It should be understood that this "life body," as we can also call it, has nothing in common with the hypothetical "Life Force" postulated in the 19th century. The physical body consists of the solid constituents, the mineral substances of the body. The formative forces are active in the liquid elements of the body. Therefore "when we concern ourselves with whatever circulates, the circulation of the absorbed food or the food substances already transformed in the blood stream, then the directing forces are cosmic and not terrestrial forces."[21]

As we have seen, man is not only endowed with life, he also has a soul and a spirit. The soul is carrier of sensations, feelings, drives, and passions. These organize within man and form the "soul body," just as the life forces constitute the "life body." The soul forces are intimately involved in human nutrition: life forces are pushed back wherever consciousness occurs. If a feeling, a sensation, is to arise in the living organism, the life processes must recede, growth must cease, reproduction must decrease. Their place will be taken by breakdown processes. All organs of the body are filled with such constructive and destructive processes in varying proportions. The liver—nomen est omen!—is primarily subject to the constructive, the life processes; its cells have an exceptional regenerative capacity. And yet the breakdown processes are also powerfully active in this organ, e.g., in the formation of bile. In the sense and nerve organs the life processes recede early in life; both harden and solidify. If an eye shall see, an ear shall hear, their own life processes must be excluded. The eye becomes a physical apparatus. It has to be nourished from without by a fine circulation. The brain could not become the instrument of thinking if the neuron did not relinquish its reproductive capacity. "Conscious thinking does not occur in processes of growth and formation; it builds up its organs; it breaks them down again when feeling occurs in the soul's consciousness.

The Ego builds up its "Ego-organization and breaks it down again when the will is active in self-consciousness."[22] With these Ego forces, man establishes his own realm and elevates himself above the animal. He becomes carrier of a spiritual organization. This member of man interacts with the bodily processes by way of warmth. In this sense, the liver, as the organ with the greatest formation of warmth in man, can become the bodily foundation of the will. Unless we take these relationships into consideration we will not understand the significance of warmth in nutrition. In a similar manner the human "air-organization" is carrier of the soul body. The respiratory function of the lung is at the same time a soul event. Like warmth, the "air-organism" is active in the whole body.

19

Ego forces interacts via WARMTH (liver — foundation of warmth/will)

lung – astral – "air"

Nutrition Appropriate to Man

The Ego-organization transforms the food substances so that they become "appropriate to man." If it becomes impossible to fulfill this function because of the inability of Ego-organization forces or some deficiency of the physical body, then death must occur.

Conversely, we can say that the formative force organization, via nutrition, constantly battles against death. As long as man can nourish himself, so long does he hold back death.

Through nutrition the etheric body receives a continuous stimulation and revitalization, and becomes thereby the carrier of the healing forces. But, as we have seen, consciousness could not arise out of this organization. To that end the etheric body has to be pushed back, resulting in a paralysis of the healing forces. Feeling can then arise, depending on the extent to which this paralysis has occurred. If, however, the equilibrium between these two poles is disturbed, illness results. Every pain is a feeling that is too strong, an excessively intensive activity of the soul organization in the body. This equilibrium is very labile and has to be renewed continually. With every intake of food it is brought out of balance and then re-established. The old Arabian physician was correct when he said: "By eating man becomes sick, he returns to health by digesting."

Rudolf Steiner explained these relationships in a lecture for young physicians: "Just as one can abstractly say man consists of a physical body, etheric body, astral body, and Ego, so one can be very concrete and say man consists of the nutritional processes, of the continually intervening disease processes and of what is a continual death process, which is always held back until the death processes are, so to speak, summed up, are integrated and death occurs."[23]

With this we have outlined a number of basic questions of nutrition. We can recognize now that only a true image of man enables us to examine all aspects of nutrition. The resulting detailed consequences will be evident later.

Because it was unable to fully comprehend man, the science of nutrition was already on a dead-end road at the beginning of the 19th cenury. Rudolf Steiner's Spiritual Science reconstitutes the complete image of man. The image of nutrition is an organic part of this picture. The image of nature, out of which we take our food, also arises from this image of man, and enables us thereby to perceive in a new way the interaction of man and nature in nutrition.

We can then not only understand how the present problems in nutrition arise, but also how it can be possible to counter this situation with new and healing impulses.

20

Chapter 2

WHAT IS THE PURPOSE OF NUTRITION?

Scale and Thermometer in Nutritional Research

The answer to the above question, superficially considered, appears to be so obvious that frequently it is either not asked with any seriousness or is just barely mentioned. Since Lavoisier established the doctrine that life is a chemical function and foods are the "combustibles," it appeared to be a simple matter to answer the question concerning the meaning and purpose of nutrition. Since then (1780) one used "the scale, the thermometer and the principles of chemistry to establish the quantitative energy relationships between food, work, and the organism."[1] The complete process of nutrition in man was considered to be a "combustion process," wherein the various foods as "carriers of energy," with the participation of oxygen, unfolded their activity. This "energy" was measured in terms of the calorie. One merely needed to determine how many calories a nutrient contained.

As early as the end of the last century there were voices which questioned this all-too-simple calculation. Gustav von Bunge (1844-1920) was one of the first to observe that there is also "life without oxygen," i.e., that Lavoisier's recipe could only be applied to intake and output, to ingestion and excretion. The destiny of the various substances within the organism, however, appeared to be subject to different laws. It was said that not only combustion, in general, is necessary for life, but that the liberated energy, i.e., that all energy-yielding processes are necessary for the organism. Thus the study of "intermediary metabolism" took the place of metabolic energy relationships. Further studies revealed that various proteins have a different

21

composition and cannot merely be exchanged for one another in nutrition. Within the last few years such research led to the results with which we will still have to concern ourselves.

The Constitution of Food Substances as Measure of Quality

As a result of Bunge's experiments, it was shown that the "constituents" of food, e.g., milk, do not bring about actual nutrition. The addition of constituent substances did not suffice for adequate nutrition. Although it became evident that the older theories of nutrition were untenable, such experiments nevertheless led to the discovery of new quantifiable substances. Consequently, the prevalent thinking only concerned itself with quantity, even though the "vitamins" discovered in this manner often approached the limits of quantification.

Through these discoveries a change in direction occurred in nutritional science. There was no talk anymore about "carriers of energy" which could be measured calorically. Instead, one heard of so-called "protective substances," among which we today include vitamins, minerals, and water. These substances are of course necessary for nutrition, but they cannot be measured in calories. They are designated as "those nutrients which contribute to continuous functioning of all parts and the totality of the organism."[2] Thus we have to recognize the purely functional, i.e., the qualitatively effective character of such substances. Today, such a "protective function" is even ascribed to proteins and certain fatty acids; therefore, a qualitative activity is ascribed to those substances which were formerly considered to be exclusive calorie carriers. A. Gigon remarked, in 1951, that the "value of a nutrient can be grasped neither by examining its calorie production nor by its analytical composition."[3] What other point of view remains then besides the qualitative one?

The Law of Energy and Its Limitations

The quantitative conception of nutrition was criticized from still another angle at the turn of the century. These criticisms, however, have not yet been taken seriously. Since the last century, one of the pillars of scientific nutrition was the so-called "law of the conservation of energy." Julius Robert Mayer (1842), from certain observations made when he was a naval physician, was the first to voice his opinion of this subject. He frequently expressed it in the phrase "Nothing comes out of nothing." With this law he wanted to establish the theory that the universe contains a constant sum of forces, which are only transformed into other forms, e.g., thermal, mechanical, or chemical force,

22

etc., and which can neither increase nor decrease in number. The question arose, then, whether this law, applicable to the inorganic, was also valid for living organisms. Helmholtz believed to have established this in 1847, but it was not until 1894 that M. Rubner published his own results, according to which the law of conservation of energy had full validity for animal life. Other scientists believed they had found verification of this law in man also.

Accordingly, it appeared to be conclusively established that man, too, transforms his food only quantitatively into another form, uses it up as work and excretes the rest. This not only closed the "sequence" of mineral-plant-animal-man and the universe, it also made man into a mere piece of nature, only a link in the infinite circulation of substances and forces of the universe, only "transformed sunlight."

Again G. v. Bunge raised an important objection: "The only remaining question is: What about the life of the soul? Our sense perceptions, feelings, affects, drives, representations—are they too only transformed sunlight? Or are we to assume that the world of the inner senses is not subject to that great law which rules the world of the outer senses with uniform and iron necessity?"[4] Bunge was unable to answer this question. Modern physiology, however, discovered the surprising fact that mental work does not increase the rate of metabolism. Does that not imply that human psychological and mental activity, especially thinking, is not subject to the law of conservation of energy, that man's mental activity is free of bonds of natural law?

Based on purely spiritual research, Rudolf Steiner answered this question in his *Philosophy of Freedom*: "The plant transforms itself because of the objective laws within it; man remains in his incomplete condition if he does not take up the transforming substance and transform himself through his own power. Nature makes only a nature being out of man . . . only he can make a free being out of himself. . . "[5] He can do this, because "the human organization has no part in the essence of thinking."[6] Rudolf Steiner's *Philosophy of Freedom* appeared in the same year in which Rubner claimed to have verified that the law of conservation of energy also applied to man: 1894.

We can understand why Rudolf Steiner later considered Rubner's law a great obstacle to an understanding of man. He did, however, specify that man is the only being in which new forces are formed, while in all other realms of nature, up to the animals, the law has validity. Man is not a mere spectator in the world. He breaks the bonds of natural laws by reaching with his being up to the supersensible, the spiritual. This makes him an individuality and allows him to unfold an individual spiritual life. This recognition has a fundamental significance for human nutrition, because man is in the position to individualize the substance of his body, i.e., to free it from subjection to the natural laws.

23

The Biochemical Individuality of Man

In 1963 Roger J. Williams published his work "Biochemical Individuality." In a later essay (1967) he wrote:

> The biochemical individuality is actually an immense and far reaching subject matter, in which much remains to be discovered. The fundamental fact of the uniqueness of each individual—biochemical individuality is a part of this—represents a pillar of biology. . . . One does not usually think about the fact that each one of us has his own peculiar metabolism-personality, has his own unique biochemistry. We may all use the same amino acids, vitamins, and minerals, but how we use them in isolated instances, and the effects of their individual utilization, that varies infinitely in all of us.[7]

Rudolf Steiner came to such a recognition through his purely spiritual research. He wrote in 1925: "Down to the smallest particles of his substance, man's formation is a result of this Ego-organization."[8]

Destruction and Resurrection of Matter in Man

If man is to reach the point of actually individualizing himself down into his substance, then he must be capable not only of transforming the foods he takes in into other forms, but also of destroying the ingested substance in order to build up his individual substance. Were this not so, man would merely be a metamorphosis of nature. Rudolf Steiner discovered a "place" in man where work is done without an energy equivalent: in the formation of consciousness. The content of our soul life is given as a fact of consciousness, but soul life "can only exist if substances are destroyed," and that means that in us there is actually no preservation of force and substance. Through the destruction of substance, space is created for the development of thought life. "In fact, only in man does destruction of substance occur."[9] Through this, man does not only become an individual being, a thinking and self-conscious personality, he also becomes the point of origin for creative activity. Outside of the human organism, in the rest of nature, the law of conservation of energy and mass applies fully. In man, however, anthroposophy teaches us about "a complete disappearance of matter and a resurrection of matter out of mere space."[10]

Nutrition as Resistance Against Nature

From the first moment of the nutritional process, when we begin to

24

transform our food, we resist nature. In the 19th century, Justus von Liebig wrote in his "Chemical Letters":

> Through the forces originating in his body, man resists the natural forces which continually strive to destroy his existence. This resistance must be renewed daily if his existence is to be secure for a period of time. . . . Man needs food for heat and energy production. Through it, he creates in his body a resistance against the influences of the atmosphere which receive a part of his body every day.[11]

What Liebig states is important insofar as he stresses the significance of the resistance which we have to exercise in our nutrition process. We can only maintain ourselves against the destructive effect of nature if we are able to provide sufficient resistance against it. Food gives us the stimulation, the means, to unfold these forces within ourselves. Thus we do not take in the substance and forces of nature in order to utilize them directly, but rather to create through them the forces which counter the destructive force of nature. We cannot actually approach nature without being threatened with destruction; we must overcome its substances and forces. In this overcoming we gain the forces which we need for our existence, and it is through nutrition that we must bring about this transformation in the right way.

> If man takes up something from the outer world, it is injurious to his inner organism, and it is essential that he overcome it. . . We really do not eat so that we get this or that food into us; we eat so that we develop those forces in us which overcome these foods. We eat in order to resist the forces of this earth, and we live on the earth because we exercise resistance.[12]

This helps to answer the question: Why do we nourish ourselves? The reality of nutrition is thus something quite different from its appearance. Yet this answer raises a few further questions: Why do we need different foods, since the resistant force at first seems to be uniform? Of what sort are the forces in the foods against which we resist? And finally, how do these forces act upon the different organizations of man, his life organization, his soul, his spirit? With these questions we address the problem of quality in nutrition, because the purely quantitative consideration of these questions would soon be exhausted.[13] Thus we have delimited a number of questions with which we will be concerned in the next chapter.

Chapter 3

GENERAL ASPECTS OF
THE PHYSIOLOGY OF NUTRITION

Man and the Realms of Nature in Nutrition

Man's food consists of mineral, plant, and animal substances. We notice at once that there are important differences among them. While the fraction of mineral substances in our foods is minimal and has no caloric significance at all, it is nevertheless essential for life. On the other hand, although the fraction of foods from the animal realm continues to rise in our time, it is neither necessary for life nor indispensable. Most of our foods come from the plant realm. That seems to indicate that there is a special relationship between man and the world of plants. A fact of world nutrition is that the majority of the world's population subsists by eating only food from the plant world. Only about one tenth of human foods actually consists of animal products, if milk and milk products are included. Thus if we consider our relationship to the realms of nature in general, we can say we are closest to the animal realm and furthest from the mineral realm. The plants take a middle position. This can be schematized as follows:

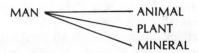

The path from animal to man is the shortest, from mineral to man the longest. From this point of view, man needs the least force in overcoming

27

foods from animals and the most force in overcoming foods from minerals. In the same sense, he needs more force to overcome foods from plants than from animals. We can understand that man, with his present constitution, is able to take up only very little of the mineral. Plants make up the greatest fraction of his mineral needs and are in a position which is closer to him though he takes up some minerals via the animal.

Following this line of reasoning, one might easily conclude that food from animals is best. Did not the animal—depending on its level or organization— take the nutriments closest to man? Man only has to take one more step to humanize them; for plants he needs a doubled effort. In reality the situation is quite different. Rudolf Steiner frequently emphasized that man actually has the forces to overcome the plant organization; otherwise, he would not be able to take the greatest fraction of his food from the plant realm. It is just here that a law applies of which modern biology is fully aware: an organ, which is not at all, or only insufficiently, active, atrophies or degenerates. This also applies to the human organization which actually depends on such an appropriate force activity. The organism has to "call up totally different forces" if it is a plant eater, rather than a meat eater; nevertheless, the forces necessary to overcome plant foods are still present. If they are not sufficiently active, then they, as it were, recoil back into the organism. Their effect on man is then essentially very tiring and disturbing.[1] This important observation will concern us further when we discuss the characteristics of vegetarian and animal forms of nutrition. Through it we are led to the important insight that nutrition "consists of work, not of substances," and that it is most important "to know that life does not consist of eating cabbage and turnips," but of what one "must do" when "cabbage and turnips enter man." In brief, what is essential is the dynamics of nutrition.

The "overcoming of nourishment" by man presupposes, as we already pointed out, the foreign nature of foods. It is therefore a prerequisite for the digestive process that the overcoming forces of the organism are sufficient, for insofar as man can develop soul and spiritual forces, he also always carries in his organism the possibility of illness. This is very relevant to nutrition. Every ingestion of food raises the question of whether man can overcome the foreign nature so that he can humanize it. Eating is like an invasion from a foreign world that threatens to annihilate man and also wants to impair his soul-spiritual activity by allowing natural forces to penetrate him. Every ingestion of food thus initiates a disease process. When man has eaten, he has introduced something foreign into himself and he is "actually sick." He must first "overcome the illness" through his inner organism, through the function of his inner organs. In other words, "One eats oneself sick and digests oneself back to health," according to the old Arabian proverb. In this sense we can understand Rudolf Steiner when he says: "Actually the de-

28

velopment of illness is nothing other than a continuation of what happens when man eats."[2] Such a view gains particular importance in our time, with its ever-increasing diseases connected in one way or another with nutrition. Nutrition, as a pathogenetic factor, thus plays an important role in today's medicine.

It is by now evident that nutrition is related to the human organism through many recognized connections. The calorie has been proved an unsatisfactory measure. Inadequate also is the so-called "biological value," which many have frequently attempted to establish. In order to attain a true measure of quality, we have to take the interaction of food and the whole human being into consideration.

Fundamental to these indications is what Rudolf Steiner stated in the *Agricultural Course* in 1924: we should not concern ourselves with a relationship of mass in metabolism, but rather with "whether, in our foods, we can take up the vitality of forces in the proper way."[3] That presupposes, of course, that we are aware of such forces in food. Plants are permeated and organized by the same kind of formative forces which we can also observe in the human body. Animals have, in addition, an organization of differentiated soul forces. These force-organizations are in no sense "parallel" to the physical substances; instead, they permeate them and raise them to higher stages.

The life forces of plants work against the physical laws. A living plant is filled with forces that take its substance into spheres which are cosmic rather than earthly. Plant life is not possible without sunlight. So in the living plant, earth substance "departs from its community with the earth." It is taken in by forces "which radiate from all sides, from the extraterrestrial to the earth," and, "in the interaction of terrestrial and cosmic forces," the plant originates.[4] Man is involved with these etheric formative forces of the plants when he eats plant foods. These living formative forces continue to be active in the plant even when it has been picked. Here all the questions arise which we will discuss in subsequent chapters: the problem of uncooked foods, the great problem of food preparation, cooking, baking, etc., and also the question of preserving. Relevant to these considerations will be the fact that animals take their food directly from nature, while man does this rarely, usually preferring to "prepare it."

We must clarify here that the animal has a higher force organization which enables it to form not only living, but also "feeling" substances. In their book, *Fundamentals of Therapy*, Dr. Steiner and Dr. Wegmann expound upon how, in the plant, substance is transformed into living substance by the forces radiating towards the earth. This living substance interacts with the lifeless substances, and in the animal, the feeling substance forms itself out of the living, just as in the plant the living forms itself out of the lifeless. This

29

"feeling substance" is the result of the soul organization, the astral body of animals. Out of that "originates the animal's external form and also the internal, the organs."[5] Consequently, when eating meat, one has to interact with the continuing effects of the animal formation. The animal organ is not only permeated by etheric formative forces, but also by astral forces. A piece of veal is different from a piece of fish or a goose liver. Likewise, in every case, the animal foods differ qualitatively from plant foods.

Mineral nutrients, on the other hand, are not permeated with after-effects of such higher organizations. Although they are most removed from man on the one hand, on the other, they approach human organization the most closely, insofar as their digestion does not involve an opposing life or soul-force.

The Four Steps in Digestion
Mouth Digestion

Digestion occurs in four great steps: in the mouth, in the stomach, in the small intestine, and finally in the colon. The first processes occur in the mouth. Significantly, there, events can be accompanied by human waking consciousness: chewing and salivation. It is remarkable that the quality of saliva depends closely on the kind of food. For example, watery saliva is secreted when one takes an insoluble substance, e.g., a small stone, into the mouth. An actual "digestive saliva" is secreted only in response to stimulation by a nutrient. The composition of this saliva varies, depending on the nutrient. The saliva, which moistens the oral cavity, is continually secreted.

It is remarkable that this play of saliva formation and secretion is not only elicited by sense impressions such as smell and taste, but also by sight, sound, touch and warmth. It can even be elicited by purely mental activities, such as imagining certain foods. This shows clearly how the human soul organization intervenes in the conscious or unconscious activity of these glands. The glands are able to create, out of the blood, a changing salivary composition corresponding to that required by the prevailing situation.

Rudolf Steiner considered the latter relationship from still another point of view. In general we can designate every gland activity, insofar as it takes place in the fluid organism, as an expression of the etheric formative forces. But we have not only the formation of saliva—or any other gland product— we also have its secretion. Through this secretion, the substance secreted confronts the nutrients. It resists their peculiar, foreign nature. This resistance elicits, however, a specific soul experience which is usually unconscious. It is like a "bumping" into a strange world—one which is connected with becoming aware of the self. If this perception becomes

30

gland activity – in the fluid organism — etheric form. forces stronger, then it enters consciousness as pain. The self responds to the inner experience with conscious awareness: "I have bumped into something." Such a process occurs, in an intimate form, during every formation of saliva, when saliva is separated from the blood. Rudolf Steiner called this process, which permeates the organism continually and in various forms, "becoming aware of the self." He also pointed out that because of the secretory activity in our bodies, the possibility exists that each organism "is being enclosed within itself, experiencing itself." This self-experience is kindled by virtue of encountering resistance.

This inner gland activity, which clearly presents itself as interaction of the etheric formative force organism with the soul body, continues towards the outside in the meeting of the gland product and the nutrients. Here, too, such a "resistance experience" occurs. The gland activity is thus a direct expression of the necessary overcoming of the foreign character of foods. It is an expression of the maintenance of the individuality which announces itself in the "becoming aware of the self." It is evident in thinking about food and experiencing feelings related to it, as well as in the direct perception of food. Of interest here is that the glands respond with special intensity to favorite foods. The more favored the food, the more the mouth waters. That means that one wants to assimilate its inner quality and therefore has to resist it with particular intensity. This also applies to the stimulating effect of spices and aromatic substances on digestion. Because they promote salivation, they have assured themselves preferential treatment in digestion and subsequent utilization.

Gland secretion is significant from still another aspect. It is another indication of "the formative forces stepping out of the organ into the thought." Rudolf Steiner directed attention to this in the first medical course.[6] As we have seen, when a gland secretes, the event is connected to a certain conscious or instinctive soul state. This is most evident in crying, but it is also apparent in sweating, insofar as it is connected with fear or psychological exertion. Here it is evident how the soul forces are, as it were, separated from the life activities. A part of the occurrence takes place in the soul realm, another in the life realm of the organism. That means, "If I hadn't thought like that, my gland would not have secreted." A part of the gland's formative forces is removed and transferred into the soul region. The secretory events, starting with salivation and continuing down through the secretions of the stomach, intestines, etc., thus represent a specific interaction of soul and life forces. Just this fact is of great significance for our understanding of the role these organs play in the digestive process. It reveals how closely human nutrition is connected to the life of the soul.

Considering saliva specifically, we become aware of its unique significance for speech. A gland secretion is put at the service of a soul-spiritual activity.

31

The same holds true for tongue and teeth. The human oral cavity is not only a digestive organ, but an organ for the direct expression of the soul and spirit. Just here, in the uppermost part of the digestive organization, essential functions and organs are clearly removed from purely vegetable activities and put in the service of higher activities. Thereby the whole nutritional process in man is steered in a different direction than in the animal. While in the animal nutrition is completely instinctual, man can develop a "culture of eating," which raises him above the animal stage. Man can learn to eat; the animal is condemned to feed.

Saliva has a specific function in digestion. This resides in ptyalin, the enzyme which enables man to break down starches in the mouth. While fats and proteins remain undigested there, reaching the stomach as foreign substances, the preparation of glucose is initiated in the mouth. This casts a special light on sugar and its properties. Its sweetness, which becomes evident when starch gets broken down after thorough salivation and chewing, is thus still accessible to conscious experience in the oral cavity. The mouth digestion of starch thus contributes to an experience of consciousness which is characteristic of human nutrition. It calls up forces of the human organization which reside neither in the vegetable nor in the animalistic parts of his being, forces that serve his spirit, his Ego, in the unfolding of consciousness. Thereby the oral cavity is penetrated by forces which enable the same space to become a tool for speech. In this way we can begin to comprehend Rudolf Steiner's words:

Man can be conscious only through what is active in his Ego-organization in such a way that nothing overwhelms or disturbs it, so that it can unfold fully. This is the case in the region where ptyalin is active.[7]

Warmth is also a contributing factor here, because it receives the nourishment in the oral cavity and interacts with the warmth or coldness which enters from the outside.

The Overcoming of Foreign Nature in Nutrition

As soon as food reaches the oral cavity, it is taken up by the living organism and it becomes subject to its laws. In addition to the soul and spiritual forces, insofar as they are active in the body, the human formative forces are also activated. The foreign nature of foods is thereby worked through by man's own forces. The first result is that food is more or less liquefied. But what does that really mean?

When a nutrient is solid, maybe even mineral, like salt, then it is subject to gravity. In older world views salt formation was considered equivalent to subjection to gravity, to terrestriality. To the extent that such a substance is water soluble, its gravitational subjection is reversed in the oral cavity. Salt is brought into solution. The salt formation, the actual earth formative element, is overcome. Salt is taken back to a condition in which the solidifying forces of gravity cannot act on it. Foods taken from living nature are also dissolved and thereby removed from the influence of earth forces. This is the direct effect of the etheric organization, which, as we have seen, lives in the fluid element, for "human nature has within itself a kind or organic necessity to reverse, to fight against, certain processes which take place in outer nature."[8]

This force which dissolves the mineral, which is active in the oral cavity, is an activity of man's organization. It is similarly active on plant and animal foods although the salt formation process has already been overcome by the etheric forces of the respective organisms. Nevertheless, for human digestion, these plant and animal formative forces are also "foreign bodies" to man's etheric organization. We would deceive ourselves if we believed that we were able to take the foreign etheric forces of foods directly into our own life bodies. The same applies to the astral forces which are organized within the animal. They want to unfold their activity in man when he eats meat, but man's own astral and Ego-organization have to confront them.

Thus the first essential step in human nutrition is that "every trace of outer life is removed from them [the foods]." Rudolf Steiner described the events which transpire when man eats meat. Through digestion one drives "out everything which the foods represent in the animal body. In addition, everything which belongs to the plant food, by virtue of having been part of a living plant, must be driven out."[9] This is mirrored in the oral cavity in the liquefying, dissolving, and breakdown processes. If man is not sufficiently successful in overcoming these foreign processes, then the effects of nature continue to operate in man to a certain extent. That calls forth disease. In this sense we can recognize the validity of the previously mentioned proverb: "One eats oneself sick and then digests oneself healthy."

The complete digestive organization, from the oral cavity to the intestines, represents an everted inner world of man—or an inverted outer world. Activities can take place in it which are not yet completely subject to the laws of the inner organization. They represent a field of conflict between inner and outer forces. Only when the stream of nourishment has reached the intestinal villi and appears in the lymph and blood channels has it reached the stage where it can and must follow the laws of man's inner organization.

Rudolf Steiner discussed this problem in a lecture to physicians. He held that if one confines oneself exclusively to the intestinal contents, natural scientific considerations are adequate. When one considers "that outer laws enter in a certain sense into the life of the digestive tract, then, for this limited area, one gets along quite well," providing one holds to what can be observed in man's physical organization.[10] However, Rudolf Steiner con-

33

liquefying food = overcoming earth formative element; this is the effect of the etheric form. forces

tinued, one should be fully aware that the digestive and nutritional process is not completed within the confines of the intestine.

Stomach Digestion

Characteristic of stomach digestion is the hydrochloric acid-pepsin mixture. In contrast to the weakly alkaline saliva, digestive processes in the stomach take place in a strongly acidic milieu, which primarily breaks down proteins. These processes point to the intervention of a further organization principle of man; the astral body expresses itself in the acid. In the oral cavity, processes of consciousness take place which mirror themselves, for example, in the carbohydrate digestion. The life processes are also active in the alkaline milieu. In the region where pepsin is active, however, the astral body predominates over the Ego-organization: "The Ego-activity immerses itself in the astral activity." Although not always interpreted correctly, the effects of these processes are well known and thoroughly studied today. Thus, in the case of chronic gastric hyperacidity and gastric ulcers, one talks about connections with the autonomic nervous system which innervates the digestive organs. Nevertheless, H. Schäfer, in his book, *Medicine Today*, wrote in 1963:

> Even if it can be verified that an ulcer follows the experimental stimulation of certain autonomic nerves . . . nothing decisive is established. We would first have to ask how specific autonomic nerves get to be stimulated to such an extent, what somatic centers activate the autonomic impulses, and where the activating disturbances originate.[11]

Such scepticism is understandable insofar as there are still no answers to these questions, and it is likely that no answers can be discovered unless man is observed through the methods of Spiritual Science. By using this method, however, Rudolf Steiner established that in the sympathetic nervous system "the etheric body is primarily active." The nerve systems under consideration behave similar to living organs. The astral and Ego organizations affect them "not by organizing them from the inside, but from the outside."[12] For that reason their influence is said to be a strong one: "Affects and passions have a lasting, significant effect on the sympathetic nervous system. Suffering and worries have a destructive effect on this system." The consequences of such disturbances then become evident in the most varied disease manifestations.

For our discussion here it is important that we gain insight into the activity of the higher members of man in digestion, especially the effects of the astral body on the functions of the stomach.

34

Ego organisation dominates in mouth. Processes of consciousness in CHO breakdown
Life process active in alkaline milieu then
Astral forces active where pepsin/acid found — stomach

This is evident in still other phenomena, e.g., in peristalsis, the rhythmic movements of the stomach, which also depend on the autonomic nervous system. These peristaltic waves, not consciously experienced by healthy persons, can increase to such an extent that they are manifested as cramps which represent an excessive intervention of the astral body. Also, "a state of nervous irritation can lead to peristaltic unrest of the stomach," as Landois-Rosemann writes in his work on physiology.[13] From this is can be seen how important the soul mood is for digestion and nutrition. It is also interesting that, for example, "meals which are ingested with relish, are able to move through the stomach even in the absence of hydrochloric acid." Evidently one's soul orientation to the food, or the fact that a meal is appetizing, contributes to its digestion. "This psychic motility significantly encourages the emptying of the stomach."[14] Thus meals which "lie heavy in the stomach" remain in the stomach too long, not only because of their composition (e.g., excessive fat content, etc.), but also because of the soul mood during and after eating.

It is also known that during the churning of the stomach contents, brought about primarily by peristaltic movements, sounds can develop. These sounds can also occur when the stomach is empty and can even cause pain, the so-called "hunger pangs." They result from the presence of gases in the stomach. Like water, these gases are not only physical substances. While the liquid element is the medium used by the etheric formative forces in the physical realm, the gaseous element is lifted even more out of the physical and becomes a carrier of the astral forces. (See. R. Steiner, *Light Course*, 1921.) The ever-present gas bubble in the stomach provides man's astral body with a path of entry to the activities of this organ. When the "pangs of hunger" result because of this gas, then we should well be able to think of the connection between hunger and pain in the soul life of man.

Digestive Processes in the Small Intestine

The digestive processes which take place in the small intestine, at first in the duodenum, are even further removed from consciousness than are the stomach digestive processes. While mouth digestion is still accessible to waking consciousness, the act of swallowing marks not only the entry to a new place of action, but also to a different level of consciousness. Man's relationship to digestion in the stomach can only be compared with dream consciousness. This state of consciousness changes to dreamless sleep consciousness when the nourishment has completely reached the small intestine.

Decisive steps in digestion take place in the upper small intestine. The three primary food substances reach this organ in totally different stages of breakdown. We pointed out that carbohydrates are subjected to digestive enzymes in the mouth. In the small intestine they undergo the third step of breakdown. Proteins pass the oral cavity unchanged and are broken down to polypeptides in the stomach. They still need the further, thorough destruction of their foreign nature in the small intestine. Fats remain essentially unchanged, even in the stomach. Only here, in the small intestine, are they split into glycerol and fatty acids. Apparently they are least foreign to man's inner organism.

Rudolf Steiner described all these processes, yet he frequently attributed a different significance to them than that given by present physiology. He described how nutrients first must become dead in us before they can be revived. This is so because we would be unable to tolerate a continuation of the life present in the animal or plant which provides our food. We could not, for example, eat cabbage and allow it to approach our intestinal villi when the same etheric forces are still present in it which the cabbage has by virtue of being a plant. "The nutrients' etheric and astral forces must be done away with."[15]

There must be not only a chemical breakdown, but an elimination of the life and soul forces connected with our food substances. In the small intestine there is actually a threefold attack on the nutrients: by the intestinal juice, the bile, and the pancreatic secretions. All three fluids, which, in the sense of our discussion of gland secretion, provide resistance to the entry of foreign substances, are active in the breakdown of fats, carbohydrates, and proteins.

Up to this point, fats have remained practically unchanged: here they are subjected to the breakdown effects of all three glands. After emulsification by the bile so that they can be split into water soluble products, both intestinal and pancreatic secretions are active in their breakdown. Rudolf Steiner characterized this process as follows: "fat, as food, gives up its nature most easily, and is absorbed more easily into the human organization." This property is made possible only by the fact "that it carries very little of the nature of a foreign organism (of its etheric forces, etc.) into the human organism."[16]

The small intestine is the site where protein is digested most actively. Besides the effects of erepsin, which originates from the intestinal mucosa, the activity of the pancreas, mediated by trypsin, plays the central role in protein digestion. Trypsin first enabled analytical chemistry to split proteins into amino acids. However, we must be very precise here and realize that these 20 amino acids are breakdown products and not "building blocks" of protein. To provide a foundation for this assertion, we will have to examine the events in the small intestine in more detail.

Modern research into metabolism clearly established the dominating role and unique position of the pancreas in digestion. Bohlmann, for example, writes:

> It is most remarkable that the pancreas always secretes exactly those enzymes which are most needed to digest the particular nutrients. If fats predominate, lipases increase; if they are rich in starches, amylases increase; and if there is much protein, then much trypsin is secreted. The relative quantities adapt themselves almost slavishly to the quantities of the corresponding foods, so that one could be tempted to compare the pancreas to a thinking being.[17]

Further animal experiments established that the pancreatic activity is independent of the brain but is in close connection with the ganglia of the solar plexus.

The pancreatic activity is especially important in the individualization of protein in man. Steiner and Wegmann speak of "two kinds of protein substances." In the beginning of the digestive process protein is still a foreign substance; at the end it has become man's own. In between there is a state, during which the ingested protein has not completely relinquished the prior etheric effects, "and has not completely taken up the new." In that moment it is almost completely inorganic. This devitalizing of the protein occurs "where trypsin is active in the digestive system."

In the stomach digestion we were primarily concerned with the astral body; here in the small intestine, the previously described "Ego-organization" makes its appearance. Only by its forces are food substances broken down and devitalized to the extent that they can become integrated into the laws of the individual human organization, because everything which comes into the realm of the Ego-organization dies.[18]

The pancreas can thus be seen to be the central organ of the digestive occurrences in the intestine, and these brief comments concerning the digestive functions of the pancreas make evident to what extent it is burdened, especially with today's nutrition. Thus we can understand why pancreatic diseases continually increase.

Rhythmic Events in the Intestine
Significance of the Spleen

While the oscillating movements of the intestine, brought about by alternating contraction and relaxation of the circular musculature, lead to a rhythmical segmentation and mixing of the intestinal contents, the actual peristalsis brings about an advance of the contents. These movements, too, adapt themselves exactly to the nature and constitution of the nourishments,

37

in small intestine: Ego-Organisation,

that is, they perceive them. This process is mediated by the autonomic nervous system and the solar plexus, which is here especially active. In his *Occult Physiology* (1911), Rudolf Steiner speaks of the task of the sympathetic nervous system. It must carry over into the blood, "the inner life of the organism, which expresses itself in warming and nourishing."[19] The impressions of the sympathetic nervous system on the blood must not, however, enter consciousness; they must be left in the subconscious. That the inner digestive events take place in sleep-consciousness provides the precondition for the ordered rhythmical activities. Every breakthrough of the boundary marks the beginning of illness.

We must now talk about an organ whose significance in this connection is hardly recognized today: the spleen. In 1911 Rudolf Steiner clearly pointed out the importance of its activity. He described how the spleen is inserted into the inner world system of the metabolic organs to fulfill an important regulatory function. The movement of blood, as that of all other bodily fluids, proceeds according to strict rhythmical laws which must be maintained at all costs so that man remains healthy. Opposed to this are man's eating habits which can make use of the digestive organism almost at will. The spleen's function as a rhythmically active organ is to balance this irregularity in the passing of nutrients into the blood rhythm. The spleen is a "switch organ, to balance out irregularities in the digestive tract, so that they become regularities in the blood circulation."[20] Rudolf Steiner attributed a great significance to the rhythm of nutrition.

One should not be pedantic about the matter, but it would be very desirable if the rhythm of eating "would become increasingly regular—especially for children." The state of affairs is actually quite sad when we encourage the excessive snacking and irregular drinking habits of our children. Exceptional demands are made thereby on the spleen, which radiates its rhythmical effects over the whole organism. Rudolf Steiner emphasized this point when he spoke to physicians: through the respiratory system (and in connection with it the circulatory rhythm), man is bound to the strict world rhythm. His irregular eating continually interferes. The spleen acts as a mediator. Rudolf Steiner advised physicians to treat patients with abnormal spleen function by having them eat little at main meals and many smaller portions during the day. This relieves the spleen activity and it is therefore better able to fulfill its rhythmical function. Thus Steiner's advice should be noted as an important suggestion for the practice of nutritional hygiene.

We must return once again to the intestinal peristalsis because this movement is still only part of the great rhythmical organization which permeates the human organism. It is to Rudolf Steiner's credit that he was the first to recognize and describe this rhythmical organization as an independent

Spleen: regulator of digestive processes in dig. tract;

38

RS said: eat little at main meals, many small portions during day.

constituent of man's being. In his book *Riddles of the Soul* (1917),[21] he described the nerve activity, the breathing rhythm, and the metabolic activity, as three forms of activity which interpenetrate, but form the "bodily apparatus" for thinking, feeling, and willing, which include within themselves independent realms of function. An understanding of the threefoldness of the human organism can open new perspectives and insights in understanding the human being. Thus it is essential to the study of nutrition stimulated by Rudolf Steiner.

The Rhythmic Organization
The 24-Hour Rhythm

Modern research into biologic rhythm also shows that rhythmic occurrences play an essential role in the organism and can no longer be overlooked. Sollberger (1972) writes:

> Until recently, anyone who believed in biologic rhythms was held to be more or less crazy. The change can be attributed to several factors: the stubborn persistance of a few biologists and physicians who really believed what they saw with their eyes, namely the successful demonstration that an organism has spontaneous rhythms even though the environment remains unchanged, and that this also happens in metabolism.[22]

Intestinal peristalsis is only one of many such rhythms which are involved in metabolism. Nevertheless, this rhythmic movement is of the greatest significance for the whole digestive and nutritional process. One has only to consider the immediate pathologic consequences that acceleration or retardation of this rhythm has to grasp its importance. These, of course, are very prevalent today in the far too numerous cases of diarrhea and constipation. We can therefore completely agree when Sollberger writes:

> The recognition that knowledge of physiological rhythms is important for diagnosis and treatment of diseases has finally reached the practicing physicians, although much too slowly, in view of the fact that scientists have emphasized this point long ago.

Fundamental studies in this field were made by Rudolf Steiner in the twenties, and in 1952 Günther Wachsmuth published his work on this theme: *Earth and Man, Their Formative Forces, Rhythms and Life Processes.*[24] The 24-hour rhythm (today also designated "circadian rhythm") is thoroughly dis-

39

cussed in this work. Forsgren (1931) also contributed significantly to studies of this rhythm in physiology, and Jores (1933) was one of the first to point to its clinical significance. Through this rhythm, man communicates with the earth and indirectly with the cosmos, especially with the sun.

The following is especially significant to our consideration of the subject of rhythm:

> Modern research has established the surprising fact that the daily variation of metabolism does not depend on the time of food ingestion, but rather, that many metabolic processes in the organism proceed in a definite 24 hour periodicity and are characterized by definite daily maxima and minima.[25]

Not only the activity of the liver, whose "rhythmically alternating assimilatory and secretory activities are, to a high degree, independent of meals," but also fat absorption in the intestinal mucosa, blood glucose enrichment, etc., proceed in these 24-hour rhythms. Jores, in 1940, described the character of this rhythm:

> We are familiar today with a great number of functions in mammals and in man which have a 24-hour periodicity. . . . . Consequently, for life in general, there must be something similar to a central, temporary directory. . . . The multiplicity of the phenomena observed impels us to assume that an inner clock must be made responsible for their direction.[26]

In 1972 Sollberger confessed: "We must admit that the fundamental synchronizing mechanism of biologic rhythms is unknown. We cannot even localize the clock itself."[27] Such an attempt will never succeed, because at the basis of all these rhythmic occurrences is the organization of formative forces, the supersensible force body designated by Rudolf Steiner as "etheric or life body." This force body gives life to the plant, permeates the animal and fills the human organism with individualized life force.

> The organization of formative forces not only builds up the spatial arrangement of specific polarities, regions, organ systems, and single organs, but also affects the course of development inasmuch as specific formative forces intervene in temporal succession. Consequently, depending on the time, one or another kind of formative force dominates, or a rhythmical intervention of centripetal or centrifugal formative forces occurs.[28]

Basis of 24 hr. rhythms: etheric body

40

The same force organization is also active in the earth's atmosphere as Kepler and Goethe have pointed out. In a lecture given December 9, 1909, Rudolf Steiner pointed to this important phenomenon and referred to Goethe, who attempted to establish that the cause of the rise and fall of the barometer lies in the earth.[29]

Although man, with his individualized body of formative forces, has partially emancipated himself from these rhythms, we still find that the 24-hour rhythm is one of the foundations of his life processes. That is why it is necessary to be aware of the full significance of this occurrence. W. Menzel, a prominent rhythm physiologist, justifiably writes in his book *Human Day-Night Rhythm and Shift Labor*:

> No normal life process proceeds without rhythm! The variety is limitless. It extends over plant, animal, and man, to the single cell as well as to cell groups in organs, to the form processes and to time. It extends beyond the "events of life" in the non-living world, into the atmosphere and into the cosmos.[30]

Thus we can say that the total process of man's nutrition is integrated into this rhythmicity, and we can conclude that from these observations the nature of digestion can be significantly illuminated.

Rudolf Steiner asked once: What actually is digestive activity? His answer was: "It is metabolic activity which pushes towards the rhythmical, unfolds itself towards the rhythmical. Digestive activity is metabolism which takes up the rhythm of the organs of circulation."[31] In this activity the substance disappears, as it were, into the rhythm. Thus the muscle activity, which begins with chewing and continues in the peristalsis of esophagus, stomach, and intestine, is also a raising of substance into the rhythmic organism. Similarly the stream of nourishment, when it reaches the threshold of resorption in the small intestine, when it is mineralized and reduced to its basic elements (chaos), is taken up into the inner circulatory rhythm which courses through lymph, blood, and tissue fluids.

It is known that there is a strict relationship of 4:1 between the circulatory rhythm and the respiratory rhythm. This relationship, itself a rhythm, represents that interaction of earth and sun which Rudolf Steiner has frequently emphasized in his lectures: If we calculate the number of breaths per day at 18/minute, we get $(18 \times 60 \times 24) = 25{,}920$. This is also the number of years which the sun needs to travel once through the zodiac—the "Platonic year." That means that man himself is built up according to a world rhythm. And the rhythmical organization manifests itself in respiration and circulation.

41

digestion: breakdown to chaos, then a raising to the rhythmic organisation

Platonic Year: 25,920

Processes which today are so strongly subject to arbitrariness, such as ingestion of food, must become rhythmical to escape the varied illness-bearing impulses and to be incorporated into the health-giving forces of the rhythmical events. "Rhythm heals, arhythmia weakens and makes ill." This phrase, which can be said to be the quintessence of Wachsmuth's findings,[32] and which may even be the most essential criterion of rhythm,[33] is especially applicable to the processes of nutrition and indicative of an important demand for a renewed nutritional hygiene.

Absorption

Nutrients cannot be absorbed until they are sufficiently divested of their individual nature. Every trace of their origin must be destroyed. This process is completed only when the nourishment reaches the small intestine. At the moment of moving from the intestine into the lymph and blood, the chyme nearly becomes subject to outer physical forces. That is how Rudolf Steiner described the digestive process that takes place at the border of the intestinal mucosa.[34] At the same time, he emphasized that this breakdown of food is a specific characteristic of human digestion. It corresponds to the demands and necessities of the Ego-organization, the individualization of the human substance. In the animal this does not happen to the same extent. Its astral organization is not able to destroy foods as completely as man's: "what enters the animal's body still remains similar to the outer organization." Thus the animal is not as far removed from the outer world, the source of its nourishment. Its vegetative and soul qualities are only partially emancipated from the environment.

There are several significant aspects to this assertion. First, it tells us something essential about animal foods. They carry within them the effects of not only the terrestrial, but also the cosmic environment. The lower the development of the animal, the more strongly are these effects in evidence. Consequently, food from a fish, an oyster, or even a snail has a totally different inner quality in relation to man than does beef, for example. (We will further concern ourselves with this issue in our discussion of different kinds of food.) Secondly, it points up the fact that the excretions of animals are correspondingly different from human excretion. This raises the problem of fertilization, which also has to be taken into consideration in evaluating food quality. Finally, the above assertion casts a significant light on the limited validity of applying results of metabolic experiments in animals to man. The entire metabolism of animals is actually determined by processes different than those of man. They are similar and comparable only insofar as the animal organization achieves an ensouling of the body substances. This takes place—as we will see subsequently in more detail—also in man, but in

42

man it is prepared for the still higher condition of penetration with individual forces.

The intestinal digestive processes, of a remarkably vital nature, are closely connected with the digestive processes started in the mouth, but their realm of origin lies in the inner organs of man. They are still experimentally approachable in absorption, insofar as they take place in the blood and lymphatic vessels of the intestinal mucosa, especially in those of the duodenum.

When the chyme reaches this step, it encounters a truly important inner organ of man, namely the intestinal mucosa. Physiologists have long been concerned with the functions of this barrier. Without going into detail, it is evident that this intestinal wall is a highly specialized, living organ that continually impresses scientists with the uniqueness of its construction. It is covered with millions of small formations called villi. There are 2500-3000 of them per square meter, which expand the intestinal absorptive area to approximately 40 square meters. Every villus has within it a central lymph vessel, fine nerve fibers from the solar plexus, and a small artery which branches out into a capillary net. Smooth muscles are everywhere. One can see that all members of the human being are united in these highly specialized organelles: the life activity of the lymph, the unconscious soul forces in the nerves, the Ego-organization in the blood. These villi move rhythmically; every villus contracts independently of the others, but all move in a uniform rhythm, approximately six times a minute. The contraction is more rapid than the relaxation, i.e., they move in the rhythm long-short, corresponding to the trochee. With this rhythmic gesture they immerse themselves in the chyme, move forward, sense it and take it up. They are not only active in life activity, but also in perception. It has actually been discovered that they are extraordinarily sensitive. They taste, as it were, the liquified food as it moves through the intestine and are stimulated in the most varied ways. From within, too, via the nerves and the blood, as well as hormonal activities, the movement of these fine organs is regulated.

It is thus apparent that when we speak of digestion we are not concerned with merely passive activities subject to physical-chemical laws, but with "active achievements" which take place in the living intestinal mucosa. When—as is frequently the case today because of poor food quality—unphysiological substances, foreign to the body, against which digestive enzymes are ineffective, reach the region of absorption, then—as proved by experiment—absorption occurs according to the physical-chemical laws of diffusion. The higher activities of the mucosa do not become active at all or are only insufficiently active. The vital and sensory functions of the villi appear to be paralyzed. Something similar occurs in cases of food allergies, which are ever increasing. In such cases, because of an abnormal mucosal

43

permeability, certain protein substances, insufficiently denatured, penetrate into the organism. There they elicit hypersensitivity reactions, which have a variety of manifestations, e.g., eczematous formations. Everywhere we can see how a paralysis of the higher activities is manifested in pathologically abnormal reactions, which lead to delayed, but frequently violent defensive reactions.

On the intestinal wall there is not only a "sucking in," but also a separation of the different constituents of food: substances destined for fat formation are channeled into the lymphatic vessels, the others into the blood vessels. Here, too, the synthesis of individualized substances takes place. In fact, the newly formed, individualized substances appear everywhere in the organism after a very brief time, although modern metabolic research reports that the necessary processes are exceedingly complex.

It will not be our goal in what follows immediately to report all the results of modern research or to attempt to integrate them into the picture which Rudolf Steiner's Spiritual Science developed. That will be done later with a few examples in our discussion of proteins, carbohydrates, and fats. Instead, we will attempt here to sketch with a few strokes the great picture which Rudolf Steiner developed of this aspect of nutrition and to explain what led him in his lecture of October 27, 1922, to begin his presentation with the words: "It is at this point that for the first time our way of looking at things has to become heresy when contrasted with official natural science."[35]

Devitalization and Revitalization of Nourishment

The processes which have led the ingested nourishment to the intestinal mucosa are essentially destructive. They bring about the removal of every trace of external life. We have observed particularly that minerals require the least transformation in us; they are already inorganic outside of man. This holds also for sugar, insofar as it is almost completely mineralized by external preparation. However, everything we take as nourishment from plants and animals must lose its life as well. The animal food must in addition be divested of its typical animalistic character. This means that the human organism has to be capable of performing a definite function. The manner of preparation, cooking, baking, etc., also plays a role. As a result of all these processes, there must be this "de-vitalization" before the human organism is able to take up the nourishment into its life and soul organisms.

Rudolf Steiner described these processes concretely when he said that we cannot allow our nourishment in its natural state to approach the intestinal villi. The etheric and the astral aspects of foods must also be removed,[36] and their removal must be accomplished on the threshold of the intestinal wall.

the villi

As we have shown, this is also an organ, full of life forces and sensitivity. It is the location where, as it were, the whole inner aspect of the human organism mirrors itself, and where the inner organs, especially, send their activities.

We must understand here that man's inner organs, the liver, lungs, kidneys, etc., represent centers which are permeated in a manifold manner by etheric and astral forces, within which the Ego-organization acts in a differentiated manner. This is evident, for example, in that the protein of every organ is of a specific nature. Every organ thus has a sort of sphere, within which it is active in the vicinity of its physical formation. Such organ spheres are also active in the intestinal wall as dynamic activities.

The first process which takes place on this threshold is the taking up of broken-down nutrients into the individual etheric body. Thereby a revitalization occurs at the moment when they reach the blood and lymph vessels of the intestinal villi. Rudolf Steiner points out, however, that this is actually a function of the heart-lung organism, which leads "the food which has become completely inorganic, into the living." There it is "caught up" into the etheric organization, and a "vitalization" takes place. This is only possible, however, because the etheric body is able to continually renew itself with the help of inspired oxygen. It is oxygen, then, which "makes into living earthly substance what would otherwise disappear into the etheric body." That means, by combination with oxygen, the substance is not only revitalized, but is also integrated as vitalized substance into the terrestrial laws. "The whole etheric system is pulled down . . . . into the physical." Were this not the case, substances would dissolve into the purely etheric.[37]

step one (etheric)

The carbon structure of the individual organization, as well as of foods, serves as a point of contact between this activity and the physical. It is carbon which provides the basic structure of all organic substances; it "fixates the actual physical organization." Were we to stop this life-giving act (the new creation of vitalized substance, especially of protein, in our organism), then we would be unable to unfold a soul life, much less a spiritual life. A further step has to be achieved: the ensouling of vitalized substance. This too takes place in an organ sphere: the kidney system.

In his *Occult Physiology*, Rudolf Steiner described how the heart and circulation must be able to continually harmonize the activities originating from without and from within.[38] This can only be done because we have in our kidney system such an equalizing organ which can continually remove the excess resulting from this harmonization. In other words, the kidney system continually has to remove and excrete the remnants of the inner activity of the blood system. This activity is mediated by the kidney system when it excretes the useless excess. This whole process is connected with breakdown processes. We can follow the necessity of this breakdown to substances which again approach the organic, e.g., urea, uric acid, etc.

O_2 + nutrient + etheric body → vitalized

ensouling of vitalized substance → the kidney sphere

The astral body is active in this devitalization and deformation. In this sense the astral body embodies itself in the kidney. The secretion out of the blood which takes place there conveys to man the subconscious experience so "that man confronts the outer world as an inner being. . ."[39] Thereby he becomes aware of himself. Kidney function is subject to laws of pressure and gases as they are evident in osmosis, indicating that the gaseous, the airy, is active in the kidney. The laws governing gases mirror themselves in the formation of the urine. This holds true for the forces active in blood pressure as well as for the pressure and suction activities involved in the formation of urine in the kidney. Steiner adds that ensouled man cannot come about unless there is a direct interchange with his air nature.[40] From this "gaseous organization" the astral-organic forces radiate into the human organism. The kidney itself, as physical organ, is made possible by this radiation process. In this way the whole human organism is permeated with perceptive abilities. The ingested substance, lifted to the stage of life by the heart-lung system, becomes ensouled in this way.

The forces radiating from the kidney, which represent the counter pole to urine production and excretion, extend over the whole organism. Its sphere includes all organs and all parts of the body, including the head. In this way everything we have taken up as nutrients is "delivered" into the astral body. Contrasted with the pure life-forces active through the heart-circulatory system, this astral radiation is a formative force. This is why the kidney system acts in such a way that that which through the heart activity is "liquid, swimming away, is now formed into certain organs. . . . The formation of these organs is mediated by the kidneys." This happens with the help of the head system, which halts the radiations originating in the kidney, and gives the organs form. Rudolf Steiner illustrated these relationships in a verbal picture.[41] We can understand his description if we imagine someone throwing up a substance with one hand and catching it and shaping it from above with the other. The first activity corresponds to the activity of the kidneys, which become organs once their substances have been caught and formed. In these dynamic processes the kidney uses nitrogen, both excreted to the outside as urea and uric acid, and inwardly again to structure proteins.

In old times such knowledge was used in urine analysis. One spoke of an "astral mummy" that could be discovered in the constitution of the urine, by which one could diagnose the health or diseased state of a man, and from which one also could know what remedies and special diets were to be prescribed.

Modern physiology has established that the content of uric acid, insofar as it moves through the brain, is correlated to some extent with human intelligence. Steiner and Wegmann point out that this uric acid, as it is secreted into the brain, provides there the foundation for the nerve-sense activity which makes waking consciousness possible.[42] Thus this substance, which is, as it were, secreted into the brain, does not establish a relation to the soul, but rather to the spirit part of the human organism. It thus enters the service of the Ego-organization.

The Humanization of Nutrients
The Role of the Liver-Gall Activity

We have now arrived at the fourth stage which substance must reach on the way to humanization. This is at once the most important and most decisive step: the incorporation of substance into the Ego-organization. While the first three stages are also realized to some extent in the animal, this last one takes place exclusively in man. It is the step which, even today, continues to be an enigma to physiology and anthropology.

The formation of the human brain is recognized as far exceeding that of even the highest animal forms in size, complexity, and function. And it is also known that no one human brain is like another. Yet the key has not been found to unlock the riddle of this individualization of form and substance and the arising of the waking Ego-consciousness connected with it. One scientist literally demands that "a specific immanent organizational principle must be presupposed in an organism." (Bertalanfey, 1949) Yet with resignation others acknowledge: "A peculiarity such as the spiritual is not explained by this model. . . . What we know is determined indirectly and with extreme uncertainty."[43]

Such quotations are in no way meant to diminish the serious and significant character of these studies. On the contrary, they show how complicated these problems are and how we can get nowhere with simplifications. But what is decisive is that the method of Spiritual Scientific research established by Rudolf Steiner makes it possible to recognize the spiritual in matter, to comprehend that "everything which surrounds us as matter is an effect and expression of the spiritual. Thus behind everything material, which we take into ourselves through nourishment, there is the spiritual. . . . Thereby we establish through nutrition a relationship to the spiritual, a substrate of the physical."[44] We, today, with the help of the method of Spiritual Science, can put ourselves into the position of evaluating and ascertaining the results of Spiritual Scientific research by comparing them with the most recent results of the natural sciences. What may be more important, however, is that we can comprehend with our own thinking that these results are true and can be verified in daily life.

In rising to the fourth stage of the inner nutritional processes, Rudolf Steiner's presentation takes up from the heart system and kidney system into the liver system. "The liver system, which, with its secretion of bile, drives everything into our actual Ego."[45] Although it will be asserted that animals also have liver-bile organs, it should be clear that they are not taken hold of by the same kinds of forces as those in man. In the higher animals we have, as it were, attempts to incorporate a higher formative principle, and we can study these animals and learn how this principle is active. Nevertheless, even in these studies, we must not fail to recognize the special position of man.

Bile represents a separation from the blood which meets the chyme, especially the fats, in the small intestine. In the formation of bile, the liver acts in a sucking manner on the blood and removes toxic substances and products of breakdown activities. In this sense the liver is, via the bile formation, the great blood cleanser in man, the detoxifier. In this way it also regulates the composition of the blood itself by stimulating, through bile secretion, the formation of blood. Just as the formation of urine in the kidney provides relief and at the same time initiates an impulse for new activities, so too, the formation of bile by the liver cleanses the blood and stimulates its production. Thereby the liver becomes the instrument of the Ego-organization which is active in the blood. It must guarantee continually and simultaneously that the blood can become a cleansing and productive instrument. It does this, as we have already explained, according to the model of the 24-hour rhythm, which Rudolf Steiner has characterized as the actual "Ego-rhythm."

At the same time, the liver actively participates, via secretion of bile, in the digestive process in the small intestine. Here one can see how these inner nutritional processes also take hold of events on this side of the intestinal wall. The liver activity actually begins, as will be evident later, in the mouth.

The fatty acids contained in the ingested fats will only become soluble and subsequently absorbable when they combine with the bile acids. This combination, however, is rapidly dissolved again and the bile acids are transported back to the liver via the blood. One speaks therefore of an "enterohepatic circulation of the bile acids." As a result of the combination of bile acids with food fats, very small fat droplets form, which present an enormous surface area for the pancreatic lipase activity. The lipases are secreted into the small intestine when bile covers the mucosa and are activated by bile.

Bile is also necessary for the further digestion of proteins in the intestine. The small undigested fats surround the protein and thereby prevent the access of water soluble enzymes. If the bile is prevented from being active, or if not enough is formed, then protein breakdown as well as fat digestion suffers. Undigested protein begins to decay in the colon and forms a source for far-reaching disease processes.

48

Effects of Cholesterol

Here we must mention cholesterol, the substance which, in the last few years, has led to many erroneous opinions. Formed only in the human and animal organism (thereby revealing its astral nature), cholesterol is also involved in the "entero-hepatic circulation." It is formed in the liver and also in the intestinal mucosa. It is furthermore the starting substance in the synthesis of bile acids.

This substance can be found in all body fluids and tissues and has without a doubt a universal function. Since it is synthesized primarily in the liver, it also represents a function of this organ. It appears to be especially significant that its main location and, indeed, its main activity in the organism is in two organ spheres: the brain and the adrenal glands. In the latter, cholesterol is completely involved in the dynamics of metabolism in that it participates in the building-up activities of the kidney system, in the sense of astralization of substance. By contrast, in the brain, where it predominates quantitatively, it appears to be stable, i.e., its mass and concentration do not appear to be subject to nutritionally dependent variations. Today one even suspects that it "is embedded in the brain for the duration of life," and "probably does not participate anymore in the general metabolism."[46] In any case, it is there ordered into the restfulness, the lifelessness of the human nerve-pole. This does not happen, however, until about the fifth year when the formation of the brain is completed. Chiefly, it is found in the white matter, the "think-substance," as Rudolf Steiner called it, less so in the gray matter which primarily serves metabolism.

It is important that the amount of cholesterol derived from our food is far exceeded by that synthesized by the liver. One can hypothesize that the food cholesterol only represents a stimulus for the liver synthesis, and that the two interact. Thus it seems clear that too much food cholesterol can bring about an imbalance in the whole cholesterol metabolism. Cholesterol can also be excreted via the bile, and the fact that it contributes significantly to gallstones makes evident what the manifestation of such an imbalance could be.

These observations in no way exhaust the activities of cholesterol. It is known today that, besides involvement in the synthesis of bile salts, cholesterol is also the basic substance in the synthesis of the multitude of steroid hormones. Thus it is evident that this substance is necessary for life, or more accurately, that it is essential for the functions of the astral body. The dangers of a loss of equilibrium, and its consequent effects on the heart, are well studied today. When we realize, for example, that the excretion of cholesterol is inhibited by animal foods, while it is stimulated by plant foods, then we are already in the midst of important questions raised by modern nutrition.

49

Carbohydrate Metabolism *liver – Ego org*

The nature of carbohydrate metabolism, which is one of the primary functions of the liver, has been significantly illuminated by Spiritual Science. Rudolf Steiner pointed out that carbohydrates develop in the plant by virtue of the sun forces. Without the cosmic light and warmth radiations of the sun, no sugar formation would be possible on the earth as it is now. Ultimately, this is also true for fats and proteins. Through the release of oxygen by the plant in the formation of carbohydrates, men, as well as animals, depend indirectly on the sun forces for their earthly existence. Interacting with earthly forces and substances, the plant condenses its bodily substance out of the cosmic sun ether. This consists primarily in building up carbohydrates out of the carbon skeleton. In this sense M. Bircher-Benner also spoke of the "resounding of the cosmic sun" in our foods.

The liver has a special relationship to these substances. The starch, as it is formed in plants, undergoes a reconstruction in the liver into glycogen. This is formed as a mirror image, as it were, of the densification of cosmic radiation in the liver. From there it is poured into the human organism via the blood. Active in this transformation is man's highest member, the Ego-organization. This result of Rudolf Steiner's Spiritual Science casts a significant light on our relationship to sugar. Not starch, but the glucose derived from starch is a substance "which can be active in the realm of the Ego-organization. It corresponds to the taste of sweetness which resides in the Ego-organization."[47] More precisely, when the starch is transformed into sugar, the taste of sweetness is not in consciousness. "But what goes on in consciousness—in the realm of the Ego-organization—when sweetness is experienced, penetrates into the subconscious regions of the human body, and the Ego-organization becomes active there."[48]

This "region" of the Ego-organization is, above all, the liver, whose sphere of activity on the one hand extends up to the taste organs in the mouth, and on the other, permeates man in the blood. It is important to emphasize here that this Ego-activity is delimited by clear and strict boundaries. This is demonstrated, for example, by the fact that the blood glucose content, which is regulated by the liver, is held near a relatively constant level of 0.1%. Too much as well as too little blood sugar makes man sick. One should not be led by Steiner's indications to the foolish conclusion that the more sugar one eats, the stronger the Ego-organization becomes. The activity of the Ego-organization is ordered by strict boundaries of quantity and quality of sugar. This will become evident later in our full discussion of sugar metabolism.

Here these indications were given just to point out another central function of the liver, which establishes this organ as the center of the metabolic activity of the human Ego-organization. All these and still many other functions allow us to designate the liver as a "chemist," and the indications of Spiritual Science can lead us still further. "Man has within himself a 'chemicator.' He has within himself something of the heavenly sphere in which the origin of chemical actions lies. And what is active in such a way is strongly localized in man," namely the liver. And we can study this extraterrestrial sphere "when we study all these magnificent actions of the human liver."[49]

This should also make it evident why the liver is actually a sort of "enclave" in man, one in which processes occur which are most similar to processes outside of man, "so that man is actually least man in the liver."[50] Just as the eye is directed towards the outer world and perceives what approaches with the light out of cosmic expanses, the liver is also a sense organ which has "a fine sensitivity for the nutritive value of different substances," which we ingest. The liver continually perceives what enters from the outside as chemism, but also as another cosmic force, namely warmth.

Warmth as Carrier of the Ego-organization

We will later see the practical consequences of the "enclave" character of the liver, but here it will direct us to the Ego-character of its functions. Through the Ego we again open ourselves to the world after first separating ourselves from it. In this way the substance in us, after it has been ensouled by the kidney system, is taken up into the Ego-organization through the liver-gall system. And here warmth serves as the medium in which the highest human organization can live. For what exists in the warmth-structure, in the liver-gall system, "radiates in such a way that man is permeated with what the Ego-organization is, which after all is bound to the warmth differentiations in the whole organism."[51]

The foregoing comments bring us to a decisive point in our presentation. The liver, which is not only the center of chemism, of the fluid-organism, is also the center of the warmth-organization of man. With its temperature of 41°C it is not only the warmest organ, but also the one that regulates the warmth metabolism. And while the kidney uses the air for its activity, the Ego-organization takes hold of the warmth in the liver to regulate all warmth differentiations. To that end it utilizes hydrogen, the chemical element closest to warmth, just as the kidney uses nitrogen and the heart-lung system uses oxygen.

This warmth activity is closely related to the sugar process. For when the liver transforms plant sugar into human sugar, then "it hands over this inner sugar to the whole body which thereby receives its inner warmth."

Warmth — medium where Ego lives [51]

Liver: center of "chemism" and warmth. Used H_2
kidney: ensouls substance (astral) uses air
heart/lung: uses O_2

Warmth, which, just like sugar, is held constant in the human organism, is a guardian over the activity of the Ego-organization. Too much or too little blood warmth means illness. It is evident from the central role of warmth, especially in relation to the Ego-organization, that man is a being of warmth. His total bodily, as well as soul-spiritual, existence is organized with reference to warmth. This is also a decisive factor in the evaluation of temperature in nutrition, of the significance of warmth in the preparation of meals, etc. Only from this starting point will it be possible to attain a rational point of view concerning the application of warmth and coldness in human nutrition.

Now we have arrived not only at a decisive point in the content of our discussion, but also at a methodologically important point. Warmth actually forms the bridge between the sensible and the super-sensible. It is soul-spiritual and at the same time it is of a sensible nature. These two aspects of its being are not separate, but are bound together, especially in man: the Ego-organization, which is similarly active in both directions, combines the sensible with the super-sensible and creates a bridge between these two worlds in man himself. Because of his warmth, man participates not only in the warmth organism of nature, but communicates at the same time with the warmth-force of the world spirituality. Through warmth, the human Ego not only kindles the normal waking day consciousness, it also "warms" itself with moral ideals, which manifest themselves to the extent of increasing the warmth in man's warmth organism.

Rudolf Steiner devoted three lectures to this "cardinal question of man's view of the world," as he called it.[52] The methodological aspects of these lectures are fundamental for our theme because they show that with the help of Spiritual Scientific research methods we can learn to justifiably speak about the fact that "behind everything material lies the spiritual." Furthermore, they illuminate a far-reaching problem which we have mentioned earlier: the necessity and ability of the individualization of substance in man. Rudolf Steiner asks in these lectures: "Where lie the sources of life?" His answer is that they lie in what "stimulates the moral ideals which inspire man." We find this "source of world-creativity" if we direct our attention to man's warmth organism. We can recognize that with our intellectual, abstract thinking we have a "chilling" effect on the warmth organism. It also has a "paralyzing" effect on the air-organism, an "extinguishing" effect on the life in us. From this cold pole of his nature man streams out an actual death process extending down into the physical body. These death forces, which we carry in our head as breakdown forces, and which enable us to think abstractly, are the same which bring about the disappearance, the destruction of substance and force us "down to the zero-point." But just by virtue of that destruction do we first achieve our self-consciousness. Our Ego, which tolerates no foreign life within itself, ignites our self-consciousness on the combustion, the turning to ashes, of the world substance. "We become conscious of the world and we become human beings only when the thought process has left all life behind." But after the old natural substance has passed away in the dying-off, a new sprouting begins, a new beginning, a future. In the warmth-fire of our will-being the new substance develops as an instrument for the individuality. At the same time the soul-spiritual lives in us as moral force in these new substances. "A world that has passed away dies in us down to substance, down to force. And only because another one arises right away, do we not notice that substance disappears and arises again." This process is hidden today because it also passes over the customary time relations. In fact, modern researchers like Professor Manfred Eigen have demonstrated that many metabolic reactions in the human organism proceed not only within seconds, but within fractions of seconds.

These findings lead us to a recognition of what is contained in Rudolf Steiner's words: When we follow the bodily to warmth, then we will be able "to cast a bridge from the warmth in bodies to what acts out of the soul into the warmth of the human organism."[53]

Man carries a cold pole in his being. It is localized in his head, his nerve-sense organism, his brain. It makes possible abstract thinking and also the waking consciousness based on the body. But man's true nature lies in the still germ-like warmth-will organization. He has to overcome the coldness of the head to overcome the paralysis of the limbs. He must create anew and revitalize the destroyed substance with the cosmic will forces and impress on it the seal of his entelechy. This fire nature of man creates its source of warmth in the liver.

Thus it is not surprising that modern man is endangered in just this organ. It is also clear that our nutrition has to take this fact into account, and that the question: "What does the Ego-conscious consumer expect from nutrition?" is exceedingly relevant today. One might even rephrase this question by asking: Of what does our nourishment have to consist in order to speak to these Ego-forces, to further, rather than to paralyze them, to awaken, rather than to undermine them?

With the penetration of substance by the forces of the Ego-organization, as it happens through the liver-gall activity, the nutritional process has reached its culminating point, its completion. Insofar as this happening interacts with processes in the intestine, still further processes play an important role. They reach from the small intestine over to the large intestine. We are led thereby to the excretory processes which are also of special significance for all of nutrition.

Significance of Intestinal Peristalsis

Two occurrences in the intestine are indispensable for digestive processes and for excretion: peristalsis and the presence and activity of the intestinal flora. In describing the peristaltic movements, we have thus far only pointed to the rhythmic villus movements which play such an important role in absorption in the small intestine, but the intestinal movements themselves also participate in the digestive occurrences.

While the chewing movements of the jaws, which submit foods to their first working over in the oral cavity, proceed in consciousness and therefore need man's attention, this consciousness disappears with the act of swallowing. The movements of the esophagus proceed subconsciously. There the rhythmical movements begin and continue in a differentiated manner through the whole stomach-intestinal tract. Only at its end, at the rectum, consciousness again enters into the movements. Actual elimination in man is somewhat subject to willful control. That is why this process is more accessible to consciousness and presents, like the act of chewing, a rather frequent source of dangers, which we will discuss later. In between lies the unconscious rhythmical movement, of which we become painfully aware only in illness. This movement can be divided into three main sections: the stomach peristalsis, the small intestinal movements, and the large intestinal movements.

This whole movement organism (we purposely avoid the usually applied term "mechanism") is determined by a multiplicity of factors which are all intricately interrelated. It becomes quite evident here how sensitive all these organs are and how strongly perceptive processes are involved in their function. Thus the process of nutrition depends not only upon the kind and quantity of meals, their condition, consistency or temperature, but also upon the psychological state of the consumer. It is important, for example, whether eating occurs with a good appetite or with repugnance, i.e., what the soul mood is during eating. The various conditions at mealtime therefore significantly affect nutritional hygiene. Not only can inadequate food quality disturb the appetite and in that way paralyze digestive processes, but the environment also can have its effect, depending on whether it is "appetizing" in the widest sense of the word. It is perhaps not fortuitous that in Latin the word *humores* designates not only the body juices, i.e., the digestive juices, but also humor. A bad or depressed mood, worry, or uneasiness are just as detrimental to nutrition as inadequate quality of foods and insufficient chewing.

Clearly the soul processes accessible to our consciousness thus influence the subconscious occurrences in the intestinal tract. They are experienced there, especially in their interference with the movement processes, by slowing them down or speeding them up. All too frequently pathological processes are the result. Steiner and Wegmann have this in mind when they speak of the sympathetic nervous system which innervates the digestive organs. The organs of this system affect the inner movements by speeding them up or slowing them down. They are, as the name "vegetative nervous system" indicates, "primarily only living organs." Influences of the higher members of man—the Ego and astral body—"do not organize them from within, but from the outside."[54] That is why their influence is so strong. "Affects and passions have a lasting, significant effect on the sympathetic nervous system; suffering and worries gradually destroy this system." That such soul states are often related to stomach or intestinal ulcers, as well as increased stomach acidity, is well known.

These soul influences play a lesser role in the small and large intestinal movements. The latter proceed primarily in a state reminiscent of deep sleep, inaccessible to man, while for the stomach there is still a sort of dream consciousness. But the peristaltic movements, which advance the chyme in the intestine, can be increased by soul disturbances, for example, fear, which results in diarrhea. Chemical influences are also known to affect intestinal movements. Besides the advancing movement, there are also oscillatory movements, consisting in a back and forth movement of intestinal contents. Significantly these movements depend on the intestinal temperature.

To these considerations still other aspects are important. B. Thomas has made an especially significant contribution in his work, *Die Nähr-und Ballaststoffe der Getreidemehle in ihrer Bedeutung für die Brotnahrung.** In his convincing demonstrations he comes to the conclusion that whole grain products are very important for an orderly digestive process. Their presence in foods increases intestinal motility, because the peristaltic movements "proceed with more vitality, the more the content of the foods consists of undigestible and chemically-mechanically stimulating substances."[58] The effects of such an increased intestinal motility are summarized by Thomas in the following points:

—more intensive mixing of the chyme
—increased excretion of digestive secretions (including bile and cholesterol)
—enhancement of blood circulation and the resorptive activity of the
intestinal epithelium

*The Nutritive and Roughage Substance in Flours in Their Significance for Bread Nutrition.

—more rapid absorption of fermented food substances
—more rapid transfer into the blood and more rapid flow of venous blood out of the intestinal mucosa
—transport of resorbed substances from intestine to liver and partial acceleration of chyme transport.

We can see from this list what significance can be attributed to food quality when it stimulates intestinal motility and thereby stimulates digestive processes on both sides of the intestinal wall. All this is also confirmed by Rudolf Steiner in a lecture to the workers: "If one can tolerate coarse bread, then it is actually the healthiest nourishment."[56] We will pursue the question of tolerance later, but in what follows we shall show how Spiritual Science has brought still different points of view to bear on the issue of intestinal function.

Polarity of the Human Configuration

We pointed out earlier that, in the sense of a dynamic nutrition, we must take into consideration the polarity of the human configuration as it expresses itself between the restful head-formation, as center of the nerve-sense organization, and the metabolic organization, completely based on movement and localized in the organs of the digestive tract. Rudolf Steiner suggested, for example, that we engage in comparative studies of intestine and brain development in animals, especially of the forebrain, which is so important for the evolution of consciousness. In his own studies he arrived at the astonishing result that "the highest soul-spiritual activity found in the human physical world, insofar as it is bound to a complete development of the brain, is dependent at the same time on a corresponding development of the intestine."[57] For the activity of the brain, the dynamics of intestinal movements and processes play an essential role. When, for example, because of stagnation, protein digestion in the intestine is inadequate so that decaying processes predominate, then there will be disturbances which express themselves, among other ways, in "headaches and impairment of spiritual processes."[58] This is also evident in chronic constipation, in which the prolonged stay of the feces in the rectum brings about such an interaction.

This "intimate relationship between the intestinal formation and the brain formation" has concrete significance for both areas. "So that on the one side they are relieved of physical activity for the benefit of thinking, they must burden the organism on the other side in the developed colon."[59] The duration for which the feces, returned again to solidity, subject to gravity and accessible to human consciousness, remains in the rectum must be proper in

56

order to effectively "relieve" the other side. Through this process what is prepared for excretion can be adequately devitalized, and at the same time subjected to formative forces as a sort of mirror image to the formative forces in the human head. In this sense Rudolf Steiner spoke of an "imitation of the silica-forming process" through the brain, i.e., that form-giving effect of substance which plays such an important role in the formation of the sense organs and the brain.

We can evaluate the significance of this polarity, this metamorphosis from above downwards, from still another perspective. Just as the senses predominate in the head, the whole digestive process presents itself as a transformation of sense activity, at least up to the moment "where the nutrients are given over by the intestinal activity to the lymph-and-blood-forming activity." The further this sense function extends downward, the more it immerses itself, as it were, into an organ-like activity.

Out of the understanding of the digestive process as transformed sense process which functions in an organ-like manner (Steiner speaks directly of a "continued taste-sensation process"), Rudolf Steiner arrived at the following conclusion: "If one really knows how to appreciate such a fact, then one establishes the foundation . . . . for all of dietetics."[60] Such a way of looking at the matter leads to real and practical results. Thus we have a concrete point of contact for nutritional hygiene stimulated by Spiritual Science.

In the same lecture Rudolf Steiner also makes an important observation with respect to tooth formation. This formation, terminating in a mineralization of a high degree, represents an opposite pole to the mobility of the intestine. For the peristaltic movement "is intimately related to what on the other side is taken care of by the tooth formation." This too has practical consequences: namely, when the dentist finds that the teeth become carious, then he should make certain "that the whole digestive activity of man is decreased somewhat in intensity," by, for example, giving "remedies which quiet down the digestion."[61]

Such an indication reveals that Rudolf Steiner considered the causes of caries to be primarily determined from within—a concept which is quite prevalent today. Later we will further discuss this whole complex of questions, including the significance of flourine, insofar as it plays an important role in nutritional hygiene.

Significance of Intestinal Flora

Another relationship which also illuminates our understanding of the total being of man is the significance of the intestinal flora in the digestive processes. It must be considered quite remarkable that man's large and small intestines are populated by a rich flora, by foreign organisms, which have

57

entered into a symbiotic relationship with man.

Fr. Baumgärtel, one of the foremost authorities on the intestinal flora, wrote an important work on this subject.[62] In it we find that at least seven different kinds of bacteria, each with a different function in digestion, are "obligate" inhabitants of the human intestine. While the upper small intestine is normally free from bacteria, the actual microbial flora begins in the subsequent portion of the small intestine. First the coliform organisms and the aerobic lactobacilli predominate. Further down in the cecum, the actual "fermentation chamber" of the intestinal tract, besides the coliforms, there are *Bacterium saccharobutyricus*, fermenting carbohydrates, and *Bacterium putrificus*, breaking down protein. Towards the rectum the masses of bacteria die off and are predominantly excreted with the feces. Thus there are continuous fermentation and decay processes in the populated intestinal segments. It is essential to understand that just in the region which is inaccessible to consciousness, there is an active life activity; the continuous dying off of bacteria necessitates uninterrupted multiplication and new formation.

The normal healthy digestive processes proceed in an exceptionally meaningful interaction of the most varied factors. They are regulated by a multitude of glandular secretions and enzymes and are in a balanced relationship with the microflora activities which are dependent on alkaline or acid milieus. The intestinal flora appears to be tamed, as it were, by the organism's activity mediated by glands, enzymes, etc. This is, however, a labile interaction which is reestablished with every digestive activity. It can be disturbed in many different ways, but it can also be stimulated by the quality of foods and also by the upper digestive processes. Today the disturbances predominate and bring about many of the prevalent intestinal diseases.

How is it possible that such an extensive population of organisms from the lower plant and animal realms can populate man's intestine? This population is started in the first hours after birth by an "infection" from the mother during birth. One can even say that when the human child is born, one of the conditions of its life on earth is that it become host to the intestinal flora. The discoverer of the intestinal flora of the infant, Escherich (1886), remarked, "that every individual has his own race of B. coli."[63] It appears that the appendix is the breeding place for these individual B. coli, which, from there, spread out over the rest of the intestine. These "personal B. coli" are today considered to be "a consequence of the natural acclimatization of this bacterium to the intestine of the individual."[64] For that reason a pathological deterioration of this "biologically normal" flora can occur, i.e., because of the "individualization" of intestinal bacteria, their pathological deterioration is favored.

Insofar as the plant process continues in man, it meets, especially in the

58

small intestine, an atmosphere which at first encourages this vegetative life. There, in the state of deep sleep, is a milieu which supports plant life through its alkalinity. Nevertheless, we also find impulses here which oppose outer natural processes and thereby bring about the need for a continual adaptation of these coliform bacteria (which are also very prevalent in outer nature) in the individual carrier. Thereby a pushing back of the pure plant formation processes is achieved, or, in other words, formative forces are taken away from our intestinal flora which in outer nature are bound together with it. These formative forces, pulled out by the human Ego, can then be used for higher activities.

In his first medical course Rudolf Steiner said: "What goes on in outer nature as flora is parallel to our intestinal flora, in that there are the formative forces which we pull out of our intestinal flora."[65] If we did not take these forces away, or if we were unable to take them away, then we would have to remain beings of nature in this part of our organisms. That is in fact what happens in many cases of disease. The formative force removed by one's own activity can after its removal be used by the soul-spiritual. The intestinal flora is therefore different than the flora outside, because the flora outside retains all of its formative force. And so we arrive at Rudolf Steiner's significant conclusion: "In this way we obtain a concrete concept of the relationship of formative forces in the realm of plants to what goes on in us when we develop an intestinal flora whose formative forces we take away." If we did not take them away, "we would not be thinking human beings."

In the intestinal flora, we activate, once again, a process which has also been active in the preceding digestive processes: the overcoming of the foreign nature of food, the liberation of these formative forces in order to achieve an individual build-up of our body substance. Here, in the activity of the microflora, a very particular interaction between upper and lower poles of the organism is necessary in order to liberate these formative forces out of the lower man for use by the upper man. If, however, "an inadequate opposing activity" comes from above, so that it cannot contain the lower vegetative processes, then one gets "an excessive intestinal flora," a pathological deterioration and overgrowth. The continual overcoming of this danger requires not only the activity of the Ego-organization, but also the activity of the astral body and the individualized etheric body in this realm.

Aspects of Protein and Fat Digestion
Fermentation of Carbohydrates

Three essential processes of digestion are connected with proteins, carbohydrates, and fats. The first two are directly related to the activity of the intestinal flora: the decaying processes of carbohydrates. Both are necessary, but both have to be held within definite boundaries; a continuous balance must be maintained.

Protein decay, which takes place primarily in the colon with the help of the bacterial flora, results in various poisonous substances which have to be detoxified by the liver. The presence of these substances allows for the possibility of a predominance of such decay processes. The danger of this predominance is a subject to which an increasing amount of attention has been paid. Again and again one reads of the possible dangers of absorbing toxic substances from the colon. Such absorption appears to be promoted by excessive meat in the diet, which, as we have pointed out, reflects itself even in man's state of consciousness. (We will discuss this in more detail later in dealing with specific diets.)

Notable here is what Rudolf Steiner emphasized in a lecture to workers. He directed attention to protein insofar as it is subject to the life and growth processes. He explained that, to a certain extent, the activity of the etheric body is connected with protein formation and protein digestion: "All protein is semi-liquid. The human etheric body has access to all that is semi-liquid."[66] In this sense the etheric body also has to counteract the decaying processes of protein: "The etheric body battles against, and is victorious over, decay." Today, however, the question is whether the etheric body is even able to fight against decay adequately.

The third process referred to above is that in which fats become rancid. In the digestion of fat a process takes place which today is usually labelled fermentation, but is more appropriately termed "becoming rancid." It takes place in the upper small intestine, in the duodenum. While decaying, with its associated gas formation, is related to smelling, "rancifying" of fats represents a more inward process which manifests itself in tasting. The tendency towards rancidity must be held back by man and that happens through the activity of the astral body. If it is unable to deal adequately with fat digestion, "then man has an unpleasant taste in his mouth. . . . In this way man gets stomach and intestinal ailments from the rancid fat within himself."[67]

The fermentation of carbohydrates takes place primarily in the small intestine. It results in the production of various acids such as lactic acid, butyric acid, acetic acid, etc. Of special significance is that the intestinal bacteria produce an enzyme which can break down the cellulose of plant foods. The fermentation processes continue into the colon. Just like the decaying processes of protein, these processes also have to be overcome by the inner human nature. A trace of alcohol, which always results from fermentation should not spread its effect throughout the organism, should not "rise to the head." The sugar out of cellulose must be able to fulfill its proper role in the organism. To that end it has to get into the realm of the Ego-organization. "Where sugar is, there is Ego-organization."[68] And so the

Ego-organization must work from above as opposing pole against the fermentation processes in the intestine.

The fermentation process also plays an important part in the digestion of grains, which brings us again to the problems of the role played by roughage. J. V. Liebig recognized "that the separation of bran from flour is a luxury which, for purposes of nutrition, is more harmful than beneficial." (1865) Although this was later denied by Voit and Rubner, today it has been established as an important fact in nutritional physiology. Thomas demonstrated that whole grain products are very beneficial for peristalsis and thereby for the whole digestive process. He pointed out that through the cellulose digestion activity of intestinal bacteria the production of toxic products in protein decay is limited. He also remarked, however, that this ability in man today frequently appears to be stunted, "probably because of disuse." Nevertheless, "the difficulties disappear during rapid accommodation, i.e., after an adaptation of the intestinal flora." This may be what Rudolf Steiner meant when he said: "If one *tolerates* coarse bread," then that would be the healthiest food. Because of present day food, man is not accustomed to such digestive work; in fact, he may have already inherited a weakened activity of the Ego-organization in this field, for when he eats whole grain products, he often suffers digestive disturbances. He could, however, train himself to overcome this weakness by learning how to tolerate such food and thereby strengthen his Ego-activity.

Not only is starch and sugar digestion enhanced by the intestinal bacterial activity, the same holds for proteins and fats of the nutrients enclosed by roughage (fibers), especially whole grains. Finally, high roughage content of foods also contributes to vitamin formation by the intestinal bacteria. Through a proper activation of all these processes, man's etheric body, astral body and Ego-organization are brought into a harmonious interaction. It is essential that we do not underestimate the detrimental consequences for all of mankind if these processes continue to suffer from continuing disuse and from destruction of intestinal bacteria by customary medications.

Quantity and Quality

The most elementary observation can teach us to what extent man is dependent on food. If we do not eat for a prolonged period of time or if we exert ourselves, then we get tired. At the same time we become hungry. We learn from such experience that through nutrition we obtain forces which strengthen us and enable us to work again. We can assume that our foods contain these forces.

These concerns became a major issue in the last century when the science of nutrition developed. Corresponding with the then prevalent conceptions of nature and man, scientists attempted to solve these problems. The teaching of the so-called energy metabolism was founded. Energy was considered to be the capacity to do work. Work in the physical sense is defined as the product of force and distance. Since it was known from physics that the achievement of work was connected with the development of heat, it was quite natural that these concepts were also applied to man and animal.

The results of this kind of thinking are contained in the theories of nutrition established by Liebig, Voit, Rubner, Dubois-Reymond and others. They rest upon concepts such as those expressed in Ludwig Büchner's work, *Kraft und Stoff*. One reads for example:

> Force and substance are fundamentally the same thing, only considered from different points of view. . . . We know today as little as was known in the past, and we will probably never know what *force in itself* is, or what *substance in itself* is. But we do not need to know it, since . . . . the separation of both existences in themselves is possible only in thought and not in reality, and since both words, just as the words spirit and matter, are only designations for two different aspects or kinds of manifestations of one and the same, which in its actual nature is to us an unknown being or ground of all things.[69]

Force and substance thus are unthinkable separately, "and when there is no substance without force, no force without substance, then no doubt can remain in us that the world as such is not created. . . . , rather that it is eternal." A beginning or end of this world "is to be relegated into the realm of spiritualistic or theological reveries. For it was already evident that "what we call spirit, soul, consciousness, disappears with the cessation of the material individual existence."

This concept does not prevent Büchner from agreeing with Joule's and R. Meyer's thesis that the sum of forces in the universe is constant, but subject to the capacity of transformation. It can become "latent," or else manifest itself as heat or movement, but it always remains unchanged and only appears in a different form. The "circulation of force" becomes "circulation of substance" and vice versa. In the final analysis it originates from the sun as the "central body of the world." Büchner concludes: "The force with which a locomotive races along is a drop of the sun's warmth transformed by the machine into work, just like the work which creates thoughts in the brain of the thinker or forges nails through the arms of the worker."

Not far removed from these concepts, despite the thesis of the impossibility of a world creation, is the assertion "that matter existed long, long before the spirit, and that in the archetypal world fog, out of which our solar system densified and developed, all future formations, including rational

62

beings, had to be contained as capacity or ability." On the other hand, the world appears to such a way of thinking as "a molecular or atomistic composition," although that is to be considered only as a "scientific hypothesis."

We have quoted these thinkers extensively because it is our purpose to show how such thoughts contain all the basic concepts upon which the science of nutrition in the nineteenth century was based and how the inheritance of those ideas continues into the present.

Let us consider a contemporary work, for example, *Sinn und Unsinn unserer Ernährung* (Sense and Nonsense of Nutrition), by Hermann Mohler, published in 1972.[70] In the chapter on "energy metabolism" one reads how "energy" can occur in a variety of states, just like work. For an understanding of bioenergetics the laws of thermodynamics are supposed to be just as valid in the living organisms as they are in the dead world of machines, i.e.: "The energy of the universe remains constant," it did "not originate out of a void." On the other hand, the "entropy" of the universe increases: "It is the inescapable destiny of atoms finally to achieve a state of total disorder, which one designates as heat death." Now follow the decisive sentences: "Also the living organism is subject to this change. The organism escapes heat death by eating, drinking, breathing," etc. "*The real foundations of our nutrition are incomprehensible without thermodynamics.*" In other words: man only delays the inescapable heat death through nutrition, which yet takes place out of an immutable necessity. Büchner summarizes the consequences of this world-view: "Not only in death, but even during life does this body transform itself"; it is therefore "in a higher sense, immortal, since not the smallest particle of it can be destroyed." For "the same atom which today mediates the proud gait of a ruler or a hero may lie in the dirt at his feet tomorrow," and the same atom "which today dwells in the brain of a sheep may help tomorrow in the thought work of a thinker or poet."

The fundamental concepts of the science of nutrition have actually developed as a consequence of such thinking. Scientists attempted to establish a "substance-force balance in order to calculate out of it the energy turnover." The calorie was to be the unit of measurement, i.e., the heat necessary to increase the temperature of 1 L of water from 14.5°C to 15.5°C. This presupposed that all energy quantities could be expressed in heat quantities, "because the law of the constancy of energy is valid for the organism as well as for nonliving nature."[71]

. Based on this supposition Rubner then calculated the standard values for the caloric value of carbohydrates, proteins, and fats, and established his so-called law of isodynamics, according to which 100 gm of fat are iso-caloric with 230 gm of carbohydrate or 230 gm of protein.

The contemporary work on nutrition cited above limits such concepts somewhat. Mohler writes: "Although heat is the simplest and best-known medium for energy transfer, it is useless for the transfer of energy in biologic systems," because the human body is isothermic, i.e., "it has a constant temperature."[72] "The cell cannot work like a heat machine," because it does not have a temperature gradient. Despite these limitations both of Rubner's laws are still considered valid, and according to them, one can calculate the "physiologic heat value" of every nutrient. Actually this does not turn out to be the case. It soon becomes evident that the given values are only valid for "pure nutrients," i.e., for a condition which does not exist in nature and can only be established by chemical analysis or synthesis.

We are here reminded of Bunge who pointed out that "all of our natural foods are not individual chemicals but mixtures."[73] From that Bunge came to the remarkable conclusion that from nutrients such as artificial chemical substances, one expects **a priori** detrimental consequences for health." Those who engage in this type of chemical thinking today admit that "the utilization of the three main nutrients by the body is usually much less efficient and complete," and that "the values cited in the literature are subject to remarkable variations," but they nevertheless believe that the calculations on the whole are correct. Adherents to this theory conclude that the cell is comparable to a chemical factory in which CO_2 as well as H_2O occur as "energetically useless end products." These chemicals receive their values through energy from the sun, which "develops out of atomic energy." Thus "the sun energy appears in the final analysis to be the source of all biological processes." An isolated chemical compound, adenosine triphosphate (ATP), supposedly represents the material substrate of the "human accumulator" out of which almost all life processes receive their energy. "Sun energy is stored in ATP." These are the crowning words of the undeniably imposing edifice of modern physical-chemical nutritional research.[74]

We have a special reason for broaching this theme a second time: we want to demonstrate how almost all of the essential elements present during the establishment of the science of nutrition, which continue to be active and unchanged, act like a strait jacket upon present day thought habits. Although many research results could easily lead to the giving up of such outdated thought habits, many scientists fear the loss of the seemingly secure foundation of modern science.

Scientists who approach these topics from medicine and not from the basic sciences are more critical and careful in their continuing acceptance of the old foundations. Thus Glatzel, for instance, writes in his work, *Die Ernährung in der techischen Welt*, about energy requirements: "Corresponding with the nature of the subject, these numbers can give no more than rough estimations of nutritional value."[75] Regarding the validity of Mayer's and

Rubner's "laws," he points out certain limitations and remarks that much remains to be clarified. He is certainly correct when he says: "The question as to the quantity of nutrients necessary for a person can only be answered strictly for a specific person, living under specific conditions, and performing specific activities." But such a person exists only in the head of the scientist, not in reality! A similar abstraction is that of the established norms of nutritional requirements "which maintain man in such a state of health that an alteration of diet would not affect an improvement." In the final analysis all such guidelines prove to be useless, because they only apply to a small part of man's reality, to his physical body. The life body has to overcome the peculiarity of the physical; it is "the fighter against physical substances and forces." The physical body itself "could not have in itself the organs which serve nutrition . . . . , were it not permeated by the etheric body."[76] In addition, this physical body also contains the effects of the astral body and the Ego-organization, thereby further removing itself from the normalized determinations of its nutritional needs. These can actually only be determined individually on the basis of general and specific conditions.

We can agree with Glatzel when he writes that the "reliability of a normative value depends on the research methods" and that "the normal person does not live according to nutritional tables and medical advice." But we would like to add that the real human organism does not adjust itself to such tables of data.

A further limitation of the customary way of looking at things is related to the trend of measuring the nutritional requirements by the needs of an athlete. Without a doubt, this represents extreme, even unphysiological, conditions. If these so-called laws of nutritional requirements appear to be especially applicable to athletic achievement, then this speaks more for the unphysiological character of such activities than for the validity of such norms. Forgotten is the fundamentally significant implication of Glatzel's statement: "Spiritual work has no measurable energy requirements."

Thus, it is easy to agree with the physician Gigon, who, from his own experience, has come to hold almost the same heretical convictions: "The life process can never be considered from the point of view of energy. . . . To say that one requires proteins, fats and carbohydrates to get a certain number of calories, is like saying that the atmosphere consists of oxygen, hydrogen, nitrogen, etc., so that it appears blue to us."[77]

In the course of these considerations it will become evident that where man is concerned we cannot actually attribute any significance to the calorie. It is certainly valid in lifeless nature, like all physical and chemical laws, but in living nature its effect is limited.

The plant lifts earth substances out of the earth's influences. Forces are active in it which do not radiate out from the earth, like the physical forces, but which radiate in from the circumference. The plant originates out of the interaction of these two forces, the one radiating out, the other radiating in, the earthly and the cosmic. Only when the plant dies does "the preponderance of the forces radiating out over those radiating in become evident."[78] The forces radiating in from the cosmos, especially those from the sun, bring the substance in the plant to life.

In this sense we can actually speak of plants as densified sun force, densified sun-ether force. What is formed, as long as these forces radiate in with the sunlight, is the "etheric body" of the plant. Consequently that force will have a special quality during the day time, different from that at night. If we pick a plant during the day it carries the aftereffects of these cosmic forces within itself much more so than if we pick it at night.

If an animal substance is to be formed on earth, it may not be solely under the influence of these two kinds of forces. A third force, which is placed above the other two, makes its appearance. It is similarly of cosmic origin, but it does not radiate in from the cosmos, rather it internalizes the cosmos. Rudolf Steiner calls it the "astral," because it expresses its cosmic origin, but brings forth sensation, not life. Through it, "sensing substance" comes into being. The physical expression for this force is the nervous system.

By this means the animal body is not only filled with life forces, but some of these forces are withdrawn insofar as sensing substance comes about. This is the case, however, only when the animal is awake. In sleep the life forces are again predominant.

These fundamental relationships are expressed by Rudolf Steiner in a precise statement: "Physical substance enters all these organisms, the physical, the etheric, and the astral, from the outside. All three have to overcome the plurality of the physical in their own way."[79] This happens in digestion, through nutrition, the processes of which we have described in our sketch of digestive physiology. They are dynamic processes and require for their understanding a dynamic theory of nutrition.

It follows that man, insofar as he also has an astral body, internalizes such cosmic forces. In other words, man, unlike the plant, cannot take up the cosmic light forces as they radiate in; instead he has to internalize this light, has to transform it into soul-force. What stimulates the growth force from the outside metamorphoses itself within the force of consciousness.

To this end man needs still a higher force, which he organizes into himself and which confronts the ensouling force. Through it, sensing substance becomes transformed again. It becomes carrier of the self-conscious spirit, of the "Ego-organization . . . down to the smallest particles of his substance." The organ which becomes the bodily expression of this Ego-organization is the blood. Rudolf Steiner presented these relationships, especially with respect to the astral body, in detail.[80] He remarked how, through nutrition, the plant substances built up out of sun forces are "dismembered, broken down and destroyed" by mediation of the astral body. Thus we always have to overcome the plant-becoming process in us; otherwise, we could not develop waking consciousness. This astral body, however, especially by virtue of being able to confront the external light activity of plants, is itself related to light in its true nature. It can be recognized by those with clairvoyant consciousness as "an inner light, a spiritual light," i.e., a spiritual light body, in contrast to the external light. The external light, as cosmic radiation, has the task of stimulating the etheric body to build up the plant organism out of inorganic substances, i.e., to build up primarily starch out of the assimilated CO_2 and H_2O. The internal light, the astral body, on the other hand, initiates the destructive processes through which alone an inner soul life is possible. By pushing back the outer light process the astral body not only ignites the inner light of the soul, but also creates for itself an organ through which it can continue this process into the body: the nervous system.

The nervous system itself is continuously permeated by the breakdown processes, and creates, therefore, by pushing back the life processes, room for unfolding of the soul-spiritual. For this reason, conscious activity as such is not associated with an enhancement of metabolism. Through this relationship of the light-formative forces to the nervous system, the plant gains a special connection to human nutrition. We take light forces into us with plant nourishment, which becomes in this sense "food for the nerves." This is especially true for the green plant. By breaking down and destroying this densified sunlight within the astral body, we stimulate those forces in us which we need for the nourishment, the formation, and the maintenance of our nervous systems.

Meat, on the other hand, is closer to man; it already contains such internalized light in the nervous system. The animal already used up the plant-light body to build up its nervous system. "So man takes up something with animal foods which does not confront him in the virginal form of plant foods, but something which has already been subject to astral forces." At first this may seem easier to digest, but actually "man has then to overcome what was affected by the astral body of the animal in the foods." He has to deal with the varied animal astralities. These affect his astral body, specifically the nervous system, by disturbing and by retarding it. Rudolf Steiner emphasized that this fact must be taken into consideration especially with regard to the nervous system as a source of disease. We are led thereby to an important justification of vegetarian diets, which are especially important in the care of patients with degenerative processes of the nervous system. (We will deal with this more specifically in Chapter 9.)

In earlier historical eras there was a clearer instinctive understanding of these issues. It was said that man was a being of light when one was able to perceive his etheric body. When this was overshadowed, it was seen as a sign of illness which expressed itself in the skin color. For that reason the tremendous influence of light on human health was still experienced. The healing forces in plants were perceived by recognizing how light is active in them.

Rudolf Steiner spoke of this subject in a lecture in Dornach.[81] He pointed out that the light which we treasure so much today was not valued in the same way by men in older times. What they valued as light actually came from the realm of plants. They felt attracted to this or that plant because they needed it as remedy or food. They experienced an inner stimulation, an inner vitalization, when they roamed through woods and meadows. That was a direct effect of the light-ether force of the plant world. "Today, however," Rudolf Steiner continued, "we are moving toward the necessity of having to comprehend light in a new way," having to understand what the nature of those forces is which can come to man through the plant world as cosmic sun forces.

We cannot continue to consider this densified sun-force as energy and measure it in calories. We have to expand our comprehension and see the sun not just as a source of atomic forces; we have to learn to look at it (just like the human astral body) from within and recognize it as a source of inner light forces. We recognize in this way that the question of food quality must be approached from totally different aspects. It is important, however, to make clear the fact that man, in his inner being, is not a continuation of natural laws. The law of entropy and the law of "preservation of matter and energy" are not valid for the inner being. For, "nature is allowed to be nature outside the human skin; within the human skin what is nature changes to what opposes nature."[82]

When Rudolf Steiner had the opportunity to talk to a group of physicians for the first time, he said: "The greatest obstruction to a comprehension of the effects of substances, especially healing substances, in the human organism" lies in the law of the so-called preservation of matter and energy, a law which is "in absolute contradiction with the process of human development."[83] Directly following this he added: "The whole nutritional and digestive process is not what it is considered to be by materialistic science." According to contemporary conceptions of nutrition there is no essential difference between a substance inside or outside of the human organization. Here the appearance continues to be deceptive because what is excreted into the outer world is again subject to its laws. And in the final analysis all "in vivo" experiments in man actually do take place "in vitro." The inside of man is then "made accessible" in some way, i.e., it is subjected to extra-human conditions. In this way one can at most learn something about the after-effects of the inner conditions—but that is a continuous source of deceptions. The reality can only be observed spiritually.

In the same lecture Rudolf Steiner explained exactly what happens to carbon, the substance we take up with all foods, especially with plants. He stated that the possibility actually exists in the human organism to completely destroy the environmental carbon through the digestive process, to remove it out of space, and return it to its original form. "Death and revitalization" of substances take place. Connected with these is a "light-formation process" within man.

When we attempt to follow the occurrences from the intake of nourishment, through devitalization to revitalization, to ensoulment and finally to permeation with the Ego-organization, then we can also comprehend that we interact similarly with the higher qualities, light and warmth, i.e., that we must subject them to a kind of digestive process. The light coming from the outside has, consequently, only "significance by stimulating the origin of the inner light." This inner light process, a spiritual process, is stimulated by the outer light. Rudolf Steiner expressly emphasizes that the outer and inner light remain separated by the human skin and "do not combine with one another." We carry, in this sense, our own light within us. If we ask which organ is involved in this process, we must, in view of our earlier discussion, point to the kidney. The urine formation and excretory process can be considered external aspects of "kidney radiation." Thus man carries within him the source of something extra-terrestrial.

The same also applies to those forces within him which manifest themselves as chemical forces. The liver, as "chemist," is also an internalized source of extra-terrestrial forces. What happens chemically to substances here on earth has its origin in cosmic regions. The correspondence of the cosmic chemical forces to the inner source of chemism, the liver, is similar to that of light to the kidney. Actually, however, we work against the cosmic forces with these inner forces, emancipating ourselves thereby not only from nature, but also from the cosmos. We individualize ourselves not only in the earthly, but also in the cosmic sense. For just that reason we achieve a new higher balance with these extra-human realms. Through the Ego we achieve a new harmony with the world. We establish ourselves as free beings down to the physiological processes.

One of the means through which this is accomplished has great significance for nutrition, i.e., rhythm. It is not without reason that Goethe brought forth the following words out of deep spiritual perception: "There is something magical about rhythm; it even leads us to believe that the sublime may be part of us." In the rhythm the substance disappears, as it were, into the process. And so we can comprehend the fundamental significance of Rudolf Steiner's words: "The organism is a relationship of activities. The essence of the organism lies in action, not in substance. The organization is not a relationship of substance; it is an activity."[84] These words actually express the motto for a "dynamic nutrition." Only when we can comprehend the essence of this statement will we be able to overcome the materialism in nutrition and get a perspective of its true nature.

If here again we pose the question: "For what do we nourish ourselves?,"it will become clear that we must be concerned essentially with activities. As soon as nourishment enters man, it is taken hold of by a stream of dynamic activities which themselves oppose what is the result of such dynamic activities. The goal of these processes is to reverse what has, as it were, jelled into a form, to dissolve the relationship of substances. By these substances we reverse what has condensed into early substance out of the cosmos. Thereby we liberate those forces which were concentrated in the substances; we take the substance back into its cosmic origin.

Matter, which in our food has reached crude material, has originated from a fine, substantial, even a non-material configuration of forces. A supersensible form of being originally lies at the foundation of every nutrient. In the digestive process the food is taken back to this cosmic form of being. Something like a "process of memory" of the substances' cosmic past takes place. The crude substantiality of our foods is thus actually a sort of interim state, a transient condensation out of cosmic origins to which it must be taken back at the climax of nutrition. We are only seemingly nourished by crude material substances. Nevertheless, the material substances are of special significance in human evolution on earth. Because of them we can become actual earth beings and are thereby able to take hold of the purpose of the human form of existence.

We must understand clearly that what stands before us as a human being today is the outcome of that long "cosmic evolution" which Spiritual Science has described in detail. In *Occult Science, an Outline*, Rudolf Steiner characterizes the three mighty steps which man and earth underwent in this evolution, as the Old Saturn, Sun, and Moon stages.[85] All earthly matter has gone through these stages. The mineral has reached the end of this development. It is in "the terminal state of being." In man, however, in the metabolic organism, this terminal state is reversed. This is only possible because this part of our being has maintained for itself a state of beginning. In the warmth, in the air, in the liquid within our body, protected from influences of the earth environment, these beginning states of earth development have been maintained. What reaches them from outside as food must assume the initial state in the smelting oven. "Anthroposophical Spiritual Science must, to supplement what is corpse-like in outer nature, find the beginning states, which are only contained in man, and which in older epochs of world-evolution were also externally real."[86]

These beginning states are, continues Steiner, maintained in what we refer to as lower man: "There one can find, as far back as the Saturn stage, what once was external reality."

70

Now what does man do in nutrition with this "beginning stage?" We have attempted to clarify that at that moment the human Ego can get involved and impregnate the substance step by step with the members of its being. In this way—through the dynamics of the heart-lung process, the kidney activity, the liver-gall activity, the substance reaches a new end. It undergoes a new densification into a new form. In the sphere of the nerve-sense organism the stream comes to rest again. It dies anew. It has taken up a new earth-form, not that of the outer world, but rather that corresponding to the individual Ego-organization. "The head depends on the stomach." What is accordingly contained in the head? Earthly substantiality, again densified, deposited, separated out of the dynamic stream of metabolism. Insofar as the brain is the central organ of the nerve-sense organism we must understand that whatever appears as substance in the brain is an excretion out of the organic process. We refer here to the *Agricultural Course* in which Rudolf Steiner described these relationships with great exactness. He stated that the matter which can be found in the human nerve-sense system, as a result of the nutritional process, is the most advanced which can be found on earth. Neither plants nor animals are in a position to produce it because they have no Ego-organization.

But this process of excretion into the head actually begins in the intestine and has its necessary counter-process in the intestinal excretion. Natural substance is thus not only excreted in the brain but also in the intestine. On this point Rudolf Steiner spoke of a "relationship" which may appear paradoxical to our modern thinking, but which was still quite vivid in the minds of men in older times, for example, in the thinking of Paracelsus. If we want to understand the animal and human organization, this paradox should not be overlooked. It must be taken into account when we ask: "What is brain mass?" Brain mass is simply intestinal mass brought to completion excretion upwards. This makes comprehensible why the intestinal contents need to remain in the colon for some time; it is because just there a process develops which is again accessible to Ego-consciousness. If the brain is to be compared to anything, then it should be compared not to the intestines, "but rather to the contents of the intestines," says Rudolf Steiner.[87] Because this intestinal process is so labile it becomes a picture of the most varied disease states. For that reason the feces were in earlier times especially important in the recognition of diseases. Rudolf Steiner suggests that even today one could make better diagnoses from feces than from urine. He goes so far as to say: "In his excretion man shows of what spirit he is."

From such suggestions we begin to recognize the purpose of nutrition: it is primarily to provide the foundation for the Ego in the brain. For that reason the human brain is by far the most complete and, relatively speaking, the biggest in size. But it is at the same time the most individual in its formation.

71

"Of all organs in the body the brain has the most complicated structure. . . . Every brain shows its own peculiarities, none equals another."[88] These words by A. F. Marfeld clearly point to the special nature of the human brain. But Steiner's suggestions prompt us to ask yet another question: If in the brain, the nerve substance represents such an "excretion" of matter, how can the tremendous formative force of this organ, which exceeds that of all other organs, be explained? In order to answer this question we must realize that not only are substances active here, but so, too, are certain forces.

Brain substance is of a special nature in that it breaks down more easily than any other substance in the body. Modern physiology supports this with findings which suggest that ganglionic neurons have to renew their substance after nine hours, because, by then, their life-force is exhausted. Thus the matter which is excreted into the brain has already been deprived of most of its life. The life forces it gains on the path of formation, through the "etherealization" in the realm of the heart-lung organization, are just as quickly taken away again. Under the influence of the astral and Ego-organization it is again devitalized. At the birth of the organism, neurons are unable to reproduce. The formative forces, which are taken from them so early, can, by virtue of their liberation from the brain substance, be applied to the higher task of soul-spiritual activity.

However, the necessity of a continuous renewal of substance which is excreted into the brain requires an exceptionally intensive metabolism in this organ. This has to be maintained by nourishment, which is one of the reasons why we have to eat several times a day. (We will return to the seeming exceptions—for example, fasting.)

Only a small part of the brain consists of nerve substance in the narrower sense. The nerve fibers (the "white matter") represent a smaller fraction of brain mass than the neurons in which metabolism takes place. While the ganglionic neurons, on which the axons end, still belong somewhat to the nerve activity, the neuroglia appear to be totally concerned with metabolism. According to estimates by neurologists, the brain contains about 15 billion neurons and about 100 billion neuroglia. The latter have preserved the ability to divide and multiply. These cell groups thus represent the actual "nutritional colony" of the brain. This corresponds to Rudolf Steiner's assertion that the gray matter "exists essentially for nourishing the brain . . . . while the white matter is of significance as thinking substance."[89] This aspect of the question of brain nutrition is in fact significant for all human nutrition, a fact that we will deal with in greater detail later.

Substantiality and Force Activity

In the fifth lecture of a cycle given in England in 1923, Steiner directed his attention to the problem of the substantiality and activity of the forces which we must distinguish in each of the three members of man, i.e., the nerve-sense, the rhythmic, and the metabolic organization. He explained: "Substance and activity are actually one and the same; but they are active in the world in different ways." This seems to be a confirmation of Büchner's statement cited previously: "Force and substance are basically the same thing, only considered from different points of view." Büchner, however, claims that force, i.e., something supersensible and spiritual, can only exist on the basis of organized matter which existed long before the spirit." Modern spiritual research, however, came to the reverse conclusion: "The spirit is the origin of all being." Matter, or substance, represents a densification of force, but—as we have seen—only a transient densification.

If we first consider the human head we will recognize that it is formed substantially out of the physical world. This formation begins in the embryonic stage and the head and brain development far exceeds that of the limbs and metabolic organs. It is during this time especially that the activity intervenes which, as formative activity, works in the physical substance by plastically forming the head. This is a cosmic, not an earthly activity. "In my head I have substances taken from the earth, but they are formed plastically in such a way that earthly forces could never have formed this human head." The forms of the head and the brain are "so to speak, a creation of the heavens."

This unique wealth of forms and differentiations of the human brain (far exceeding every animal formation) must appear mysterious and inexplicable to modern research because it cannot possibly be explained by physical laws. In fact, from the point of view of earthly forces, it even appears contradictory. Not only the external form, but the inner structure of the brain is highly differentiated. As A. F. Marfeld writes, in his *Cybernetics of the Brain*:

> While the liver, for example, has approximately the same weight as the brain, the liver shows essentially the same tissue at every section; the brain, however, shows an altered microscopic structure, often within a few millimeters or even fractions of a millimeter.[90]

We consider this a good example of the opposing qualities of the metabolic organization and the nerve organization. Thus we have in the nerve-sense organism of man an interaction of earth substances with cosmic forces.

On the other hand, we observe in the realm of the limbs and metabolism how the earthly forces are active. If in this system, we were not subjected to gravity, we could not be incarnated as earth man. Our human Ego utilizes the constant overcoming of our heaviness. "The forces and activities of the metabolic-limb organism are taken from the physical world." The chemical processes, too, as they first proceed in the digestive organs, are determined by earthly activity.

But what is the substantial basis of the metabolic-limb organization? There are many obstacles to a thorough understanding of the answer to this question. When we consider that within 24 hours our brains renew their substance twice, and that we nevertheless maintain our identities without interruption then we must recognize that a concrete conceptualization of these facts is almost impossible. For our normal daily consciousness is based primarily on the stability of our bodily existence. At first we are not even aware that this bodily existence is a mere semblance. The existence of our metabolic-limb organism appears similarly to be based upon an earthly stability. Spiritual Science, however, says: "The limbs and the digestive organization of man are formed completely out of heavenly substance." But what does this mean? By referring to the works in which Steiner has been more precise in his explanation, we will attempt to work towards a solution of this new and difficult problem.

We have pointed out so far that all foods have not only to be divested of their foreign character, but must also be taken back into a non-material, etheric state, before we can densify them anew and make them our own. This process has been recognized by modern nutrition. A. Gigon. for example, writes: "The nutrients must be transformed into body substances before they can be utilized by the organism."[91] Nevertheless, many still think of a matter-force continuity mediated by various physical-chemical processes. Gigon confesses that it is a miracle that the living form manages to assimilate a foreign substance into its own structure, and he further states: "It is undoubtedly erroneous to believe that a living organism functions according to mechanical principles." Thus it is at least admitted that the present-day natural scientific methods and thought patterns are unable to comprehend these processes. Gigon comes even closer to reality when he finally quotes Aristotle: "Not food, but the soul nourishes." The possibility, then, that higher principles, which are accessible only to corresponding higher methods of cognition, are involved, is not excluded. Rudolf Steiner developed such methods but was impelled to say: "One can despair when one observes how science confronts the findings of spiritual research which reveal the truth."[92] Despair results because it is so difficult to communicate with modern science. This has not changed even today, although modern research has made many discoveries which do not fit in with its theories concerning these processes. Many of these new discoveries, however, will help us in our goal of approaching Spiritual Science.

When, as we have said, man "etherealizes" the nutrients, he proceeds in different ways with different substances. He must transform all mineral nutrients into "warmth ether," all plant nutrients into "air form," and all animal nutrients into "watery form."

In his lecture of November 10, 1923, Rudolf Steiner once again emphasized that there can be no question of a continuation of chemical and physical processes in man, because inside man, "everything is different from outside of him." "Whether we take in salt or anything else, it somehow has to first take the form of warmth ether, before it is utilized by the human organism."

Plant substances in human digestion are given "the opportunity . . . to return not only to the light realms of the cosmos, but also to the spirit realms of the cosmos." Corresponding processes in the liquid realm, i.e., the chemical ether, take place in man when he digests animal foods. If he is not able to bring the processes to completion, he becomes ill. Today, more than ever before, man is continually exposed to this danger. Rudolf Steiner mentions in reference to this that a person unable to take sugar back into the warmth ether state will develop diabetes.

At this point it is important for us to remember that man must take his food, before he can use it for himself, back to the etheric state. He must remove it from the effects of physical laws and transform it into a non-material form, i.e., release it from subjection to the "law of the conservation of matter and energy." This applies not only to substances but also to natural forces. In other words, although man takes in earthly substance, he does not nourish himself in an earthly but in a cosmic etheric manner. Thus he must proceed with the second step: to re-densify this cosmic-etheric nutrition back into substance, which he, as we have already indicated, thrusts as "excretion" into the nerve-sense organization. In this process man rebuilds the substances, in a mirror-like fashion, into proteins, carbohydrates, and fats. He thus uses his nutrients as an exemplary model.

Origin and Goal of Nutrition
Earthly and Cosmic Nutrition

We may here ask whether our present day nutrition has not evolved out of an earlier one in which the food was of a finer, more etheric substance and man had not descended so far into the physical. Such a condition is suggested by Spiritual Science when we hear of an "archetypal albumin atmosphere" in which beings lived, as it were, in a living nutritive liquid. Rudolf Steiner pointed out, for example, that in earlier times mother's milk came to man as food from his surrounding atmosphere: "Then the situation was simply such that what man had throughout his life was like milk."[93] While our air today consists of oxygen, nitrogen, etc., in those times, which Spiritual Science describes as the Lemurian epoch, there was a "very thin milky soup in which life existed." There "milk was taken in from the surrounding environment." Milk was still a cosmic substance. Does not the old legend speak of the land "where milk and honey flow"? In this sense, the plants with

75

milky sap represent remnants of ancient plant formations. Our milk today still carries such a memory of ancient times insofar as it can stream as living nourishment from one organism to another. Milk is an after-image of the original cosmic nutrition and at the same time a transition to earthly nutrition. It is therefore the first nourishment of the new-born; it acts as a means of transition to the coarser foods taken in later. Milk is thus the bridge between cosmic and earthly nutrition.

It may now be more comprehensible why Spiritual Science must talk about the fact that today we take in etheric substances besides the coarse earthly substances. In 1923 Rudolf Steiner pointed out that the substance of the metabolic-limb organization is not built up out of earthly substances. "As incredible as this may sound at first, you carry in your metabolic-limb man what, as substance, is not built up out of the earth, but instead . . . . out of the substance which exists in the spiritual world."[94] In a lecture of February 9, 1924, Rudolf Steiner again spoke about this problem. He stated that all living organisms and even the earth itself depend on such a two-fold stream of substances. Plants and animals (especially the lower ones) depend on this nourishment from the environment. Similarly, "the earth nourishes itself from these fine substances which are present everywhere in the cosmos." The earth continually takes up "nutrients from the atmosphere."[95]

Such indications have indeed been confirmed by modern science. We hear, for example, of "cosmic radiation" which brings fine substances to the earth. In his work, Die Schöpfung ist noch nicht zu Ende (Creation Is Not Yet Complete), F. L. Boschke remarked upon this "interchange with the cosmos."[96] He emphasized how hydrogen, which is bound least by gravity to the earth and can most easily leave the earth's gravitational field, behaves. The "cosmic radiation" just referred to consists primarily of hydrogen nuclei, but it also includes the so-called "sun-storm," which has gained in importance lately because of the astronaut studies. Boschke writes: "The earth receives not less than 1.6 tons of matter every second from a 'sun-storm.'" This consists primarily of atomic nuclei of hydrogen.

Rudolf Steiner gave a whole lecture about hydrogen to the workers at the Goetheanum. He spoke of the close relationship between this substance and phosphorus, which is spread out in the atmosphere and also plays an important role in living organisms. Hydrogen is closely related to warmth and is an important structural element of proteins. As such, Rudolf Steiner characterized hydrogen—as well as oxygen, nitrogen, and carbon—as a substance which harbors formative forces. In this context hydrogen develops a relationship to the heart system: "Through the heart system man allows his hydrogen to be prepared, which then is carrier for the preparation of the thinking apparatus." We hear in the same lecture that we take up hydrogen (and phosphorus) through the skin and the hair. It is thus active in man and all living beings and brings about, in conjunction with other substances, a substance in the brain which "can be the mediator of thoughts."

Thus hydrogen is one of the substances which moves between earth and cosmos and which plays an essential role in cosmic nutrition. It is, as it were, a refined breathing, not only through the lungs, but also through the skin and, as Steiner emphasized especially, also through the sense organs. "We continually take up not only light, but also substances. [But] especially through our noses do we take up a tremendous amount of substances without noticing it."[97] In a lecture to physicians on December 31, 1923, Steiner had made prior references to this aspect of nutrition. After mentioning that the usual metabolic activity produces just the building blocks of the nervous system, he went on to say that through the activity of the nerve-sense system, in relationship with respiration, "substances out of the cosmic environment are taken up in an exceptionally finely dispersed state," which are then integrated into the organism and "substantially replace whatever is excreted."[98] In a lecture of January 7, 1924, we find another related comment: "In the atmosphere all substances are present in very fine dispersion." Man inhales them, but he also takes them in through his eyes and ears. From this follows an important indication: man on earth depends on earthly foods insofar as he engages in earthly activities; otherwise, "he would not need to eat at all; he could attract everything out of the cosmos."[99] Through eating earth substances we obtain support for working with our bodies.

Present-day science is well acquainted with the fact that substances radiate into the earth atmosphere out of the cosmos. After describing cosmic radiation, in which nitrogen, carbon, and hydrogen are included, Boschke writes: "Furthermore very small quantities of many other chemical elements reach the earth: iron, nickel, lithium, berythium, boron, etc. The earth also takes up many atoms of elements which can be discovered by analyses of star light." It is well-known that "cosmic material" falls to earth with snow and in meteoric showers, through which massive quantities of iron, cobalt, and nickel fall to the earth. According to Boschke, 0.000014 gram of nickel is contained in 1,000 cm^3 of air. That is the result of a yearly precipitation of 5 million tons of cosmic material! Boschke concludes: "Clearly great quantities of cosmic material in a fine rain of powered metal continually reach us." Thus we have not far to go to realize that this cosmic stream is taken up not only by the earth, but also by earth organisms, including man. A "cosmic nutrition" of all living beings on the earth takes place continually.

The coarse nutrition, accepted today as the sole basis of the nourishment of man, is necessary for his earth existence. Through the daily overcoming of the resistance of the earth substances, man gains strength especially in his soul-spiritual organization. This overcoming has to lead, especially in man, to a destruction of substance, i.e., to an etherization of substance, so that the

77

Ego can begin anew with the creation of man's earth body with each ingestion of food. Thereby he is freed of the constraint of natural forces in the nourishment. He carries the beginnings of the earth within his digestive organs and can form the nourishment according to the image of the world, but with the individual impregnation of his Ego. He becomes a physiological individuality.

The stream of substance which man thus densifies again becomes the substance of the nerve-sense organization, which is therewith built up of earthly materials. The brain becomes for that reason the instrument of the unfolding consciousness. Earthly nutrition is therefore primarily nourishment for the brain.

The forces which man takes up with earth foods must be overcome. Whether they orginate from mineral, plant, or animal, he cannot allow them to enter him as such. This requires a mobilization of various counter-forces, which in addition create certain counter-images which continue to work in man. Through the forces of earth food, our limbs gain strength and we are able to work. In brief, the substance of earth foods stimulates the formation of consciousness; the forces, the energetic components of earth foods, stimulate our limb-metabolic system. Since both are continually used up, we have to renew them through daily nourishment.

The stream of earth substance is confronted by a stream of cosmic substance. The primary receptive organs for this latter stream are the skin, the sense organs, and the respiratory organs. They must be continually renewed by the earth foods so that they can take up the cosmic stream of substance. This stream, too, divides in man: it leaves its forces in the nerve-sense organs; it is combined here with the earthly substances and forms them into highly differentiated organs, in order, from the aspect of formation, to serve the same goal which earth substance serves for the material aspect, the formation of consciousness. In this interaction nerve substance breaks down and must be continually renewed.

The cosmic stream of substance also densifies and pours itself as substance into the metabolic-limb organization. As earth food must first be etherized so that it can then be densified anew, so the cosmic stream of nourishment must also be densified into earth substance. By direct impregnation of the etheric form of this stream through the soul-spiritual organization, this substance too receives the signature of the personality.

The upper man, consisting of the respiratory and nerve-sense systems, is thus of a completely different nature than the lower man, consisting of the circulatory and the metabolic-limb systems. Both meet and interpenetrate in the heart, which mediates between upper and lower man. Respiration and circulation in man together form a central system, the rhythmic organization. In it there is an interpenetration of spiritual activity and material substantiality. "Heavenly substantiality and activity stream in, earthly activity and substantiality stream in."[100]

The image of man and his nutrition developed so far differs remarkably from the prevalent scientific and popular conceptions. Nevertheless, when we study the results of modern scientific research, we find that they do not contradict the results of spiritual scientific research. The new image, developed from Spiritual Science, however, liberates us from the one-sided materialistic manner of thinking and facilitates bridging the gap to the soul-spiritual processes in man. Once these are no longer separated from the bodily processes, together they allow us to recognize the path to a comprehension of the interaction of the various realms of forces.

Rudolf Steiner presented an additional aspect of earthly and cosmic nutrition in one of his last lectures.[101] In taking in cosmic nourishment with our breathing, he said, we "take up not only material substance, but also soul substance." The finely dispersed substance which we inhale also contains soul substance. Thus these substances are not merely minerals; they are also carriers of life forces and, beyond that, carriers of an objective force which we can designate "world-astrality."

It is well known today that we also take up such forces with our earthly nourishment. In fact they determine certain properties and qualities of our food. If animals were in a nervous and fearful state before slaughter, their muscles would be modified down to the chemical constituents. M. Pyke reports this in his book, *Bread for Four Billion*, and writes that this does not directly damage the nutritive value of the meat, but it does diminish its quality. He also points to the fact that "the physiological state of the animal clearly influences the taste and odor of its meat."[102] Actually he refers here to various soul states, e.g., the state of sexual excitement. The muscles and fat of hogs, for example, develop a repulsive odor during the rutting season. The concentration of aromatic substances is high enough to render the meat unpalatable.

The odor and taste of a food substance has a far-reaching significance in the quality of food. However, before we turn to a discussion of the problem of aroma and taste, we will conclude this chapter with two examples of how nutrition, as described here, is applied to life situations. These examples will show how, for Rudolf Steiner, the results of Spiritual Science, seemingly far-removed from practical nutrition, always led into concrete life situations.

In a discussion concerning a child in need of curative education, Rudolf Steiner pointed out that although the child had a strong limb organization, it had a remarkably poor appetite. This poor appetite had "impaired the nutrition of the head," of the nerve-sense organization, and for that reason the head organization had remained weak, which led to certain physiological disturbances. The limb organization, on the other hand, was strong because "its substance is not built up out of foods, but out of the cosmos by way of the respiration and sense activity." The therapeutic suggestions given for this child took these points of view into consideration.[103]

In the *Agricultural Course*, Rudolf Steiner was especially concerned with developing insights into nutritional processes that could become fruitful for daily practice. For that reason he had to emphasize that everything spiritual—as well as etheric—has to have physical carriers on the earth. Materialists, however, "take only the physical carriers and forget the spiritual." This relation of the physical to the spiritual is especially important in nutrition. He also emphasized the great importance in earthly nutrition of whether we are able to properly take up "the vitality of forces" in our foods. These are needed for our daily activity in work. The actual substance of the food, on the other hand, is taken up in very small quantities and then solidified in the organism. It is solidified so far that it must be cut off in nails and hair. Thus, "it is wrong to set up the formula: ingested food, passage through the body, nail and skin sloughing etc."; in reality it is "respiration, very fine intake through the sense organs . . . passage through the organism, elimination." The forces taken in with earthly foods are important because "they bring the forces for willing into the body."

Based on such a concept of nutrition, Rudolf Steiner established his new teaching on agricultural fertilization. It forms the basis of bio-dynamic gardening and agriculture.

Chapter 4

SMELL AND TASTE: SPICES AND AROMATIC SUBSTANCES

Introductory Viewpoints

An understanding of the significance of spices and aromatic substances in human nutrition requires a consideration of the sense of smell and taste. The deep significance of these senses will be revealed to us when we attempt to illuminate the results of modern sense-physiology with the results of Spiritual Science. Modern physiology, despite a plethora of minute data, admits that "the way in which aromatic substances stimulate the sense receptor cells is still unknown."[1] The same is true for the sense of taste. Rudolf Steiner's Spiritual Science, on the other hand, states that "we experience the living relationships of macrocosm to microcosm in our tasting." Understanding that "will result in a healthy hygiene of eating," which we need, "because the unconscious, instinctual way of living will gradually be lost by humanity and must be substituted by a conscious relationship to the cosmic environment."[2] These words, spoken over fifty years ago, have become exceedingly relevant today as evidenced by the far-advanced deterioration of human instincts.

The Significance of Aroma

A substance can be perceived by smell if it is in the gaseous state. This simple statement has a far-reaching significance. Aromatic substances in the "macrocosm" must therefore have the potential to go from the solid or liquid state into the gaseous state. Likewise, the "microcosm" must develop a fine and highly differentiated organ to perceive such gases.

The interaction between the transitional potential of macrocosmic substances is demonstrated by the following example. The characteristic fragrance of lime tree blossoms results from their volatile etheric oils which easily pass from the liquid to the gaseous state; they are easily ignitable and burn with a bright flame. Thereby they proclaim their connection to the light and warmth element, having almost no relationship to the liquid and solid. Resins, waxes, and fats are dissolved in them, but salts are not. Thus they withdraw from earthly form and gravity and strive to give themselves up to the forces of warmth and light radiating in from the cosmos. Radiating out, they integrate themselves into a higher lawfulness. As gaseous substances they attain the ability to interpenetrate and continuously go through immeasurable rarefactions and densifications and form an "aroma-sphere," which, carried by air, light, and warmth, represents the breathing sphere of the earth organism. This penetrates plants, animals, and man. Thus we must learn to speak of an "aroma-sphere" within man, which makes use of the sense of smell as an organ of perception.

In the last few years modern research has investigated this aroma-sphere. The development of gas chromatography has contributed significantly to our knowledge of aromatic substances. Substances which serve as primary aroma carriers have been identified. Among them are the sulfur-containing substances and those substances which originate only when a nutrient is roasted, e.g., grains, coffee, malt. A surprising discovery in these studies was that about 70 chemical compounds contribute to the formation of aroma when bread is baking. The list of discovered coffee aroma substances is over 300 in number.[3]

Although the goal of the analysis of aroma is "to imitate every natural aroma by a correct selection and mixture of its components," hardly any practical results have come about from these studies.[4] Nevertheless, the study of fruit aroma has led to deeper insights into the nature of the formation of substance. Many of the aroma carriers have been found to be breakdown products of certain carriers of metabolism. Accordingly, the formation of aroma is now known to be not a synthetic process, but rather a catabolic process, comparable, for example, to fermentation or the formation of blossoms and fruits. The latter is not a continuation of pure life-processes; it is the intervention of external warmth and light processes in the ripening plant. In the blossom and fruit formation the plant is touched by forces, which, in plant and animal, are active from within and are manifested as soul and spiritual forces.

Rudolf Steiner once described how the plant blossom strives to unite with the "soul of the sunbeams." The sunbeams, however, are permeated with

82

the same forces which we have internalized in our astral bodies. These activities do not manifest themselves physically in life processes, rather they are active in breakdown processes, in pushing back synthetic activities. The formation of aroma carriers thus initiates, as it were, a process which, internalized, represents the capacity for consciousness. This statement will be very significant in our further considerations.

Here we may point to a conclusion of the results of modern aroma research: "No man will be satisfied for any length of time with a nourishment that tastes and smells of nothing, regardless of how rich it is in proteins, vitamins, and trace elements. . . Every food has its own specific aroma problem."[5]

Rudolf Steiner pointed out how forces radiate into the gaseous substances in the air permeated by light, through which the gaseous bodies are lifted out of the earthly influence and are subject "to the influence of the unifying sun being."[6] In other words, in the aroma-sphere "something spiritual-astral closely approaches the material. Matter is most spiritual in fragrance." And we can also understand: "When the spirit . . . most closely approaches the physical earth, then we have the perception of fragrance."[7]

The formation of fragrance thus represents an interaction between terrestrial and extraterrestrial forces. The fragrant plant is taken hold of by certain forces to which it answers in a specific manner: in the manner of a lily, a violet, lavender, an onion, etc. This process, which, for the plant is an excretory process, is at the same time an active intervention of the cosmic environment. In the formation of fragrance the plant becomes an "organ of smell" through which it communicates with the world. It becomes creative in this activity by filling itself with extra-terrestrial forces which give it specific qualities.

Thus it is an illusion when we assume that the plant is delimited by its physical contours. Actually, a rose, which we can smell from far away, extends itself into the whole atmosphere. That extension is just as real as the rose which we see in definite contours. Despite our limited sense of smell, we perceive the rose, we take it up into our own air-body, our own astral body, and we assimilate it there.

In one of the lectures to the workers, Rudolf Steiner concretely described this process of fragrance formation in the plant. He explained that there are beings which can simply smell the world: these are the plants. "The plants smell the cosmos and arrange themselves accordingly." The violet, for example, "beautifully perceives what radiates out from Mercury, and it forms its fragrance body accordingly; likewise, the asafoetida finely perceives what radiates out from Saturn, and it forms its gaseous body accordingly; it stinks." Thus every being in the plant world, when it smells, perceives "what can be smelled out of the planetary world." Also those plants, which, for human olfaction, have no odor, actually do have an odor.

We frequently perceive it as a "refreshing odor." This actually mediates "what comes from the sun."

How significant such a remark is for nutritional hygiene! This "refreshing odor," this freshness, is one of the important signs of quality which we look for in vegetables, leaves, and roots. When we "refresh" ourselves with such nourishment, we partake of the sun forces, the pure light and warmth effects which, from out of the cosmos, combine with earthly substance. The "fresher" a plant smells, the more fragrant it is, the more will it procure these qualities for us. We need these qualities for our nourishment and for the maintenance of our actual digestive and nutritional processes.

Considering the fact that the aromatic qualities of our foods today suffer enormously from prevalent agricultural and processing practices, such insights are very significant. They also contribute to the value of the "biodynamic method of agriculture" initiated by Rudolf Steiner, which attempts to raise products which are true carriers of aroma and which will thereby retain their nutritional value. This value is, as we have seen, not determined by proteins, vitamins, etc., but by the ability to "aromatize," to bring the plant into the proper interaction between earth and cosmos.

In his *Agricultural Course* Rudolf Steiner indicated how important it is for the health of an animal, and therefore also for the quality of the foods prepared from it, that it "freely seeks for its own nourishment, guided by its organ of smell, seeks for the cosmic forces." It matters not only what kind of feed the animal receives, but also "what the value of certain feeding methods has for the whole animal organization."[8]

This applies to man also. The nutrients necessary for the nerve-sense organization, which provide the substantial foundation for the unfolding of consciousness, gain in value when permeated by cosmic aroma-forces.

At this point we will attempt to acquaint ourselves more fully with the human sense of smell. A comparison to animals will be illuminating. The dog's sense of smell, as well as that of most other wild animals, far exceeds man's. What such animals sense, often over distances of many miles, is nothing other than a fine perception of the aroma-sphere. The animals use this capacity not only to search for food but also for perceiving their own species. Every species has its own peculiar odor, and the "odor-sphere" has enormous significance in the social instinctive behavior of animals. A herd stays together because of the shared odor. Through the scent the animal perceives the astrality common to the species. The group-soul of the animals manifests itself in the formation of fine aromatic secretions which the animals perceive. The highly developed sense of smell is thus an instrument of the animals' supersensible organization, of their common soul-organism, which is not yet individualized and is therefore bound to the species.

At this point we can understand better what Rudolf Steiner says about the perception of smell: it is called forth because "the spiritual-astral approaches very close to matter." The plants, through their characteristic fragrances, communicate with the cosmic forces of the planets; by doing so, they actually act as the physical organs for the perception of the world-aroma, for communication with the stars, with the astral world. Exuding fragrance and smelling are simultaneously active and passive activities; they are processes in the continual formation and perception of the world aroma. If you are familiar with the fragrance of lime blossoms, then you are acquainted with the process. For that, explains Rudolf Steiner, is a smell that occurs "because the flowers have refined nostrils for everything that streams from Venus onto the earth. And so we actually confront the heavens in the fragrance of plants."[9]

What, we may ask ourselves, happens when the fragrance of roses and carnations is cultured away? What happens to the quality of our nutrition when plants lose their aroma through our current production methods? Are they thereby removed from their cosmic origin? Can they still live together with the cosmic forces, with the spirituality active in the aroma-sphere?

Must we not remind ourselves here of what man has done and continues to do to the aroma-sphere when he pollutes the atmosphere with the waste gases of his factories and his motors, and when he continuously permeates it with foreign substances? Is the atmosphere not already totally poisoned? Are not the beings living in it—plant, animal, and man—diseased with it? From this point of view the ravages of civilization gain a different perspective. Much more is destroyed than is evident, namely, the interaction of the earth and its inhabitants with the cosmos. This means a tying off of the umbilical cord between earth and cosmos, a drying up of the nourishing and maintaining streams between them.

In view of such a development, can a responsible human being remain uninvolved? Obviously not. But how can one get to the root of the problem? The first step must be to attain correct knowledge, to gain an insight into the reality of the situation. Man can achieve this if he makes use of his potential. He is able to do this because of the metamorphosis of the sense of smell into faculties of consciousness.

We have already referred to the remarkable olfactory capacities of animals, especially of hoofed animals and carnivores. Yet, by comparison, the perceptive capacity of many insects is far greater than that of other animals. The olfactory surface, i.e., the actual sense organ, in the dog is 1/80 of its skin surface area, while in man it is only 1/8000 of the skin surface area. In insects, however, the olfactory organs are independent of, and separate from, the respiratory passages. Bees, ants, and butterflies have exceedingly fine olfactory organs in their antennae and feelers. It could be said that they still live directly in the environment through these organs. With these physical organs they are actually more tools than actors of the cosmic forces.

Man, however, has emancipated himself step by step from his earthly and cosmic environment. He has internalized himself and to that end it has become necessary that he liberate himself from the excessive influence of his environment. Thus he has developed higher senses such as the sense of sight and the sense of hearing, which still reach into the physical-sensory world. But these higher sense qualities do not require outer sense organs anymore; instead they require an advanced brain development as the basis for the formation of consciousness.

The retrogression of the olfactory organ in human development is well known. Not only is the olfactory epithelium atrophied in man, but also the "olfactory brain," the rhinencephalon, of man is small when compared to that of most animals. This brain formation in man has, however, not actually diminished in size; instead it has become enlarged to make a mighty formation, the forebrain, and has thereby given the human head the typically human aspect. In other words: the olfactory brain in man has metamorphosed into the "thinking brain." It has withdrawn from smelling in order to think about the impressions of the world, in order to communicate directly with the cosmos.

Rudolf Steiner describes this situation as follows:

> All the intelligence of the dog is actually placed in the sense of smell. . . The more civilized man becomes, the more the significance of the sense of smell decreases in importance. . . Man has in the front of the brain, just at the point where the disdained nose sends in its nerve, actually an exceedingly noble organ.[10]

Here Steiner is referring to the forebrain, which he terms "the noblest part of the brain." The metamorphosis he describes goes hand in hand with the development of the uprightness of man. That man developed the upright walk gave him the potential to liberate himself from his earthly and cosmic environment. He could do this to the extent necessary to unfold his own personal innerness, to develop individual soul forces, to incarnate his cosmic super-sensible being, his Ego, into his physical body. Thus Rudolf Steiner once formulated the statement: "All our thoughts are actually transformed odors."[11]

Despite the importance of this conceptual activity, however, the significance of man's sense of smell should never be underestimated, because the recognition of the place of the human sense of smell in evolution allows us to appreciate its importance for nutrition. We must further recognize that the human capacity for smell is still remarkable. When, for example, we are still able to smell one millionth mg ethyl ether, 5 millionths of a nanogram (10^{-9} gm) vanillin and 40 millionths of a nanogram mercaptan, then that means that we are able to perceive quantities of substances which cannot be chemically verified anymore. Thus man's nose is still capable of detecting finer substances than the best chemical analysis, even though it gets weaker with increasing age.

The healthy adult person is especially dependent on the stimulation of aromatized nourishment. Thereby he not only stimulates his digestion, not only communicates with the cosmic environment, he also provides himself with the material foundation for supplying his brain, including his forebrain, with a daily renewed stream of substance, which is filled with cosmic forces. The human brain needs this stream in order to be able to serve as an instrument of thought-formation. A healthy hygiene of eating, based on a living relationship between macrocosm and microcosm, will only be achieved with the help of such forces of consciousness, "because the unconscious instinctual living of humanity will gradually disappear"; thus it requires replacement "by a conscious relationship to the cosmic environment."[12] This must begin in agriculture. It must be done by awakening the consciences of food processers to their responsibilities and by providing the consumer with insight into the significance of an aromatized nourishment. Only such a nutrition can decisively prevent the "decadence of vegetable life" from becoming a decadence of the human soul on earth.

Such a consideration of aromatic processes may clarify how close we come, through such an aromatization of substance, to the problem of "cosmic nutrition." The "fragrance body" of a plant, for example, represents the dissolution of solid or liquid substances, a reversal of earth processes, a striving towards the etheric. Thereby the "fragrance body" interacts with the aroma-sphere of the environment. "In the spreading, sweet fragrance of the lime blossom the plant etheric interacts with the astral which fills the cosmos."[13] This process of dissolution can be compared to a fire process which dissipates substance into warmth; we have here a "combustion process held back." It penetrates the whole digestive canal, stimulates there all digestive activities, and finds, as it were, its counter-pole in the organ system which embodies the internalization of the astral, the kidney. The perception of aroma by a sense organ means that something etheric establishes a relationship with something astral. The kidney system also represents, as we demonstrated earlier, such an internalizing and at the same time an opening up to the outside.

87

Taste Processes
The Problem of Spices

As in the lower man, where the digestive processes are separated into kidney and intestinal processes, so, correspondingly, in the upper man, the sense of smell is separated from the sense of taste. The tongue, as organ for the sense of taste, offers a large contact area for the dissolved substance primarily because of its exceptional capacity for movement.

Just as we unite with the airy element, the carrier of the astral, through our sense of smell, so we immerse ourselves in the fluid element through our sense of taste. We thereby enter the realm of the etheric formative forces.

Whatever we want to taste must be soluble. This requirement is fulfilled in the oral cavity insofar as the taste experience first occurs there. Our taste impressions depend on the solubility of substances in saliva. In our foods this solubility, in a certain sense, is already partially prepared for. In the plant, for example, there are certain chemical processes, analogous to fragrant, gaseous substances, that appear as liquids. These can be found either as secretions or as liquids permeating the plant tissues. The latter group includes many leaves and stems which we use as spices, but it also plays an important role in the development of fruits and seeds. In developing taste substances, the plant permeates itself with its typical etheric formative forces, which are of course frequently tinged with aroma from the astral. This is important in reference to the concept of quality in nutrition when taste is considered in relation to aroma. The lime tree, for example, manifests its forces more aromatically in the astral sphere, while lemonbalm unfolds its forces more in taste, in the etheric realm. The sphere to which a plant opens itself will determine which process the plant will stimulate in man.

Let us now turn to a consideration of the organ of taste. The two "chemical senses," smell and taste, are justifiably regarded as the "most important control organs which test food and drink" (v. Frisch). By virtue of their positions at the entrance of the digestive tract, they can guard against the ingestion of unsuitable substances before swallowing. Though the sense organs are primarily found on the tongue, they are also located on the soft palate up to the uvula. The various kinds of taste buds are not evenly distributed over the tongue, however. The tip is most sensitive to sweetness, the posterior parts to bitterness. Salt is tasted chiefly on the anterior border of the tongue, sourness more towards the middle border. Of interest for us is the fact that man is least sensitive to sweetness. In order to be tasted, sugar must be present in a dilution of at least 1:200. Salt can be detected in a dilution of 1:400 and sourness in a dilution of 1:430,000. We are, however, most sensitive to bitter qualities. Quince, for example, can be perceived in a dilution of 1:2 million. In other words, we need much more sugar in order to taste it than salt or even bitter substances! These are remarkable facts when we recall that sugar has a special relation to the Ego-organization, while the sour is more closely related to the astral-body of man. We must also recall that bitter substances are often constituents of poisons. They announce themselves to our taste perception in the smallest quantities.

Now what is the relationship between taste in animals and taste in man? We touch on the question here only because it will give us important insights into the nature and significance of tasting for human nutrition. It is evident from many studies that the sense of taste of many animals far exceeds the human sensitivity. Especially sensitive are fish, about whose sense of smell Rudolf Steiner made important observations.

The fish lives in a medium which provides the preconditions for the possibility of taste. Consequently we can assume that fish taste continually, insofar as the water represents a solution of taste substances. It is known that fish are able to perceive sugar solutions in dilutions a hundred-fold greater than those man is able to detect. Furthermore their "taste buds" are also distributed over the body surface, often up to the tail tip. A blind catfish, for example, tastes the food which approaches his tail and turns just as quickly to devour it as if he had seen it (v. Frisch). In a lecture to workers Rudolf Steiner mentioned that the fish's sense of taste is a kind of skin sense organ, but one that must also be considered in relation to the organs of movement. "When something pleasant approaches him from any side, then he tastes it and his fins immediately move towards it." In their migrations fish direct themselves according to their tastes. They "taste when a little salt enters into the mouth of a river and then they swim out into the sea." So "they swim over half the earth according to their taste."

The taste organs of many insects, though somewhat more peripheral, are still connected with the limbs. The admiral, one of the most beautiful butterflies, can perceive a much more dilute sugar solution with the taste organs at the tips of its legs than can the fish. A butterfly in the American tropics exceeds with the tips of his legs, by a factor of a thousand, the taste capacity of the human tongue. For that reason Karl von Frisch calls him "the greatest gourmand on earth."

Through such research it has become evident that in most animals the sense of taste is still a kind of skin sense, and that these organisms, especially the insects, live completely "outside" in the environment and are only a part of this environment. Only in the warm-blooded animals is taste an inner experience. These animals internalize their soul-organism and have taste a soul-content separated from the environment. For that reason Rudolf Steiner said: "All our thoughts are actually transformed odors," and "in man it is interesting that his taste transforms itself into forces of feeling. . ." In this metamorphosis the capacity to taste loses its intensity as the capacity for inner experience is enhanced.

The human taste experience has a totally new purpose. On the one hand it internalizes itself from a peripheral tasting in the oral cavity to an actual "organ tasting." On the other hand, there is a metamorphosis of the taste process towards the nerve-sense side.

In the eighth lecture of the first medical course Rudolf Steiner pointed out that tasting continues down into the whole digestive tract, that digestion is actually metamorphosis of the taste process. That means that "good digestion is based on a capacity to taste with the whole digestive tract, and that poor digestion is based on an incapacity to taste with the whole digestive tract." This process becomes even more concrete when we hear that we can speak of differentiated tastes, of organ tastes: "Every organ has its definite, specific taste experience; the stomach . . . the liver, the lungs, and the heart have their specific taste experiences." In fact the normal development of human life is based on the development of this organ tasting.[14]

How is this development stimulated and maintained? By tasteful nourishment!

> It is actually true and not merely symbolic when I say: some plant which grows outside is tasteful for only a specific human organ, it is not tasteful to other organs; a specific organ can be stimulated by the forces of this plant.[15]

To establish a completely new, healthy hygiene of eating based on forces of consciousness, it is necessary that we learn to taste fine differences in the composition of our meals. At the same time, this will provide us with the basis of a new art of cooking. This new hygiene of eating will also be the best prophylaxis against the loss of the organ tastes which is accompanied by the occurrence of organ diseases.

The metamorphosis of tasting is equally important to the nerve-sense organism. As tasting is internalized and continues down into the metabolic events, it undergoes, in the nerve-sense organism, a shift towards the outside: "Our seeing is a metamorphosed tasting." Through seeing we distance ourselves from the inner life, push it back a little bit. Only that enables us, as internalized beings, to receive an objective perception of the environment which we can individually internalize in the thinking process. The brain takes the place here of the organ tasting; it objectifies and individualizes the perceived world as an instrument of consciousness formation. We must continually learn to go through this metamorphosis independently, to refine it, to enhance it. For this process, too, we need a new

90

hygiene of eating. It will facilitate for us not only the organic aspects of this process, but also the soul aspects. In the final analysis, what gives taste to plants and nourishment in general is of a feeling quality. Although the sensation of taste occurs in the liquid, in the realm of the etheric formative forces, it creates at the same time reflections of the astral in the etheric milieu.

Man has grown beyond animality through the internalization of tasting. He has elevated taste experiences from the level of the mere astral sphere onto the plane of the sphere of the Ego. This has created the path for the transformation of tasting into the upper metamorphosis, towards the nerve-sense side. "The animal, unlike man, cannot perceive in this objective-subjective manner"; it is confined to subjective experience. Now, however, there is a real danger that man will again be pulled down to the animal level of tasting and smelling. He can become animalistic again not only through the prevailing mode of nutrition with its preference for meats, fish, etc., but also through alcohol. "Perception becomes immoral to the extent to which the higher senses are pushed down to the character of the lower senses." Then "you do not hear the thoughts or words of the other; you perceive them instead in the manner that Mosel wine, or vinegar or another food is perceived."[16] The danger is imminent that our food, by becoming progressively more devoid of cosmic formative forces which bring about taste and aroma, will become a pace-setter for the degradation of man. The progressive brutalization of humanity impresses on us the importance of a nutritional hygiene appropriate to our time.

Chapter 5

RHYTHM IN NUTRITION

For man in older times, it was an archetypal experience that all life in humans, in the earth and in the cosmos, was permeated by rhythms. Man lived with these rhythms during the course of the year and the day. Not until the 18th and 19th centuries, however, after the natural scientific consciousness began to be developed, did the research of rhythmic phenomena begin. Goethe was a pioneer in this field. The modern study of rhythm actually began with his thoughts about "earth respiration," and they have, especially since the middle of this century, played an undisputed role in the medical and biological sciences. Rudolf Steiner, taking Goethe's work still further, provided important insights into rhythmical occurrences and their practical effects and significance in human life. He pointed directly to the central concern of rhythm in nutrition:

> What actually is digestive activity? It is metabolic activity which unfolds itself towards the rhythmical. Digestive activity is metabolic activity which is taken up by the rhythm of the circulatory organs.[1]

We can readily say that the essence of nutrition lies in the activity of taking up nutriments into man's inner rhythm. But to understand this better we must consider, on the one hand, the external digestive occurrences and, on the other, the rhythmical occurrences within man. In order to do this we will have to draw upon and supplement the expositions in Chapter 3.

Although the eating habits of various peoples are still related to traditional meal times, civilized man has become accustomed to eating at various times of the day or night between these traditional meal times. This has frequently led to taking in the mid-day meal in a very short time and to a shifting of the rhythm of eating. Doubtlessly this makes difficult the organism's task of taking up the nourishment into its own rhythm. As a guardian of this activity, however, we have the spleen. In the first medical course (1920) Rudolf Steiner remarked: "Man is predisposed to live in the strict world rhythm through his respiration. His irregular eating habits continually interfere with this strict world rhythm. But the spleen acts as a mediator."[2]

The rhythmitizing activity of the spleen begins the moment food enters the mouth. Just as the activity of the whole organism is stimulated here, e.g., liver and brain, so, too, the spleen activity also begins at the moment of food intake. This is not an example of a "chain-reaction," but rather an effect of man's "formative force organization," which becomes active everywhere simultaneously when the nutritional process begins. This supersensible force organism, also known to us as the etheric body, is of a rhythmical nature. It manifests itself physically in the fluid organism and has its center in the circulation. All liquids in man move rhythmically, not only in the blood, but also the tissue fluids, the lymph, the cerebro-spinal fluid, etc. The various glands are also active in rhythms. In this sense the activity of the salivary glands, the stomach, and intestinal secretions, are to be considered as rhythmical events in the etheric body. These events are initiated in a comprehensive manner when food is in the mouth, and to that extent the rhythmitizing activity of the spleen is already active here.

The muscle activity, which begins with chewing and continues on into the peristalsis of the esophagus, stomach, and intestine, also proceeds rhythmically. A great variety of rhythmic occurrences interact here in order to dissolve the nourishment into a state of chaos in which it no longer belongs to nature but does not yet belong to man.

At that moment the "chaoticized" nourishment moves from the intestine into the lymph channels, into the tissue fluids. Here the forces of the individual formative-force organization take hold of it and transform or recreate it into individual human body substance. The "state of chaos" is characterized by the fact that the nourishment is divested of the rhythms of its natural origin and must now be integrated into the human rhythmic organization. Rudolf Steiner described this process of integration as follows:

> What occurs as metabolic activity in the tissue fluids is, when rhythm confronts it, taken along by the rhythm of the circulatory organs, and the chaotic activity, the chaos, in the tissue fluids, goes over into the rhythm of the circulatory system.[3]

What is the nature of this rhythmical organization in man? What kind of rhythms permeate him? This is the rhythm of the circulatory system which is most clearly evident in the pulse. With its 72 beats per minute it is in a strict relationship to the respiratory rhythm which is four times slower. It is, however, evident how much this rhythm fluctuates. Probably even in the majority of civilized men one observes neither 72 pulse beats nor 18 breaths per minute. The rhythmical activity of the circulatory system is not able to order and harmonize the chaos of the food liquid; instead it is itself taken over by the arrhythmia of nutrition. This is a fact that should be taken seriously. The cause lies not only in the un-rhythmical food ingestion, but probably even more so in the un-rhytmitized nourishment itself. What do we mean by that?

Since Goethe, stimulated by Alexander v. Humboldt's observations, studied the "rhythmical movements of the living earth," the fact that the earth is not a dead body, as had been assumed, has become the basis of a new image of the earth. Rudolf Steiner remarked in 1909: "Just as there is inhaling and exhaling in man, so the earth also, as a living being, inhales and exhales," for "it is similarly permeated by invisible parts from which all life proceeds, as man has invisible parts, beside his physical body, which permeate him."[4] Guenther Wachsmuth was the first to give a comprehensive presentation of this subject matter in his work, *Erde und Mensch-ihre Bildekräfte, Rhythmen und Lebensprozesse.*[5]

The earth respiration has a 24-hour rhythm. The formative force organism of the earth moves rhythmically in relation to the solid earth and the surrounding cosmos in such a manner that the maximum inspiration occurs at 3 a.m. and the maximum expiration at 3 p.m. This "geo-phasic day rhythm" of the earth is especially significant because all natural beings, including man, participate in it. With reference to the plant world Guenther Wachsmuth pointed out that

the plant world is a living organ which has a significant influence on the biosphere and atmosphere. Intertwined with the great respiratory and circulatory processes in the earth's field of activity, giving and taking in the course of the day and the year, it is at the same time a living source of forces. It enriches itself and transforms the environment, not only as a reagent but also out of the activity of its own formative-force body, being a determining factor in the evolution of the earth organism as a whole.[6]

The 24-Hour Rhythm of the Liver

One of the rhythms especially important in human digestion is the 24-hour rhythm of the liver. It was first described by the Swedish scientist Forsgren in

95

1927. He began his studies by examining bile secretion, and 1935 he wrote: "I believed at that time that the activity of the liver was determined by meals." His observations, however, contradicted this belief and led him to the significant discovery that "the liver has a rhythmic function with alternating assimilatory and secretory activity which is independent to a high degree of food ingestion."[7]

The liver follows the 24-hour rhythm of the earth. In the inspiratory phase until 3 a.m. it accumulates glycogen, the result of carbohydrate metabolism; then, in the early morning hours and until 3 p.m., it pours this glycogen as sugar into the blood. The bile secretion rhythm is the reverse; its maximum is at 3 p.m., the expiratory peak, while its minimum is at 3 a.m.

Forsgren was aware of the significance of his discovery when he wrote: "since Claude Bernard's discovery of liver glycogen, the liver was considered as a glycogen depot, which was filled up when carbohydrates were taken in, and emptied during hunger and physical work." Now it is evident that the activity of the liver in relation to the blood has its own rhythm, in whose

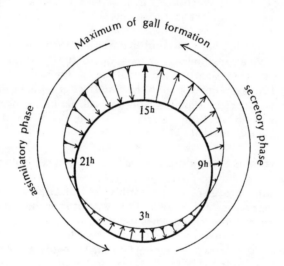

Maximum of Secretion

Maximum of gall formation

assimilatory phase

secretory phase

15ʰ

21ʰ

9ʰ

3ʰ

Maximum of Concentration
Storage of Glycogen in the Liver

The Phases of the Liver's Activity During the Day.
(From G. Wachsmuth, *Erde und Mensch*, Kreuzlingen, 1952.)

96

service metabolism and the uptake of carbohydrates are placed. In other words, the liver has the task not only of forming glycogen, but of going through this process according to a strict rhythmic law and thereby pressing its own rhythm onto the human substance. The same holds true for the bile secretion rhythm which follows the same rhythmic law and gives its character to fat-digestion. Holmgren provided evidence here that "the intestinal fat varies in a 24-hour period so that the maximum of resorption is reached at about 2 a.m., while the minimum occurs at about 2 p.m." A corresponding rhythm was also found for the pancreatic function. Holmgren concluded that "there is a rhythmic breakdown, resorption and storage of foods, which is independent of the time of food digestion." Thus we find confirmation of the results of Spiritual Science which hold that actual digestion consists of a metabolic activity which "unfolds itself towards the rhythmical."

Results of Modern Rhythm Research

Mengel gave a comprehensive overview of the 24-hour rhythm and pointed out the "deep anchoring" of this periodicity in man, plant, and animal. Nevertheless, Sollberger, who approached this problem anew, came to the conclusion that "we must admit that the fundamental synchronization-mechanism of the biological rhythm is unknown. We cannot even localize the clock itself."[8] Spiritual Science is in a position to be of help here. When Rudolf Steiner designates the rhythm as "half spiritual," whereby "the physical tranforms itself into processes, into happenings," and "disappears as matter in the rhythmic process," it becomes evident that rhythm mediates between the physical and the spiritual world; it provides the transition from one to the other. This becomes even more apparent when we consider the role of rhythm in metabolism. Rhythm is a phenomenon which uses physical substance, e.g., food substances, in order to impregnate it with a spiritual formative process and thus order it according to a higher formative principle. Through this, the physical laws are cancelled out. Although the impulse of rhythmic processes comes from purely spiritual sources, it transpires in the region of etheric formative forces. In fact the characteristics of rhythm, its periodicity, its recurrence in dynamically, not statically, placed intervals, allow us to conclude that its field of activity lies in the realm of the etheric. Goethe already established this when he discovered the rhythmical alternation of expansion and contraction as formative principles of the plant. Similarly the earth's rhythm of inspiration and expiration, as described by Goethe, represents an atmospheric phenomenon which points to the earth as a living organism and not merely a dead mineral body. All processes proceeding in a 24-hour rhythm are thus synchronous with the earth's respiratory rhythm.

The question of the primary origin and "location" of these manifold occurrences now arises. Modern science is still searching for an answer, but Rudolf Steiner, as early as 1908, provided a surprising answer. In a lecture cycle about the "Spiritual Scientific Study of Man" he discussed the "Rhythms of the Human Bodies."[9] He explained that the four members of man—the physical, the etheric, the astral-body, and the Ego—each have their own rhythm through which they manifest themselves. He also focused on the sleep-wakefulness cycle, which plays an important role in modern rhythm research. Others such as Mengel and Sollberger have made important contributions here, too, but only Rudolf Steiner clearly recognized that it is the human Ego itself, a spiritual being, which "continually undergoes certain changes in the course of 24 hours," not only in sleep and waking, but also in relation to all rhythmic processes which proceed according to this periodicity. And so he accurately identified this 24-hour rhythm, designated today as circadian rhythm, as the rhythm of the human Ego. We thus conclude that the course of the earth day corresponds to the rhythm of the Ego. In fact, through this rhythm man is united with the earth in a significant way. This is clearly evident in the fact that the 24-hour rhythm in man is strictly related to his location. This means that the liver rhythm as well as the other resorption and excretion rhythms proceed in synchrony with the location of the person and thus proceed differently in Basel than in New York or Tokyo.

The persistence of man's 24-hour rhythm, which was first described in 1938, is intimately related to questions of human nutrition. Nohara (cited in Mengel) describes his experience on the Trans-Siberia Express:

> One usually awakes at approximately the usual time after 24 hours, seemingly ¾ of an hour later every day. So after a few days, quite involuntarily, one does not appear for breakfast until noon, fortunately without eliciting the waiter's displeasure, since he is already used to the phenomenon. When riding in the other direction, from east to west, the lassitude of the human periodicity showed itself in the fact that the traveller awoke shortly after midnight and experienced a lively desire for breakfast.

The fact that Nohara continued to be influenced by the periodicity of his place of origin during the entire course of his journey demonstrated how strongly every Ego unites itself with a location on earth.

After some time, however, the Ego is able to accommodate itself to the new location. Menzel reports that for long-distance pilots the change to the periodicity of a location shifted by 12 hours takes about one week. We see here how modern technology has created new problems which are in no

98

way solved yet. Of special interest are the disturbances in man when he goes against the 24-hour rhythm by working at night. Through such rhythm disturbances serious health problems can arise which frequently affect the digestive organs. Without going into detail we emphasize here that frequent complaints consist of stomach and intestinal disturbances, anorexia, and constipation. This is supported by the following findings:

> Among employees who only had a brief eating period or frequently performed heavy physical labor without interruptions, worked in swing-shifts or worked overtime, there were eight times more ulcer patients than among employees in occupations in which a regular order of the day and an adequate meal-time was maintained.[10]

Although such extreme findings are not consistently observed, they show, nevertheless, how significant rhythmical nutrition is. In any case it becomes clear that an integration into the 24-hour rhythm encourages health, a feeling of well-being, and a greater capacity for work. As Wachsmuth points out, "Rhythm heals, arrhythmia weakens and provokes disease."

The Significance of Rhythm for Human Health

> The recognition that knowledge of physiological rhythms is important in the diagnosis of diseases and treatment of patients has only recently begun to penetrate the understanding of the practical physician; this gradual recognition, however, has come about much too slowly in view of the fact that researchers have emphasized this point much earlier.[11]

The human organism is now known to be connected with its environment in a great rhythmic relationship, and it has been proved that this rhythm continues to be effective even if man changes his relationship to this environment. For example, the maximum of bile secretion occurs at 3 p.m. even if the main meal is taken at 6 p.m. when the bile secretion is already decreasing. Fat digestion is similarly sub-optimal, as when breakfast at 8 a.m. is made the main meal.

The most important point is a still deeper one, that is, that the 24-hour rhythm is the instrument of the Ego organization. This rhythm in man is placed at the service of his highest member. This is not the case in plants and animals. Their rhythm is much more at one with the whole earth-organism. The earth received the 24-hour rhythm in a far distant stage of planetary evolution, when man, and the earth at that time, had not achieved the later stage of solidification.

When man on earth was still in another condition, this movement (which brought about the 24-hour rhythm) did not exist. . . What was first stimulated to rotate (about its own axis) was man. The human ego then actually took this earth along and turned it around itself. The earth rotation is a consequence of the ego rhythm.[12]

Man, still a cosmic being in those old times, received this rhythm from his interaction with the sun and then impressed it on the earth. Thus man and earth were actually united through the 24-hour rhythm. Rudolf Steiner mentioned in that connection that it would have been impossible for man at that time to sleep during the day and wake during the night. He would have become ill, or he would have been unable to live if he had not received his nourishment in harmony with the rhythmical laws of nature.

Nature maintains these strict laws even today. They continue to work in man, but through development of his Ego, he has separated himself more and more from his instinctive connections. This has led him progressively into willfulness and disease. Man now faces the task of becoming the creator of his own individual rhythm, of reuniting himself with the great world rhythms. Rudolf Steiner considered the hygienic task of the future to be the discovery of a regular rhythm for each human individuality which would express itself in the proper relationship between waking and sleeping. In order to accomplish this task in the processes of metabolism and nutrition, man must strive with special inner sensitivity, for in these processes he is still least conscious. Thus the eating rhythm must play an important role in dietetics and the nourishing of the sick, because it encourages those healing forces which belong to rhythm as an element of the dynamic formative forces. This is most apparent when we consider that in liver diseases and cancer the 24-hour rhythm in the organism begins to change. Sollberger reports a complete absence of such rhythms in patients with stomach cancer.[13] The studies of W. Fliess concerning the relationship of disease predisposition and energy levels to rhythmic events in man have also been met with much interest. The danger remains, however, that such recent findings will merely result in renewed subjective interpretations instead of encouraging researchers to confront such rhythmical processes objectively.

For a proper orientation we can look to the Spiritual Scientist. In his lecture, "The Practical Development of Thinking," Rudolf Steiner says that the future health and development of man cannot consist of returning to the old rhythm. That was necessary in past times when man was like an imprint of the cosmos, but now it is his task to learn to rebuild himself rhythmically from within. "Rhythm must permeate the inner man."[14]

Chapter 6

TEMPERATURE IN NUTRITION

Introductory Viewpoints

Warmth is undoubtedly one of the most important forces in nutrition. We have already discussed its central importance in the human organization, so here we shall focus upon its significance in relation to the polarity of warmth and coldness.

Thermodynamics, as developed by modern natural science, mirrors the path of the abstract, materialistic way of looking at nature—as separated from man and from the reality of world processes. Warmth and cold are only physical concerns. The result of this materialistic view is that "temperature technology" has become a dominant factor in our civilization.

If we want to comprehend the effects of warmth and cold in nutrition, however, we cannot stop with what physics has to offer. We have to expand our knowledge and, at the same time, begin our considerations with man. Both have been made possible by Rudolf Steiner's modern Spiritual Science.

Physiology of the Sense of Temperature

Let us begin with a number of phenomena which can be observed in man and with which modern sense physiology concerns itself. We experience an object as warm or cold if we touch it with our hands. In our mouths we experience soup as hot or ice cold. We are aware that such warmth and cold experiences are limited as conscious sense perceptions to our body surfaces, including the body openings. On these body surfaces modern sense physiology has discovered so-called "warm-spots" and "cold-spots" related to fine nerve terminals. The total number of "warm-spots" is approximately 30,000, while there are about 250,000 "cold-spots." Man is much more sensitive to cold than to warmth.

Actually, however, we do not sense the degree of warmth or cold, but rather the differences between them. This can be verified by an easy experiment: dipping our hands simultaneously into baths of different temperatures, e.g., 25°C and 35°C, we clearly experience the difference. If we subsequently dip both hands into a 30°C bath, the hand previously in the 25° bath will experience it as warmer, while the other hand will experience it as colder. This demonstrates that we do not perceive an objective warmth or cold, but rather temperature difference. We experience in ourselves the process of warming or cooling. We compare the external temperature with our own warmth.

Thus our "sense of warmth" does not perceive in the same way in which our eyes perceive. Nor does it perceive in the way the thermometer "perceives!" We relate all external temperature to our own warmth. As local as our temperature experience may appear at first, we still always have a "total warmth experience." "The warmth in us directly perceives the outer warmth."[1] Our sense of warmth is distributed over the whole man. The "warmth-man" is an independent organism, a "fourth man" in us, as Rudolf Steiner explained, bigger than the solid-, liquid-, and gaseous-man, and permeating all.

From modern physiology we know that this warmth organism has a basic temperature to which it adheres rigorously: the temperature of the blood. On the other hand, we find remarkable variations, the most extreme between the liver at 41°C and the tip of the nose at 22°C. Thus the warmth-man is a highly differentiated organism. It also corresponds to the daily rhythm of the earth's inspiration and expiration: the temperature is highest between 2 p.m. and 4 p.m., and lowest at night between 2 and 4 a.m.

The Warmth-Man

It is important to grasp a vivid image of this warmth-man in order to understand how he unites us with the whole earth organism, how he unites us with all of humanity, and how it is this inner warmth, especially, to which man clings intensively; for it is this inner warmth which man experiences as his own warmth, as his own property. We identify ourselves with nothing as completely as with our warmth.

The manner in which this warmth-man maintains himself against his environment can give us some insight into questions concerning warmth and

102

cold in nutrition. "Warmth-regulation" is a convincing example of how the warmth-man penetrates right into the solid, mineral constituents of the body.

Depending on the level of the surrounding temperature and the humidity, we continually give off warmth by evaporation, or else take up warmth. In that process the blood vessels expand, the skin reddens, or—when it is colder—the blood vessels constrict and the skin pales. The fine radiation of warmth, which goes on continually, increases with increasing environmental temperature to evaporate fluid. Thereby warmth is lost and the skin is cooled.

Through this evaporation, mediated by sweat from the approximately 2 million sweat glands, not only are warmth and fluid lost, but so are minerals. The insensible daily fluid loss through perspiration amounts to 1 liter in 24 hours. With actual sweating this amount increases remarkably and in the extreme may amount to 20 liters! With this fluid the organism loses significant quantities of minerals, especially NaCl, but also many trace elements.

It is thus evident that the organism is in continuous dynamic activity in the service of warmth regulation. The loss of liquid and solid substances must be balanced out continually. But is that a problem of nutrition? Certainly hunger and thirst are active participants in man's warmth regulation. But does nutrition, in the final analysis, serve to regulate and maintain man's warmth organization? No doubt it does. But it has also become evident that the aeriform-man, as well as the liquid and solid body, is placed in the service of the warmth-man. An interesting example of the warmth-regulating effect of material nutrition is found in the tradition about the Swiss recluse Nicolaus von der Flüe. During the last 20 years of his life he allegedly refrained from eating. However, a large oven was built in his cell so that he would have constant external warmth as replacement for the absent warmth formation of nutrition.

For us it is important to recognize that the perception of warmth and cold in man is not passive. The warmth regulation present at any moment represents an active function of the warmth-man. An interaction between external warmth and cold and the human warmth organization takes place wherein the latter must be dominant. Every penetration of external warmth or cold into man is the beginning of an imbalance which has to be counteracted immediately. In this counterbalancing the adaptation of warmth seems to be more important than, for example, the loss of fluid and mineral substances. That is why Rudolf Steiner said: "I must be capable at every moment to take hold immediately of the warmth from the skin and make it into my own."[2] Otherwise external warmth or cold will result in disease, in a "cold," a sort of poisoning. Like food substances, external warmth and cold behave like "foreign bodies." However, they may not penetrate into man's body beyond the body surface, while fats, for example, as carriers of warmth, reach the small intestines without modification.

The fact that man is a being of warmth, rather than cold, is decisive here. He is more closely related to warmth, rather than cold. We will return to this fundamental fact later.

Warmth Processes in Man
The Caloric Theory

In the 19th century it was established, according to the caloric theory, that every substance, every food, is a carrier of warmth which is measured by the calorie. This warmth force does not continue passively on in the human organism, however; it must be taken hold of actively, because the calories which we take in are at first foreign to us. Consequently, the "warmth force of nutrients must be transformed into the body's own before it can serve for the performance of work."[3]

Rudolf Steiner made the important Spiritual Scientific discovery that everything mineral in food must for a time be transformed to warmth by man. What is solid, heavy, dead, crystallizable must go through this metamorphosis; at least for the moment it must be lifted into levity, into a de-materialized state, into the form of pure energy, before it can be densified again and form matter in man's own physical body.

Rudolf Steiner posed the question: "How much force must the human organism call forth in order to bring the external mineral substance to the stage of warmth ether?" Trying to determine this measure is a much more realistic approach to nutritive effectiveness than is evaluating intake by counting the abstract calorie. For this ability or inability will concretely determine whether the dissolution of substance succeeds, or whether it "permeates human tissue as inorganic substance foreign to the human organism," i.e., forms various depositions in the body. Diabetes mellitus is described by Rudolf Steiner as an example of such an inability. Sugar, especially refined sugar, represents a mineralized substance that is not always successfully dissolved. Man is not so organized as to be able to effectively overcome the quantities of sugar he consumes today. Consequently, the incidence of diabetes mellitus is progressively rising.

This brings us to questions of nutrition directly related to the temperature of the foods man takes in. The warmth or coldness of food must be controlled in the proper manner. Experience shows that warm meals and drinks are easier "to digest" than cold ones. This explains the significance of the warm soup which Rudolf Steiner suggested for the beginning of main

104

meals. It also explains why ice cold foods can cause digestive problems. From childhood on, the warmth-man is overburdened by ice cold foods that must be warmed up right in the stomach, and by ice cold drinks that do not result in a real quenching of thirst.

The recognition of the dissolution of food minerals into warmth sheds new light on the significance of the mineral substances themselves. Without these mineral substances we would be unable to form a firm support for our human organization. Often, however, our foods are deficient in minerals, especially minerals built into the living substances, e.g., into proteins or carbohydrates. Whole grain foods, however, because of their mineral composition, can be considered a component of warmth regulation. It must be emphasized here, however, that minerals have practically no caloric value.

It is even more significant when we hear from Rudolf Steiner that, through the transformation of mineral into warmth, substances lose their earth quality and are thereby prepared "to take up into themselves the spiritual, coming from the cosmos."[4] In this manner the substances are rejuvenated; they strip off earth gravity and communicate with their cosmic origin, the warmth-atmosphere of the whole earth. This renewed interchange between man and world permits us to recognize still more clearly the central significance of warmth. Through the element of warmth the human Ego is led down into its firm, mineral earth existence, while it is also led up into connection with its spiritual origins.

Again Rudolf Steiner, through his spiritual research, has illuminated the depth of this secret of the development of the human Ego. In the evolution of humanity there was a point in time when a "certain quantum of warmth moved into every human sheath." The earth was then "encased in a mighty warm atmosphere," of which only the mineral warmth remains today. Then the sun spirituality lived in it. It has poured itself into every single human being as the starting point for his individuality. In the warmth of the blood it has anchored itself through all stages of substance up to the salts.[5]

Handling Temperature in Nutrition

From what we have discovered so far we can develop an understanding of the practical significance of warmth and cold in nutrition. When we are surrounded by such a warmth "that we can really say 'I' to ourselves, then we feel comfortable." When, however, we are surrounded by coldness so that we freeze, "then this outer coldness takes away the piece of warmth which we are. We are threatened with the loss of our 'I'."[6]

Not only the warmth-value of nourishment, but also its warmth-state is significant. We utilize inner warmth not only in the breakdown of foods, but in adjusting to the temperature of foods when they are taken in. The work is facilitated when food is warmed. When we warm our foods, "then man does not have to give away his own warmth." For foods are taken up into the warmth-process when we cook them, facilitating the inner digestive processes. "My body is relieved of those activities which occur in cooking, so that I bring the foods into a state in which the body digests them with more ease." Warming, cooking, roasting, malting, drying, etc., always signify an ordering of nutrition towards the human warmth organization.

The breakdown process which occurs through warmth treatment of foods is fundamentally different from the breakdown by cold-effects, deep freezing, etc. Modern physiology recognizes this and speaks of a specific cold-metabolism in frozen food products. In the methods of food preservation, the significance does not lie primarily in the maintenance of specific substances, but rather in the processes which take place in relationship to human processes. Warmth-processes direct nutrition to the central, inner functions, the individual functions through which man is related to the earth. They stimulate the metabolic-limb man, the will forces.

Coldness also has its spiritual equivalent. In the *Agriculture Course*, Rudolf Steiner speaks of the "frost effects," which bring "an enhancement of the cosmic influence," the extra-human forces. A nutrition which is not submitted to the warmth process, as, for example, raw foods, will tend toward that sphere. But that sphere is related to the nerve-sense organism, the skin, the peripheral man. There this form of food appears justified if one adheres to certain conditions. Yet one could well say that the frozen foods so prevalent today one-sidedly support the nerve-sense organization, i.e., they use the extra-human forces excessively, so that the central Ego-organization is under-utilized, neglected. This nourishment then furthers and supports the formation of abstract thought, the cold pole of man.

Such considerations are certainly not permitted the modern natural scientist who believes that he must limit himself to the physics of temperature. And for that reason he is not in a position to correctly understand the relevance of temperature in nutrition. This limitation of knowledge must be overcome. This is what Goethe demanded when he spoke of the sensory-moral effects of the color spectrum, from cold blue to warm red.

The Essence of Warmth and Coldness

The essence of warmth and coldness was always a question in ancient mysteries. Its answer was disclosed to the neophyte or priest when he underwent an initiation. He received the solution to the riddle of the winter and summer forces. The old Hybernian initiate, for example, saw in the summer landscape, which confronted his inner vision, the element of innerness; it filled him like "an all-inclusiveness in the heart" and gave him "a revelation of his self." The inner vision of the winter landscape revealed to him something of the "destructive impulses in the universe" as they reigned in his nerve-sense-organization. For "the senses belong to the winter."[7] The experiences of the initiate in the Greek Mysteries were similar. Through them he discovered: "In the warm air you feel at home . . ., in the cold water you feel yourself a foreigner. . . You can actually only feel warm air within yourself; cold water you can feel only outside of yourself. . ."[8]

Modern Thermal Technology in Nutrition

Glatzel, a leading modern nutritionalist, writes in his *Verhaltensphysiologie der Ernährung*: "No other medium besides warmth, in its various applications, accomplishes such significant alterations of the structure and substances of raw foods."[10] He also points out that biochemical, physiological, and clinical studies have shown that "heating . . . brings many more benefits than disadvantages." We have already spoken of such benefits from a broader point of view, but here we shall briefly consider the advantages and disadvantages from an orthodox medical point of view.

That milk and egg proteins are easier to digest when heated and that plant proteins improve in taste after heating has been established. Curiously enough, however, this is not true of red meats and fish; their "biological protein value" is not altered by cooking. It is said that this protein "suffers some kind of damage when subjected to strong heat," but "a loss of amino acids cannot be established."[11] Most likely this "damage" is a case of quality change that escapes a purely analytical verification.

No significant decrease in the biological value of milk protein is said to occur with pasteurization by heating to 150°C. The finer quality of milk, however, must certainly suffer. The measure of "biological protein value" is inadequate. When Professor Catel, for example, pointed out in 1939 that raw milk has a 3 to 10 times greater feeding value than when it is made germ free by heating, his findings pointed toward this conclusion. Heated milk lacks the bactericidal forces present in raw milk. Furthermore there is evidence that milk proteins undergo an obvious denaturation at 70°C. The sensitive crystallization methods developed by E. Pfeiffer provide valuable information related to these issues.

Similar problems arise when the warmth treatment of grains is examined. We know that cooking facilitates the digestion and improves the taste of starches. The swelling of starch grains during cooking, in which water also plays an important role, is crucial for making starch available. Warmth treatment is especially significant in the preparation of whole grain products, because it makes these products more accessible to the human digestive capacities. (An exception to this general rule of digestion is potato starch, which, despite cooking, is not digested any more easily.) Man would need completely different digestive forces if he wanted to eat, like the animal, primarily raw foods. Man must be partially relieved of this work, so that forces can be liberated for use in higher functions such as the formation of consciousness.

Just as there must be certain limits placed upon warmth preparation, so that food value is not damaged or decreased, so, too, limits must be adhered to in the use of cold. The method of preserving foods at a low temperature will be best in the range of -5° to +5°C. Lower temperatures, as those used in deep-freezing, bring about problems. Such methods have, without doubt, remarkable effects. These include the inhibition of growth and even death of microorganisms and the inhibition of the enzymatic activities. Noteworthy, too, is the fact that there is also a "low temperature metabolism," i.e., that certain microorganisms and enzymes first awake, as it were, at lower temperatures.

Here we must reemphasize that man is a warmth being, and his cold-pole must achieve a balance with the warmth activity. Warmth is related to the will; confronting it is the formative pole, which corresponds to coldness, rigidification and also crystallization. In a lecture to the workers, Rudolf Steiner, referring to these two formative tendencies, said: "In the cosmos everything is ordered in a crystalline manner."[12] These cosmic forces, which are especially active during the night, strive continuously to form us into mineral, lifeless formations, and would succeed were it not for the sun forces which counteract this tendency and bring the crystal formation tendency to dissolution. In this way man is brought into the interaction between warmth and coldness through the will and thought element.

In densification there is always the attempt to separate, to become independent from the environment. Every ice formation from water shows this. While warmth strives toward the formless and represents "negative gravity," as it were, those forces which lead to formation, to crystallization, to ice-formation, bind substance to gravity. In his "Warmth-Course," Rudolf Steiner spoke of a "warmth day" and a "warmth night": "in the warmth night the earth strives towards formation, towards crystallization," while during the day, under the influence of the sun being, there is a continuous dissolution, an overcoming of the striving for crystallization.[13] Thus man carries in his being, spatially, in the upper and lower pole, what the earth goes through temporally in relation to the sun. The plant, too, embodies both processes spatially; the cold-forces live in the root and the warm-forces in the flower region.

Both forces, warmth and cold, reappear in the preparation of foods. Man in primitive times, from an instinctive spiritual perception of his own being

108

and nature's being, learned to utilize these two forces, especially in the preparation of remedies from certain plants. Rudolf Steiner pointed out that in the Druid culture, 1500 B.C., man learned to submit plants to certain processes—"the process of freezing or cooling" and "the process of burning or dissolving"—as an imitation of basic processes experienced in nature.[14]

It is said that these processes were imitated "within certain boundaries." This may well point to the previously mentioned upper and lower limits of temperature. Whatever goes beyond the upper and lower extremes goes beyond the forces relevant to man and calls forth one-sided effects which harbor certain dangers.

It is well known that deep-freezing brings about a denaturation of proteins as well as fats and carbohydrates. In fats, intermediate products which are not found during the natural fat breakdown also arise. It may be true that this denaturation of proteins facilitates digestion, but it also means that the organism partially paralyzes the protein breakdown forces present in him. Occasional use may be without much significance, but with continual use of deep-frozen foods effects will be noticed. Certainly, for quality frozen products, only the best fresh products can be used; otherwise the final product suffers too much. As much as this method of preservation accommodates "modern" kitchens, the rule "thawing-cooking-eating" suggests strongly that such foods are subjected to unnatural methods not fully appropriate to man.

We will not ignore the discovery, frequently mentioned in connection with freezing, of the perfectly preserved frozen Siberian mammoths, which also attracted Rudolf Steiner's attention.[15] He remarked on the fact that the animals' meat was still so fresh that it could be eaten then.[16] This method of conserving food is considered positive, but only when the emphasis is on the freshness and palatability of frozen meat "if we were especially interested in eating such meat."

It must be observed, however, that only a moderately low temperature was involved, corresponding somewhat to the temperature used today in deep-freezing, about -18°C. It is evident that at such a temperature life withdraws (most bacteria are unable to survive) and metabolic processes cease, so that a dead image of life remains behind. Life can certainly not return after thawing. Instead, the total structure decays rapidly and the product soon becomes unpalatable.

Rudolf Steiner was in this instance not concerned with nutritional questions; instead, he used this example as an illustration of the answer to another question: that of the warmth and cold distribution on earth. He wanted to indicate that such cold conservation came about only "because the water was frozen immediately, and these animals immediately got into this gigantic Siberian ice cellar," and that the cause of this sudden change in temperature came from extra-terrestrial cosmic influences. For "the star constellations have a mighty influence on the distribution of land, water, and ice on earth."

Rudolf Steiner commented further upon the effect of cosmic influences in the *Agriculture Course*: "Frost effects are always an essential strengthening of the cosmic influence which is active in the earth." But this cosmic influence is only useful, especially in the plant world, when it is not extreme. When, however, there is deep intensive frost, then the cosmic influence is too strong and may be very damaging to plant growth. Certainly this refers not only to a direct freezing of plants, but to an excessive one-sided cosmic activity through the medium of coldness: "there, too much heaven gets into the soil."

Still another aspect of food conservation is that used by farmers, who dig burrows to store various vegetables underground. In another lecture to the workers Rudolf Steiner described what actually happens from a spiritual point of view in this conservation process.[17] Especially in the winter, the sun is active in the earth; it leaves its sun force behind, as it were, and its warmth force; it then has refreshing effects on the inner earth. From that the stored potatoes, etc., profit. The vitalizing sun force, which radiates back under the earth surface in winter, plays an important role in conserving the buried fruits.

Drying and Roasting

Modern drying processes have also been learned from nature's methods. In seed formation, for example, it is astonishing how effectively water is removed. While various grains still have a water content of 12 - 14%, in many nuts it is reduced even more: in walnuts to 7%, in hazelnuts to 6.5%, in almonds to 4.5%, and in coconuts to 3.5%. Evidently the modern recognition that all life is bound to water, and that the less water a substance contains the more its life processes are pushed back and inhibited, is demonstrated by nature. Here, however, warmth is first active in order to evaporate the water. This kind of natural cooking takes place during seed formation, and we imitate it in roasting and drying. In this sense, such processes represent a continuation and an enhancement of the natural warmth effects. In the *Agriculture Course*, Rudolf Steiner points out that the seed formation of the plant is primarily a plant metabolic activity, which calls forth a corresponding stimulation in man. Here the forces of nutrients are important. When we eat fruits or seeds, then this earthly force effect is significant. If we artificially continue the warmth process by drying, malting, roasting, etc., then we strengthen these effects; we bring "force into the limbs—force into the metabolic organism." Without doubt the rationale for the good effects of

110

dried fruits in the liver diet lies here. Not only are their effects enhanced thereby, but also an aromatization is brought about which increases the tastiness and palatability of such products.

While these drying methods utilize warmth, the modern freeze-drying methods utilize coldness. As we have seen, we can also inhibit and push back life by coldness. In the freeze-drying process the product is frozen and the formed ice is then evaporated. This process, first used in World War II, to preserve blood, has gained such popularity today that it is considered "the best and most protective means of drying."[18] Not only soup powders, but fruits and coffee powder are produced in large quantities by this method. In this process more than 80% of the water is frozen out and then removed by vacuum at low temperature, leaving only 2% behind. Without recourse to unphysiological processes this method is not possible, and that must be kept in mind when such instant-products are evaluated.

Our whole modern food technology has been developed according to methods which only take the physical and chemical characteristics involved into account. It is not sufficient, however, to look at just vitamin and enzyme losses. They reflect at most only a part of the actual nutritive value of foods. Thus when we discover that certain methods enhance the nutritive value, then we have enough justification to favor such methods. So it is satisfying to see that initiatives have been taken in several countries, and bio-dynamic quality products are available as dried fruits or vegetables. The available soups based on dried vegetables are satisfying in all respects, as are the dried fruits. Recognizing the value of such offers and taking advantage of them depends now only on the consumer.

Another method of preservation that should be mentioned is the binding of water through sugar. It is the basis of the production of marmalades and candied fruits. However, a problem arises here because of the 40-50% sugar solution which is necessary.

As a final consideration we must mention the progressive rise in the popularity of cold foods in our civilization. One need only think of the enormous consumption of frozen products such as ice cream to recognize this problem. It, too, points to a one-sided imbalance in our nutrition in favor of the cold pole. Our present discussion has hopefully clarified in what direction the effects of such products lead. In the first instance it is the liver which is subjected to an added burden, but the influences of coldness on the whole man can certainly be found in a one-sided enhancement of his nerve-sense-pole.

Consequently, new methods, based on new insights and new knowledge, are necessary here. There are promising beginnings, among them the conservation methods based on rhythmical processes. Other methods, utilizing primarily chemical substances, will be discussed later.

Chapter 7

RAW AND COOKED FOODS

Bircher-Benner's Discovery of Raw Foods

The debate concerning raw foods did not play an important role in Europe until 1847, the founding year of the London Vegetarian Society. When the twenty-eight-year-old Bircher-Benner became a follower of vegetarianism at the turn of the century, it was a highly unusual dietary principle for physicians at that time to accept. In the eyes of the Zurich Medical Society he had left the confines of exact science. However, by 1967, the father of the well-known "Bircher-Müesli" was restored to medical respectability when Dr. A. Gigon, during Bircher-Benner's 100th birthday celebration, said: "Criticism of the activity of great minds is an inevitable part of history. Their great scientific discoveries always gain in historical stature by criticism."

Bircher-Benner was not led to vegetarianism by ethical or religious convictions; instead, he observed that vegetarian foods had a better effect on his patients' health than the usual meat diet. "The vegetarian was victorious; he had taught the physician a lesson," wrote Bircher-Benner later.[1] It is significant that he proceeded in an unprejudiced and rational manner entirely within scientific limits. Because he had to admit that contrary "to my thinking and my knowledge, the patient improved," he felt that it was his human and scientific duty to explore why that was so. It is also important that his discovery was made at the bedside. He actually witnessed the healing value of raw foods.

In his attempts to find a rationale for this result, Bircher-Benner came across Ostwald's statement: "When eating plants we eat sun energy." From this he

113

assumed that plant foods must have the highest nutritional value, since sunlight, according to the laws of energy, has the highest energy value. He further surmised that raw plant foods were superior to "cooked, dead" foods.

Then, as today, a physiological verification of that conviction was hardly possible. Nevertheless, various studies have established a number of important health-promoting effects of raw foods: the diuretic effects, the diminution of the tendency toward inflammation, the help in weight control because of low fat and protein content, the activation of digestive juice secretions and the regularization of intestinal peristalsis.

Spiritual Scientific Aspects

Dr. Steiner drew attention to the fact that in a vegetarian nutrition "we ourselves must go through the whole process of which the animal partially relieves us by its own digestive processes, by taking the substance quite a distance further." If unused, those forces needed for vegetarian nutrition are not developed in man. An inner sluggishness comes about and the unused forces have a disturbing effect in the human organism.

Bircher-Benner's insight and experience was similar when he committed himself to vegetarianism. He found that the stimulating effect of plant foods, which enhances the inner forces, was strongest and most direct when they were in their fresh and unmodified state. Thus we must ask: What is actually the situation with "cooked-out" foods? Is it justifiable to use this concept? What actually happens when foods are cooked?

It is frequently argued today that man must kill off the fresh, raw foods during his digestive process. That is correct. To support this contention, Rudolf Steiner started from the fact that man is relieved by cooking, etc., of what he must do himself when he consumes raw foods. It then seems logical to assume that in making the choice between plant and animal foods, raw foods should be preferred to cooked foods. But such a comparison is only partially justified. According to Rudolf Steiner, the polarity of the human organism must be taken into consideration. In our periphery, the skin, the sense organs, and the associated nervous system, we are oriented outwardly. We are bounded by the nature surrounding us; nature penetrates into us, we perceive it, and we are thereby connected to the cosmos. This pole of our organism is therefore, in a sense, related to the raw, unmodified nature product, i.e., raw plant nutrition. If we want to integrate our organism into its periphery, we can do it with raw plant foods. We thus strengthen our peripheral organization.

If, however, we cook or dry the plants, we add a warmth process. Crucial to this addition is the realization that we then imitate externally a process that

114

is related to our inner processes. In stomach digestion we warm our foods through; when we take the foods over into the liver region, we make them completely our own by permeating them with our blood-warmth, our own individual warmth.

With cooked and warm foods, however, we stimulate at the same time the inner forces of our organization; we enhance the forces of the individuality which incarnate warmth. Thus in adding a warmth process to plant foods we favor its enhancement of our Ego-organization, which separates itself from the cosmos and is the polar opposite of the human periphery. Cooked food strengthens earthly man.

This point of view, developed by Steiner, makes possible a totally different evaluation of cooked plant foods. Cooked foods are actually "appropriate to man"; they go hand in hand with the processes of the human individuality. Cooking food represents a nutritional process in its archetypal sense. When foods are left "natural," and consumed in their raw state, then from this point of view they work against this central process. To overcome this counter-process, man needs a much greater force. And when he wants to call this up within himself, there must be a specific occasion: he actually uses this force only when he has to call forth a healing process in himself.

If one wants to affect the periphery with nourishment, or if the relationship between the peripheral and the central man is disturbed (causing the manifestation of various disease symptoms in the inner man), then raw plant foods are appropriate as healing nourishment. Such nourishment is frequently a necessity today.

Rudolf Steiner terms, as "an extraordinarily important notion," the concept "that the consumption of raw plant foods is a healing process in a much stronger sense than the consumption of cooked foods."[2] In fact a key to the question of raw vs. cooked foods lies hidden here. Bircher-Benner's first decisive experience with raw plant foods as healing and not merely as nourishing supports what Rudolf Steiner says. And because man today is increasingly subject to disturbances in the relationship between central and peripheral man, raw foods as healing nourishment have a great and far-reaching significance.

Actually, however, we must be aware that in a strict sense only raw root nourishment can be designated as raw food. The leaves and even more so the upper parts of the plant have been subjected to sunlight and sun warmth. Fruits are actually "cooked by the sun," so a raw fruit diet is more closely related to the central inner man; it is actually not pure "raw nourishment" any more. If this process is continued by cooking, drying, etc., the effect on the inner organization is enhanced.

In this connection we should also understand that there are definite limits to the human nutritional process, especially with regard to raw foods. In

115

order for man to tolerate food, it has to attain a certain degree of ripeness. This is especially true of fruits. Everyone knows about the often harmful effects of eating unripe fruit. These harmful effects provide evidence of the necessary warmth force which foods must assimilate before they can be "appropriate for man." Animals are quite different in this respect and frequently ingest both unripe and overripe fruits. Here man is much more sensitive.

The issue of proper ripeness is of some importance today, especially since many fruits are harvested in an unripe state and are then made palatable by artificial ripening methods. The question here is whether such a chemical-physical ripening can replace the cosmic warmth ripening process. Certainly the quality of such artificially ripened foods will be different.

In his consideration of ripening, Bircher-Benner started out from the second law of thermodynamics, which states that all energy finally changes into warmth and that warmth (or heat) represents the lowest stage of energy with the least value. From that he concluded that food subjected to warmth, as opposed to that only exposed to light, must be of only secondary importance in nutrition and therapy.

When, however, we take into consideration that warmth for man represents an internalizing process, an individualizing process, and at the same time a transformation into the earthly, then we can comprehend that this warmth process does not actually signify only an end. The "heat death" of earth evolution is at the same time the germ of a new world creation. The world-energy, by dying the "heat death," within the human Ego, creates the starting point of a new life. In other words the earthly termination of warmth in man is transformed into a higher metamorphosis and streams as soul-warmth from the human center into the periphery. Nutrition thus forms a source of the soul-spiritual warmth force.

These thoughts were most comprehensively expressed by Rudolf Steiner in his *Occult Physiology*:

> What the organism produces of inner warmth processes in our blood, in the warmth processes, which it finally, as the blossom of all other processes brings to expression, that also rises up to the soul-spiritual, transforms itself into the soul-spiritual. And what is the most beautiful in the soul-spiritual? That the organic can be transformed by the forces of the human soul into soul strength itself.[3]

And so Rudolf Steiner calls it a "wonderful fact" that the world-being created an outlet through which our whole organization can finally give us warmth, which we are called upon to transform through our Ego into living empathy with all beings: "In the earth mission, warmth is transformed into empathy."

Such thoughts allow us to recognize how we as human beings participate in the highest processes through our nutrition, and how we are led to such heights even though we are considering such a seemingly mundane problem as the issue of raw and cooked foods.

The Significance of Soup

Walter Ulrich Guyan in his *Kleine Kulturgeschichte der Suppe* claims that the "birth hour of soup" must be sought in the earliest times of historical development.[4] He considers the vessels found in a stone age settlement of 3,000 B.C., near Thaygen, Switzerland, to be soup pots. Throughout history various soups are mentioned. Of Ludwig XIV it is known that he kept several cooks just to prepare his soups. In the 17th century, when France was the leader in the art of occidental cooking, soup began to play a new role. It was not only the "first course," but the overture for the whole meal.

When Brillat-Savarin wrote his famous book *Physiologie du goût*, a chapter on the role of soup in the meal was of course included.[5] At that time soup was usually only a meat broth which was then enriched with various ingredients. "Some vegetables [were] added to the meat broth to heighten the flavor, and bread crusts or baked goods [were included] to make it tastier." The "soupe Parmentier," however, the potato soup, which displaced the oatmeal soup, was considered a vegetable soup. Other soups were cooked with bacon, and the well known "Rumford-soup," a "Soup of the Poor," was made from bread remnants and soup bones. From the end of the 18th century the selection of soups increased continually. In Italy there was "minestrone"; in Germany, v. Liebig developed his meat extract which was then spread far and wide as "Bouillon." Always applicable to a good soup is the pithy phrase of Brillat-Savarin: "Soup is a healthy, light, nourishing food good for all of humanity; it pleases the stomach, stimulates the appetite and prepares the digestion." And so this author justifiably praises soup as "the foundation of French nutrition," whereby "the experience of centuries in its preparation has made [France] a master of the art."

Since vegetarian nutrition has also established itself as valid nutrition in the West, more and more purely vegetable soups have been developed. In the diet of the ill the various soups have become indispensable. Two pioneers in nutrition have participated in this development and used technological advances to prepare soup powders, etc. In 1886 Julius Maggi put his cook-ready soup flours on the market and in the same year C. H. Knorr offered his first soup-tablets for sale. Through freeze-drying these products have been distributed widely, but in terms of quality they can in no way compete with home-made soups.

What a soup of good quality can achieve was stated by Mohler in his book *Sinn und Unsinn unserer Ernährung* (1972): "It stimulates, through its warmth, the blood vessels in mouth and stomach, stimulates the secretion of digestive juices, and provides liquids; for in the next hours, several liters of digestive juices are necessary."[6] That soup furthers digestive powers, especially when enriched with spices, is undoubtedly another positive property.

These advantages may have prompted Rudolf Steiner to suggest that every meal should begin with a warm soup. From personal reports it is known that Rudolf Steiner greatly appreciated a vegetable soup for his own nutrition and suggested that various fresh vegetables should be cooked and prepared as a sort of vegetable bouillon.[7]

We must, however, clarify that the "Bouillon" developed in France, i.e., meat broth, should not be confused with the vegetable soup we mean here. The appetite-stimulating properties of meat broths are more than diminished by their high salt content, their acid tendency, and their frequently low-quality animal and protein content. Thus meat broth is only seemingly the strengthening liquid that it is often held to be, even by physicians.

Chapter 8

FOODS - DIETARY SUBSTANCES - MEDICINAL SUBSTANCES

Fundamental Aspects

Fundamentally speaking, every substance taken from the plant or animal realm can serve as human nutrition, provided that it is digestible. The limitation of digestibility is a very broad one and human behavior regarding it appears quite irrational. The whole human being participates in every meal: his thinking, feeling, and willing, his consciousness and his unconscious, his bodily as well as his soul-spiritual constitution. What the individual chooses for his nutrition depends on his race and his country, as well as on custom and tradition. In the final analysis, the choice of foods is individual and that will be the case more and more.

Can we, nevertheless, beyond all these varied aspects, arrive at an objective criterion for "digestibility"? Must we not also consider the question of palatability and taste? Magnus Pyke writes: "Man must certainly eat what his body needs. Only we must not forget that in reality man only chooses what he needs when it is also tasty."[1] Could we not also say that man needs for his nutrition only what is palatable and tasty? To a large extent the animals still have such a special instinct. Man had it in times long gone. Today we must begin to replace the lost instinctive behavior with consciousness. This will be an essential task of a new hygiene of nutrition.

A prevalent concept today is that man's choice of food rests on a chance encounter and discovery of digestibility and palatability. This is, however, an unsatisfactory assumption and modern Spiritual Science points to a different possibility. Through Spiritual Science we have come to recognize that man is

119

lawfully related to the realm of nature. With the mineral realm he shares his physical body. Consequently, man is also lawfully related to the totality of his nutritients.

Relationship of the Plant to Threefold Man

The fundamental relationship of plant to man holds for nutritional as well as medicinal plants. Rudolf Steiner concerned himself with this problem in the 1920 course for physicians. Fundamental to the relationship developed there is the threefoldness of the human organism. From that aspect man represents an inversion of the plant. The plant unfolds its roots in the earth and develops its flowers, with its fruits and seeds on the top. Man, however, tends to unfold with his reproductive organs to the earth and he "roots," as it were, with his nervous system at the top. The leaf formation corresponds to his middle region. Thus we have the following relationship:

Everything rootlike on a plant has a relationship to the upper man, to the nerve sense organism. Everything blossom- and fruit-like has a relationship to the lower man, the metabolic-limb organism. The leaves and stems establish a relationship with the middle man, with respiration and circulation, with the rhythmical organization.

But we must consider also that there is a rich differentiation in the plant world. Hardly a plant will have the three members of its being harmoniously developed. In fact, the nutritional plant characterizes itself by having especially developed certain parts. Plants with specially developed roots will thereby indicate their tendency towards the terrestrial. Other plants are remarkable for their wealth of blossoms or fruits, e.g., bananas or fruit trees. They are more cosmically oriented. Still other plants have a predominating stem, e.g., the pineapple. In times of earlier human evolution these various aspects were cultivated to make plants more suitable for food production. While plants thus became specialized, they gained a relationship to certain members or organs of man. And so we can understand Rudolf Steiner when he said: "Any plant . . . is tasty only to a specific organ in man; it is not tasty to any other organs because only a specific organ allows itself to be stimulated by the forces of this plant."[2]

From such a perspective, the following words from the same lecture gain concreteness: "It is important to recognize that one should establish a living relationship to the various foods." It is not a matter of indifference whether one eats spinach or salad; for by doing so, one develops "living connections of the microcosm to the macrocosm." It is one of the tasks of modern man to develop from such thoughts a healthy hygiene of eating to replace the old unconscious, instinctive behavior.

The Medicinal Plant

So far we have described the common properties of nutritional and medicinal plants. Now we will attempt to determine their differences. Rudolf Steiner said that from a medicinal plant we must expect an effect upon man's consciousness. It should be able to normalize the consciousness which has been altered through illness, whether it is that of a single organ or of the total state of the organism. It should, in other words, bring about a return to the consciousness existing in health. A nutritional plant, on the other hand, should not affect consciousness; it should only affect the life processes. Thus when we eat we have to watch that the food is actually a food for life and is not active in us as consciousness-altering. In this sense the foods we eat must be digestible, and their nutritive value will depend on the extent to which these requirements can be fulfilled.

The medicinal plant overemphasizes one or another feature of its formation, which in turn manifests itself as a one-sided appearance of substance. In this sense, a medicinal plant can be designated as an "abnormal" or even as a "pathological formation." But this is a concept that can and certainly must be expanded: a food item can be used for something more than its merely nutritive value. When we drink coffee, we will hardly think of its nutritive value; that will more likely be claimed by the beer drinker. When eating chocolate, on the other hand, we do not like to be reminded of its nutritional value, we want to enjoy it. Our response is similar with a cupful of ice cream, a banana split, etc., which are hardly eaten for their food value. There is, of course, the coffee drinker who may claim that coffee affects him like a "medicine."

The patient who is prescribed a certain diet by his physician will claim that he needs such foods because he expects from them a certain healing effect, be it protective or stimulating. But dietary substances and mere food have both to be given in relatively large quantities, while a medicinal substance is administered in small doses.

In a lecture to physicians given in London, August 29, 1924, Rudolf Steiner also spoke about this issue.[3] He was asked why man takes up so many substances with his foods while there are relatively few medicinal substances. His answer was: "Because those substances which are not contained in foods have an especially strong effect on the spiritual in man"; they have a special relationship to the astral body and the Ego of man.

Thus we can make a medicinal substance out of a food substance by decreasing the amount taken in or by special preparation. Anthroposophically oriented medicine gives good examples: an artichoke, for example, can serve as food or medicine, depending upon appropriate concentration and preparation. It can also be used as a dietary substance for patients with liver disease. The pineapple, similarly, is used as food or after appropriate preparation, as medicine. Another example is the stinging nettle, which can be used as a vegetable, as a dietary substance, as a spice, or, with proper preparation, as a medicine. Thus we see that the boundaries between medicinal and food substances are not rigidly determined. Rudolf Steiner also emphasized this. There is no dividing line between whether someone needs pepper as a remedy or as a spice—"one runs into the other." Likewise, we find that health and disease are present in all transitions, for getting ill is basically nothing other than "a continuation of what happens through our eating."

Food and Dietary Substances

Another part of the food and dietary substance question which Rudolf Steiner especially emphasized was the social aspect. He said that through every diet man is made "into an unsocial being." He separates himself from society, through his special diet, not only in terms of nutrition, but also psychologically. For that reason Rudolf Steiner suggested that each person learn to tolerate what he is unable to tolerate, because his inner organs will be strengthened thereby, and he may even awaken an "organ-building force" within himself. To the physicians he suggested that they not continue to prescribe a special diet any longer than absolutely necessary, so that their patients could sooner return to the general eating community. "The significance of the Last Supper does not rest on the fact that Christ gave something to every disciple, but that he gave everyone the same. Creating the possibility for togetherness in eating and drinking has great social significance."

Table Salt

At this point we shall consider a substance which has value as food, spice, dietary substance, and medicine: table salt. It is one of the very few, if not the only substance, which we ingest in a purely mineral form.

Research into salt requirements and the discovery of the indispensability of salt for man began only in the last third of the 19th century, at a time when human consciousness concerned itself most intensively with the dead mineral world. Liebig, in central Europe, was the leader in the study of minerals and their significance for the plant world. One result of his studies was an important and at the same time a one-sided and erroneous concept of mineral fertilization. Consequently, the question of the role of minerals in man still remained unsolved. Lieben, in his *History of Physiological Chemistry*, remarks that, because of the complicated nature of human and animal foods, "great difficulties confronted the study of essential and non-essential minerals."[4] G. v. Bunge, who studied the consumption of salt in cities and in agricultural areas, found that with a predominantly meat diet, customary in cities, salt consumption dropped, but with a predominantly vegetarian diet, salt consumption increased. Bunge asked: Why do we need sodium chloride? Do not our foods, even plant foods, contain adequate amounts? To adequately verify his observation that salt requirement increases—even in animals—with plant nutrition, he corresponded actively with other scientists. In a letter to Bunge by Dr. L. Reinhardt we read:

> Because the Negroes eat primarily plant foods, their requirement for salt is exceptionally high, and it is a common skill among the women to leach the ash of certain plants for salt-like substances, which necessarily substitute for pure salt. Wherever it is contained in soil and water, however, i.e., only on the coast, the preparation of salt by evaporation is a profitable occupation.[5]

Similarly, Dr. L. Ranke, in his work *Der Mensch*, reported on a communication from Livingstone: "The whole area had no salt and so only the wealthy were able to buy some. The local medicine men knew the disease caused by salt-deficiency very well and always prescribed salt among their remedies."[6] It is interesting to note here how salt is used both as food and as medicine.

The result of Bunge's studies of salt can be summarized as follows:

1) Sodium chloride is necessary in mineral form in our diets.
2) Sodium chloride requirement is higher when the nutrition consists primarily of plant foods.
3) The requirement for sodium chloride drops when the nutrition consists primarily of animal products; in fact too much salt can be taken in.
4) There is a relationship between the activity of sodium chloride and potassium in the organism: plant foods contain 3 - 4 times more potassium than meat. The wealth of potassium in plants is the cause of the increased salt requirement in persons eating a primarily vegetable diet.[7]

Although these statements were, in 1905, still largely hypotheses, they nevertheless represented a new field of scientific discovery and stimulated other scientists. One of these was Bircher-Benner who determined that daily salt consumption should not exceed 3 - 5 grams. In the meantime, the daily requirement of salt has been established as 0.5 to 5 grams.[8] The actual salt consumption in civilized countries, however, is cited as 20 - 30 grams per day, a fact which led Bunge to remark that the status of salt has changed from a food item to an item consumed primarily for enjoyment, which, like others in that category, is easily abused.

What lies at the basis of man's need for salt? From Bunge's four theses it is clear that the significance of this substance can only be comprehended from a dynamic way of looking at nutrition. As is well known, sodium chloride is intimately connected with the total fluid metabolism of the organism and also with the warmth organism. Furthermore, sodium interacts continuously with other minerals in the organism, such as potassium, calcium, and magnesium. At the same time, sodium is important in the acid-base balance of the body.

The Mineral

In order to understand the essence of the salt process, we must learn to look at it in a more comprehensive manner. Modern Spiritual Science has provided the key. Relating his observation to the old alchemical teaching of Sal-Mercury-Sulfur, Rudolf Steiner pointed out that salt appears as the earthly principle, in contrast to sulfur which represents the fire-carrying, light-carrying properties of substance. When man develops a need for salt (sodium chloride in the narrower sense), then that represents a manifestation of the relationship of the life processes to the soul-spiritual in man. If a man "craves for everything salt-like, then one has a man in whom there is an excessively strong connection of the Ego and astral body with the physical body and the etheric body."[9] This is so because the higher members of man, primarily the Ego, develop a relationship to the mineral, to the crystal-like, the inorganic in the organism, those things which divested themselves of the "imponderable," of warmth, light, etc., and left behind solely the "ponderable." Thereby salt becomes permeable for the spiritual. In the sense of old alchemical cognition, salt is a "selfless substance" on which the higher nature, the soul-spiritual, can unfold itself. For that reason, all formations in man which tend to the lifeless, the salt-like, e.g., nerves, brain, skeleton, are the foundation for the unfolding of the soul-spiritual. The salt-like is related to the cold, to ice formation, through which "life becomes frozen thought."

But man must continuously overcome this process in himself. The power of death is confronted by the fire power of the Ego. In this confrontation we can understand what actually happens when we ingest salt with our food: we want to and we must reverse the salt formation process in us. Already in the mouth we dissolve the salt. Thus when somebody has a craving for salt, he "wants to reverse the deposition of salts in the organism."[10] Rudolf Steiner emphasized that a full comprehension of such processes is of special importance. Through this understanding "one looks into the relationships between the human organism and nature outside of man," and one then knows that the person craving salt "has in himself an organic need to reverse certain processes proceeding in external nature, to fight against them."[11]

Upon such thoughts Rudolf Steiner based his ideas concerning the necessity and significance of mineral remedies. In our nutrition we cannot go far beyond the plants. Most minerals are contained in the plants we eat. Sodium chloride alone is an exception. That man wants to take in sodium chloride as a mineral, in addition to those minerals contained in plant or animal foods, indicates that we have the need to go through this dissolving process, this process of overcoming dense earth formations in man. He can do this, however, only insofar as his Ego-organization is capable of handling his salt consumption. Too much as well as too little salt will result in illness. In this sense all of modern civilization is playing with its health. Modern medicine has verified this repeatedly; for example, American scientists continually point to the relationship between arteriosclerosis, hypertension, and many heart diseases and the overloading of the kidney by excessive salt consumption.

Rudolf Steiner discussed further aspects of the salt question in a lecture to workers on September 22, 1923. In this lecture we learn that salt is not merely a substance ingested for enjoyment, but that "it is an extraordinarily important nutrient"; "we salt our meals so that we can think." This emphasizes what was brought out earlier, that the minerals, especially salt, have a relationship to man's life of consciousness. Salt is placed into the service of the Ego-organization, which mediates the forces of consciousness in the upper man with the help of the nervous system. To that end, however, salt must go through the digestive organization; it must first be dissolved and then totally divested of its characteristic state. "What man makes of the salt proceeds in a spiritualized state into the brain." In other words, the human Ego-organization must be able to take this earthly, crystalline substance completely back into its archetypal state, a pre-earthly state, a pure state of formative forces, where the mineral was still spiritual. Whatever we take in as mineral is, "at least for a certain period of time, pure warmth, and as such, it is at one with the warmth which man develops as his own warmth."[12] We unite the salt-warmth with the warmth which is instrumental to, and the result of, our Ego-organization, and this must happen "before the salt is utilized in the human organism for its metabolism."

We know also that we need salt in the form of hydrochloric acid in the stomach. There it occurs in combination with pepsin, as a secretion of the stomach glands, and there it initiates protein digestion. In metabolism, salt serves other functions, and in doing so, is in the service of another member of man, the astral body.

The study of metabolism has long shown the strong connection between the astral body, the soul, and the formation of gastric hydrochloric acid. Three phases are described today. The first is termed the purely neuronal phase; it is initiated directly by sense impressions, memories, or freely formed associations. "The sight, smell, or even the thought of a favorite food can result in the secretion of stomach juices." This is called "psychological gastric juice secretion."[13] This neuronal phase, which contributes about 45% to gastric secretion, is relieved by the gastric or humoral phase, whose contribution to acid gastric juice is also 45%. Finally an "intestinal phase" is said to participate and contribute 10%. We can see that the essential stimulation comes from outside via the nervous system and the blood.

These events are actually much more complicated than our brief discussion suggests. Here we want only to direct attention to the salt formation activity in the organism insofar as it is specifically related to the upper members of the human organization, the Ego and the astral body. It should be noted here that in order to form hydrochloric acid, hydrogen must always be furnished by the organism. This is remarkable because hydrogen is the element which is most removed from the earth forces, the one that is closest to warmth, closest to the activity of the Ego.

A further example of the versatile character of a mineral salt in man is uric acid. It, too, is in the service of the Ego-organization in the brain and in the service of the astral body in metabolism. This is discussed specifically in Steiner and Wegmann's book, *Fundamentals of Therapy*. Here we want only to indicate that these functions of mineral substances in the human organism have brought about many difficulties and misunderstandings when attempts were made to study these relationships in animal experiments. Such experiments permit many interesting insights into the salt process, but in the final analysis, they give no real insight into the significance of salt for man.

Further Viewpoints

Let us summarize the essential aspect of the mineral again. On the one hand, the mineral has, in the course of earth evolution, been densified to the crystalline-solid. The spiritual view, when looking at the mineral, is led back to earlier stages of earth formation and human development. Rudolf Steiner once described these earlier stages as follows: "All minerals were in the form of mist and fog, in a light-permeated mist form"—in a living, light and warmth permeated atmosphere, resembling the so-called early Lemurian Age. Man also lived in this atmosphere at that time, only not in his present-day physical form. Those were the primal stages, which then existed externally and into which man today must transform his nourishment internally. These early conditions continue to live on in his metabolism

The mineral has removed itself most distantly from this living, ensouled, and spirit-filled atmosphere. It has, like salt, separated itself from all "imponderables." It is totally dead. But in this stage of having given up all that

126

was once its own, be it only its own life, the mineral has become especially permeable for extra-terrestrial activities. It is involved in a real interaction with forces which act on the earth out of the cosmic environment. As Rudolf Steiner once put it, we have to look at minerals as "the result of extra-terrestrial force effects."[14]

This densification and hardening process can also be recognized in man. We have encountered it especially in the organs subservient to the unfolding of consciousness. There the organ's life is suppressed so that in perceiving and thinking the world-life can enter man. The Ego-organization must continually interact with this mineralizing process. It needs this process in order to unfold its forces by battling against the mineralizing tendency in man. Thus we can understand that in nutrition, especially in salt nutrition, man has to continually go through this reversal, but in the face of the mineral he is at least able to do it. Salt serves him in this "counter-work."

At this point we must ask: under what circumstances does a mineral become a remedy? The answer is that when substances are artificially taken through processes which they naturally undergo within man in nutrition, they become remedies. This is the underlying principle of potentizing, which is used in the preparation of homeopathic remedies. In this "processed" form the potentized substances can be overcome by man's Ego-organization. They become remedies which, for a period of time, relieve man of what he is unable to do. He is able to take these prepared substances even though he is unable to overcome them in their densified form because, in that state, they are poisonous for him.

Poison Formation

Poison formation sets apart the most significant remedies and represents another aspect of the question of medical substance versus food substance. Thus we can now understand Rudolf Steiner's words: "One honors man by expecting him to participate in this stronger battle," namely, the overcoming of the mineral, "and we must in a certain sense allow the Ego to participate in this stronger battle." What matters in using remedies is not merely the use of the substances, as is absolutely necessary in nutrition; instead "it is, above all, the manner of preparation which matters," for that "represents the dynamic aspects of the process. We seek to imitate this dynamic aspect by technological means."[15] This "imitation" is related to what happens in the formation of substance in external nature, as well as in man's digestion. In this we can understand why cooked foods serve much more as nutritional substances than raw foods. In cooking and related processes we pre-digest, as it were; we partially relieve man of what he himself must do when he consumes raw foods. That is why "eating would be a continuous healing

127

process" if we did not prepare our food through cooking, etc. In that sense the consumption of raw food "is a healing process to a much greater extent," than is the consumption of cooked food.[16]

As the boundaries between medicinal and food substances are blurred, so, too, are the boundaries between poisonous and food substances. Modern nutritional science has indicated how many poisons are contained in our daily foods (often as constituents of plants), which are, without a doubt, also important for their nutritive value.

Rudolf Steiner concerned himself with the nature and significance of poison formation in his first medical course (1920). The formative forces of food plants achieve a balance between earth formative forces and extra-terrestrial forces. This balance, however, can be shifted. If the shift results in a predominance of the cosmic forces, then the plant "defends itself" in its fruit and seed formations against the earth forces. It develops the tendency to strive beyond the actual plant formative process; it attracts animal forces. Such a plant then becomes poisonous, as, for example, belladonna or hyoscyamus. These plants, with the proper preparation, become superlative remedies. They directly affect the process of consciousness which has been altered by illness. Such "poisonous plants" establish the most varied relationships to extra-terrestrial forces; consequently, they can unfold a rich spectrum of healing activities.

Such an attraction of extraterrestrial forces always occurs in the plant fruits. Every ripening of a fruit, as it announces itself in color change from the green of the unripe state, represents a contact with cosmic-astral forces. In this sense Rudolf Steiner could say in the *Agriculture Course* that fruit trees are special "collectors of astral substance," which manifests itself in their fruits. But such a food plant only interacts with the astral. In a poisonous plant, on the other hand, the astral penetrates into its etheric body. When we eat a plant, we also take in its etheric force and have to interact with it, as we have described before.

When we consume such a plant, especially a fruit, for example, "we press out the plant's etheric and take into our own etheric the force field which is at the basis of the plant."[17] Now "something very curious takes place." Using the example of eating cabbage, Rudolf Steiner explains that in the lower man "a very specific image first arises," as a picture of the metabolic activity which develops there. In accordance with it, a counter-image arises in the upper man which Steiner describes as a "real negative." "Cabbage actually brings about a very specific form in us, and its negative image is formed in our heads." This description, expressly said to be accessible to clairvoyant perception only, should not be thought of as physical-spatial. It is an imaginative perception. It applies to all food plants. When ingesting a poisonous substance, however, something else comes about, namely, "a much more defined form," a much more intensively active negative." When the poisonous plant is given to man in a tolerable dose, such a "strong structure" then permeates the human etheric body and correspondingly affects the upper man with a strong negative, that "the healing process is based on the interaction of the positive and the negative. . ." Rudolf Steiner specifically emphasized that such effects no longer depend on the "spatial distribution"; rather, such processes in the lower body call forth, as counter-image, processes in the head "without the presence of a spatial-physical dispersion."

Character of Food and Medicinal Substances

It has long been known that many plants which grow in the mountains have forces other than those of the same plants encountered on the plains. Among such mountain-grown plants we meet with many medicinal plants. Their whole growth pattern is different. They are stunted, but they are stronger in aroma, etc. The knowledge of the strength of such plants was utilized for many centuries; many healing herbs, processed into teas, powders, or tablets, formed the basis of so-called folk-remedies, and they have continually proven themselves effective as such. These plants also possess a higher quality when they are used as spices or even as foods.

Rudolf Steiner's response to a question on this subject is of interest to us here. He spoke of the strawberry, which, in its wild state, is small, but aromatic, in contrast to the bigger garden strawberry, which, for the most part, has little taste. In his response he states that the difference is based on the fact that the soil in mountains is richer in minerals; "there the plant takes into its juices very small parts of these stones and that makes them into medicinal plants." Mountain plants have an especially high capacity for taking up through their roots very small quantities of substances. The wild strawberry, for example, can readily attract traces of iron from the environment and that gives it its typical aroma. But more important, its high iron content makes it a useful dietary plant which is especially effective in encouraging blood formation. The wild strawberry also contains very high quantities of vitamin C, about 60 mg, while other berries contain a much more moderate amount: red currants—35 mg, raspberry—25 mg, and bilberry—16 mg. Rose hips are especially outstanding: 100 grams fruit flesh contains 300-380 mg of vitamin C. The mineral content of rose hips is also very high—4.6%—while wild strawberries contain only 0.7%. This mineral value also exceeds that of other berries, e.g., bilberry—0.4% and raspberry—0.6%. In the same lecture Rudolf Steiner compared the rose hip with the garden rose. The garden rose needs humus—rich and cultured soil; the wild rose, however, must develop a great activity in order to gather necessary substances for its survival. Through that activity it develops its fruits and, at the same time, directs its forces toward the formation of fruit, while the garden rose unfolds its blossom instead.

We can see from such examples how the food plant becomes a medicinal plant, and also how the food and medicinal plant, like the wild rose, can be transformed into a decorative plant under other conditions. In this connection Rudolf Steiner suggested that the plant not be used as remedy and food simultaneously. When we use the wild strawberry, for example, as a remedy, then it is inappropriate to eat garden strawberries at the same time, because the effects of each will then cancel each other out in the organism.

The spiritual forces active in the course of the year are united with nourishing and healing substances. During summer time the nutrition-creating forces are most highly developed in nature. These forces are correspondingly related to the sun forces in man, to his metabolism. Within man, the nourishing forces rise from metabolism to the respiratory system when their transformation into healing forces occurs.

> By continuing their activity into the respiratory system, they (the nourishing forces) become not only thirst and hunger relieving forces . . . they become forces which correct the ill person from within. The metamorphosed nutritional forces are healing forces. Whoever understands nutrition properly, understands the beginning of healing![18]

That is how Rudolf Steiner spoke about the inner transition from food to remedy. In between lies the dietetic use of substance. Related are those substances consumed merely for enjoyment.

In his very significant lecture of October 13, 1923, Rudolf Steiner also spoke of the existence of a highly developed instinctive wisdom in ancient times, of which Hippocrates experienced only the last remnants. At that time there were many "curious old remedies," which one can still find today in so-called primitive cultures. From these past times, however, we still have the cultured grains, fruit trees, etc. And from these often misunderstood remnants of old wisdom, other food plants have come to us, e.g., the potato, the tomato, the soy bean, and many others.

To conclude this chapter we would like to mention that Rudolf Steiner was also active in the creation of dietary substances by developing, among others, the "Aubaukalk" R (Weleda A. G., Arlesheim/Switzerland, Schwäbisch Gmünd/Germany). With this substance, whose basic constituents consist of phosphorus and calcium carbonate with added organic substances, Rudolf Steiner has provided not only a stimulant of calcium metabolism, but also a substance which supports the digestive and resorption processes of food.

Chapter 9

NUTRITION FROM THE REALM OF PLANTS
NUTRITION FROM THE REALM OF ANIMALS

Origin of Modern Vegetarianism

In our culture the vegetarian form of nutrition was not developed until the end of the last century. At that time it was a revolutionary idea to suggest that a nutrition, consisting purely of plant substances, would be adequate. Consequently, vigorous debates ensued. Physicians and nutritionists were found among both passionate supporters and convinced opponents of this new way of eating. It is still not an easy matter to deal with this issue on a purely factual basis. However, as we have seen, modern Spiritual Science can give us significant help.

The vegetarian form of nutrition has several origins. Bircher-Benner, through his medical experiences, realized the value of raw vegetable nutrition and attempted to establish it on a rational basis. His insight began as the result of a personal experience. When he was suffering from jaundice and had a distaste for all foods, by coincidence, his wife was making an apple pie. He ate a piece of raw apple and liked it so much that on the subsequent day he ate only raw apples. Doing so, he slowly recovered.

Although this interlude from 1895 was soon forgotten, Bircher-Benner soon approached nutritional questions again. In the same year he had to treat a patient who suffered from stomach disturbances. When everything else failed, he sought advice from a man who was skilled in the knowledge of natural remedies. This man advised him to try raw foods. The success was astounding. The patient recovered completely in several weeks. This was a decisive experience for Bircher-Benner. He wrote:

131

I was surprised—astonished. . . In the whole science of nutrition of 1895, I was not acquainted with a single fact which could explain the effect of this raw food diet. . . Contrary to my thinking and knowledge the patient improved.[1]

In the search for a satisfying explanation of his experiences, one that was not to be found in the medical literature of his time, Bircher-Benner sought the assistance of another pioneer in nutrition, Dr. Heinrich Lamm in Dresden. He had founded a sanatorium where he utilized hydrotherapy as well as vegetarian nutrition. Bircher-Benner wanted to know the reasons why this far-sighted physician used such a therapy. He learned that the greater wealth of minerals in vegetables was one of the reasons for Lamm's preference for this type of nutrition. This was significant, but to Bircher-Benner it was not yet the essential point, so he went to his teacher, Max Rubner, in Berlin. Through Rubner he was directed to a study of energy.

Rubner was completely under the influence of the thermodynamic laws of energy, which were generally considered valid at that time. While the first law, the law of the conservation of energy, appeared incontestable, Bircher-Benner reached the conclusion that there were still open questions about the second law. It became evident that the calorie teaching could not treat the energetic side of nutrition exhaustively. The second law states that the entropy of the universe increases continually and that therefore at the end of all development there is a "heat-death." This law was also described as "the law of the devaluation of energy." Since, as was assumed, all life processes were subject to this law, so, too, was nutrition. In accordance with this law, sun energy, as the source of all energetic processes in our world system, was determined to have the highest value. Warmth, however, that resulted from the combustion of substances, from their oxidation in the living organism, was held to have the lowest energy value. Bircher-Benner concluded that the calorie measure of foods only represented their least value in a downward curve, which begins with a much higher energy value embodied, for example, in its chemical value. Nutrition is therefore concerned with the assimilation of orders of energy, the values of which are higher the closer they are to sun energy. Such nutrition would then work against entropy, i.e., against the decay and death of the organism. Ostwald's phrase: "We eat sun energy in the plants," became in this sense a motto for Bircher-Benner. He derived from it his opinion that the closer the food is to its natural state the closer it is to sun energy, and it therefore has the highest nutritional value for man. Cooked food has already lost some of this energy. Animal foods, especially meats, have undergone further devaluation because the animal has used up the assimilated energies largely for its own life. In the preparation of meats a further energy fraction is lost. Milk, however, which the

132

animal does not form for itself but in the service of its offspring, stands higher in the rating, i.e., is closer to plant foods, insofar as it is consumed raw. Mushrooms represent the lowest category of nutritional value.

This schema was possibly the first closed system which managed to break the fetters of the calorie rules and attempted to introduce a rational concept of quality into the study of nutrition. When, decades later, the Nobel-laureate in Physics, Erwin Schrodinger, asked: "What is this precious something in our food which protects us from death?," his answer was similar to Bircher-Benner's: "Organization is maintained by removing order from the environment." In other words, the mark of a living organism, i.e., order, organization, can only be affected by order itself.

With Bircher-Benner's book, *Grundzuge der Ernährungs-therapie* (1903), there appeared, for the first time in occidental thinking, a scientific theory concerning vegetarianism. Today the following conclusion is drawn from a similar view presented by Mohler: "The human organism is accordingly no common motor which only needs fuel, for we need much more than only fuel."[2] But, given this conclusion, we must ask why in the same book, is the muscle still designated as a "mechanical-chemical machine"? And why is the cell labelled a "human accumulator," which is charged with ATP as storage of sun energy? The answer is that in the image of the life processes in the organism, we have not a mere "common motor," but an "accumulator." The accumulator is able to use up energy immediately, i.e., convert it completely into warmth, to store it. According to modern nutrition, that is how the human cell operates. It is able to store the liberated energy in the form of energy-rich compounds, e.g., glucose in the liver. As long as it can do this it works against entropy.

It is admitted in such interpretations that the living organism works against physical laws, and that it only succumbs to those laws when death supercedes. Nutrition continuously cancels out physical necessity, and so death occurs only when the nutritional process has become impossible or has been decreased to such an extent that it cannot exercise adequate counterforce against the natural laws.

Expansion Through Spiritual Science

This leads us directly to a characterization of death provided by Rudolf Steiner:

Concretely considered, death in man occurs when his whole inner organization has become so physical that no penetrating nutritional process can be initiated anymore. . .The body is unable to go through nutrition completely; it has become too physical.[3]

133

And so Rudolf Steiner establishes the polarity: "Physical Body—Nutrition." Plant nutrition, thus we may conclude, will primarily serve to fight against death; it does not actually carry death within it. For this reason we will therefore delay our discussion of energy problems to continue to pursue the question of the various forms of nutrition.

Rudolf Steiner also directed attention to the process by which the plant builds up its organism, i.e., how it densifies its body out of inorganic substances. For that it requires sunlight. This is "the wonderful force without which the plant could never build its living organism out of non-living substances."[4] With the help of sunlight the plant builds up its life body, its body of formative forces—that supersensible member of the life-world whose origin is possible by virtue of forces which radiate in from the environment. "In its transition into life, the substance must withdraw itself from the forces radiating out and subject itself to the forces radiating in."[5] Physiology shows us that man and animal carry within themselves a process opposed to that of the plant process. The plant inspires carbon dioxide and builds its body out of it with the help of the sun forces. Man and animal must exhale carbon dioxide and take up oxygen, which the plants produce. In nutrition, too, we have seen how man must break down and destroy what the plants have built up. In other words, beings endowed with soul-life do not advance the life forces in food but push them back, work against them. If we are clear about this, then we can comprehend that soul qualities, forces of consciousness of any kind, must arise in another way than the life forces which stream in through the outer sunlight. The cosmic sun force must change its direction. Rudolf Steiner described the human astral body as "an inner light, a light of spiritual nature," invisible to the external eye. In this sense the human astral body (soul body) is a spiritual light body, i.e., a kind of negative to the outer sunlight.

> The external light has the task of stimulating the etheric body to build up the plant organism out of inorganic substances. The inner light (the astral body) initiates the partial destructive processes through which alone consciousness and inner soul life are possible.[6]

But now comes the decisive insight: the organ through which consciousness can become effective, which is carrier of the soul forces, is the nervous system. And so we can say that through the nervous system the astral body works by pushing back the life processes. This shows itself in the structure of the nerve cells, which have lost their formative forces in the first years of human life; i.e., they cannot reproduce.

Thus in sunlight we have the same force which, in the nervous system, is active spiritually and manifests itself as carrier of consciousness. Thereby the

134

plant world, which has its life by virtue of the external sun forces, and man and the animals, which build up their soul body out of inner sun forces, are lawfully related to one another. By understanding such relationships, we can arrive at objective points of view regarding plant foods or animal foods. When, for example, man takes his nourishment from the animal realm, then the being from which he takes his food has in a certain sense already gone through the process which he himself would have to go through afresh if he took his food from the plant realm. The animal uses up the forces which the plant uses in building up its life body, in order to build up its nervous system and to unfold soul forces. Thus with animal substance man takes up what has already gone through the process he himself would have to go through. This might be considered a relief, but it is only a partial truth. Instead, what matters is not that man is relieved of exercising an inner force, but that he himself should unfold this force. This is a fundamentally important principle of the human being. Every force not activated becomes weak and paralyzed. Whether it is a muscle which cannot move, and rapidly becomes flaccid and atrophies, or a digestive organ inadequately utilized, or even a soul activity unused, the result will always be a weakening, not a strengthening.

The strong resistance man confronts in plant foods was reemphasized by Rudolf Steiner later in his medical courses. He explained that man "must develop stronger forces, if he is opposed by a stronger force." Thus we arrive at the difference between the vegetarian and animal forms of nutrition. When our nourishment consists of pure plant substances, "we must go through the whole process of which the animal relieves us by taking the plant a step further." Whoever takes his food from animals, consequently, does not at all develop these forces which he needs for plant foods. Here we can refer again to the schema introduced in Chapter III:

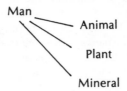

There we spoke of "paths" which the nourishment must take to get to man. From the plant these "paths" are longer than from the animal. They are longest from the mineral to man. For that reason, man can only consume small quantities of minerals directly. He must obtain minerals primarily from the plants which have taken the mineral a good step closer to him. But when he consumes plant foods, he must draw forth entirely different forces than when he consumes animal foods. Does present day man have these forces?

135

Can he mobilize them or is he already organized so that the mixed diet we consume today is the appropriate one? The question has persistently occupied nutritionists and has been answered in many different ways.

Most of the responses suffer from one-sidedness, because the differentiation of organ activities into various life activities and consciousness activities is hardly ever, if at all, taken into consideration. This differentiation is especially evident if we look at the functions of head organs. For example, the muscles of mastication are also in the service of speech and of facial expression. Likewise, the tongue is simultaneously an organ for speech, movement, sense, and digestion. Then there are the teeth which are active in chewing, speech formation, and also, as Rudolf Steiner explained, thinking.

Glatzel attempts to do justice to such claims when he writes "that factors other than food ingestion also participated in the development of man's teeth."[7] He reached the conclusion that in "their completeness the human teeth resemble neither the carnivores' nor the herbivores'." They have their own human character which enables man to consume both plant and animal foods. This means that, considered anatomically and physiologically, man has the freedom to decide between the two kinds of nutrition! The animal, however, is organized through its tooth and jaw structure towards a definite, species specific form of nutrition. Man can reform his organs into this or that direction, adapting to his nutrition, and will do this within limits in an individual manner. This adaptability also extends to his intestinal organs. Frequently one hears that man's digestive organization is not suited for a purely vegetarian nutrition. Glatzel writes: "The human intestine is shorter than the intestine of an herbivore, but longer than that of the carnivore." But to conclude from that statement that man can eat everything is just too simple. Man has the potential to break out of the rigid nutritional requirements of animals and select his nutrition according to his stage of development, his race, his constitution, his country, and finally his individuality. Such possibilities are indicated by Thomas concerning the intestinal size. He suggests that "digestive disturbances following the intake of foods with high fiber content can most likely be due to degenerative developments" and that the deficiency of a corresponding intestinal flora in man "could well have resulted from inadequate use."[8]

Rudolf Steiner, addressing himself to this issue, said that an intestine too short for a purely vegetarian nutrition does not provide proof against the possibility of transformation, although that may take generations.

Vegetarian or Animal Nutrition?

Taking all these aspects into consideration it should be evident that the question of vegetarian versus animal foods is not an either/or situation, but rather that the problem lies on a completely different level.

"The forces needed to overcome foods from plants and animals are there." If they are not awakened, or if they are inadequately utilized and instead are allowed to atrophy through disease, then "they go back into the organism as it were through a sort of kick-back." This "kick-back" has tiring and disturbing effects, while an activation of these forces through vegetarian nutrition has a less tiring effect. In fact man becomes more capable of work by activation of such forces.[9]

In the last year of his life, Rudolf Steiner told the workers at the Goetheanum: "Well, I can say I myself know that I would have been unable to go through with the strenuous activities of the last 24 years" without vegetarian nutrition.[10] He had decided upon vegetarian nutrition in 1900, the year in which he began to disseminate Spiritual Science. "If somebody can get along without meat, then he feels . . . stronger than before." The emphasis, however, is on "can" and that raises a new question with which we must concern ourselves.

We already indicated that the question of what kind of nutrition one chooses is an individual one. In the lecture cited above, Rudolf Steiner suggested that one should always consider carefully whether one can live without meat. That presupposes of course that one is able to form an adequate judgment of this question. Our discussions here are an attempt at facilitating a proper judgment. Experience shows a variety of illusions, and it is easy, despite seemingly objective judgment, to be deceived.

Rudolf Steiner established a few criteria, however. First he examined the question of whether a person is able to muster adequate forces necessary for digestion of vegetarian foods. Inheritance, for example, can be important. There are simply people "who, because of all the forces carried through inheritance, are unable to mobilize enough forces for a purely vegetarian nutrition." Only a few generations ago—especially in the country—meat was rarely eaten. It was considered food for holidays or special occasions. In the cities, however, during the 19th century, the daily plate of meat became more and more customary. The workers, however, were still too poor to afford such nutrition. So, considered merely from the point of view of inheritance the predisposition for vegetarian nutrition is quite varied.

Education

Similarly important is the education of children regarding food. The example of parents and educators often plays a decisive role here. Children in the first seven years of life want to imitate their environment. Sympathy and antipathy for certain foods are established from experiences in early childhood. The task of education can be considered to be the healthy development of the nutritional instincts native to the child. Rudolf Steiner said once: If the child likes sugar, it does not do so because of nutrition . . . , but "because of the sweetness." What matters is how the child's justifiable need for sweetness is fulfilled.

We must be clear about the fact that sympathy and antipathy, partly organically determined, play a very important role in nutrition. Thus many persons will prefer meat simply because their life forces have a strong sympathetic relation to animal astrality. Through meat consumption they feel strengthened and satisfied. "Eating meat satisfies their sensual pleasure, just as eating candies satisfies the child's sensual pleasure. . . One eats meat especially if the body loves the meat."[11]

If the organism has become accustomed in childhood to eating meat primarily, then it will become very difficult to avoid it later in life. Here, too, the power of custom plays an enormous, often undervalued, role. More and more people today are looking instinctively for clarity and insight into these questions. Young people do not want to continue mere traditions, but want to establish their own life styles. In this search they often overcome old customs, which, for them, no longer have significance. Nevertheless, the same persons succumb to one or another fashion prevalent at the time, because their power of judgment is inadequate.

Results of Modern Nutritional Science

Professor Glatzel, a typical representative of those who have done work in this area, presents several relevant arguments in his book, *Die Ernährung in der technischen Welt*. He says: "The production of animal proteins and fats requires a large expenditure of feed plants. The greatest part of the consumed energy is required by the animal for its own maintenance."[12] On the average 7 kg of plant protein are required to produce 1 kg of animal protein. In other words: "Considered from an energetic point of view, the production of animal proteins is a highly irrational procedure." This statement by Glatzel is not only of fundamental significance for political economy, but it explains at the same time what happens to protein production and utilization in the animal organism. It is an important indication of how much the animal needs for the formation and nutrition of its own nervous system. In fact, the "animal calorie" is three times as expensive as the "plant calorie." According to Pirie, the ratio is even greater: "In the production of plant foods the resulting calories exceed those of animal foods by a factor of 10."[13] We must consider, however, that the calorie measure is actually inadequate as a measure of nutrition because it neglects the qualitative evaluation. Glatzel, for example, claims that plant proteins, as nutritional proteins, have less value and that the quantities of plant food necessary to meet protein requirements "exceed the capacity of the human digestive organs." Here we have another erroneous conclusion. This evaluation is based on an estimate of protein requirement which is still debatable and unrealistic. Furthermore the evidence that the greatest part of humanity is still primarily vegetarian should show that such nutrition is entirely adequate, assuming it has not lost its value because of inadequate quality. The FAO published the following ratios of meat to vegetable consumption for 1960:

America and Australia		1:1
Europe and Russia		1:2 2/3
Developing Countries:		
Far East		1:9 1/2
Africa		1:10

Although there is malnutrition and even famine in many regions of the earth, they are in no way related to the ratio of plant and animal nutrition. Much more important are the inadequacies of food quality, the consequences of modern methods of agriculture, the denaturation of food, and, above all, the lack of an adequate measure for evaluating nutrition in general.

Attempts to establish a measure of quality can be found today, e.g., when we hear of a "biological protein value," which does not conform to the caloric value. The inadequacy of such evaluation, however, is shown by the fact that the standard measure is bacterial protein, because it is most similar in amino acid content to human protein. The measure becomes more realistic when, for example, an animal experiment shows that "protein mixtures can in every case be utilized better than single proteins of high value."[14] Professor Fleisch concludes:

It is an established fact that with decreasing protein consumption the total quantity of calories consumed also decreases. . . The stimulating properties especially of meat protein lead to an excess consumption which cannot be justified from a nutritional point of view, one that is probably not optimal, because it leads to a luxury combustion. . . Meat, beyond the effects of excess protein, must have some kind of further, specifically stimulating effect.[15]

The increased functional capacity resulting from vegetarian nutrition is

139

hardly evaluated properly today. Historical accounts are very significant here. For example, Herodotus claimed that the grain eating tribes "far exceeded those that lived by war, hunt, animal husbandry, and fishery, in arts, sciences, number, and in spiritual and bodily formation."[16] Consequently, Glatzel's observation that "the primarily vegetarian person in developing countries has a low spiritual and bodily capacity for work" is one-sided and not very convincing.[17] He applies the wrong standard here, one that is dictated by a thinking to which the realities of nutrition are foreign. That the nutritional conditions in the so-called "developing countries" are in many cases already very decadent and that these cultures are already severely damaged by the effects of western culture should not be overlooked.

Not to be forgotten is that the animal world also provides remarkable examples of vegetarian and animal nutrition. It is well known of course that many animals, such as the horse, the gorilla, and the camel, are pure herbivores. Their bodily capacity is certainly not doubted. The whale, too, who has gigantic strength at his disposal, is a vegetarian. Herder, in his *Ideas Towards a Philosophy of Humanity*, writes about the elephant as "the king of animals who has wise equanimity and purity of sense." He continues: "The lion, however, what a different king of animals! In him nature was concerned with muscles, not with gentleness and understanding."[18]

Rationale Through Modern Spiritual Science

Let us return once again to the nutrition lecture of December 17, 1908, and recall how there the specific importance of plant nutrition for the nervous system is discussed.[19] We read that man "must develop and unfold in himself those forces which permeate his nervous system. . ." This is indeed what happens when he eats plant foods. This nutritional concept is more comprehensive than a merely physiological one. We must also take into consideration that nutrition is a problem of the whole human being, of his soul-spiritual as well as of his bodily aspects. Especially the nervous system, the brain, is of importance as an instrument for the unfolding of soul-spiritual forces. Only from such a point of view can we fully understand and appreciate the statements of the spiritual scientist. They indicate that the nervous system, which includes the brain, spinal cord, and ganglia, is in connection with all other members and activities in the human being.

Through plant nutrition, which connects him with unused, cosmic life forces, man becomes much more receptive to spiritual impressions and experiences which the nervous system can communicate to him. For "nothing beclouds the nervous system" when its nourishment comes from the plant realm. And so it is by virtue of such nutrition that "man can look up to the great inter-relationships which elevate him beyond the narrow confines of this personal being. . ." Rudolf Steiner explains further:

> Whenever man elevates himself to the great overviews of existence, then he is not chained to common, passed-on tradition; whenever man regulates his life and existence from a freer and higher point of view, then he has achieved this rapid thinking, this rapid comprehension, by virtue of his nourishment from the plant world.

When we read on in Steiner's lecture, no doubt remains as to the intimate connection between the kind of nutrition we practice and what modern Spiritual Science strives to achieve for man in the present time:

> When man acts through anger and selfishness, through sympathy and antipathy, which all becloud everything and show everything in a narrowly delimited light, when he forms his judgments, when he drags himself from prejudice to prejudice, then he acts by virtue of his relationship to the animal world, his animal nutrition.

Meat Nutrition

Whenever Rudolf Steiner talked about nutrition, he made clear that he was not agitating for vegetarianism. Nevertheless, he also made clear that the progress of man depends upon the progressive predominance of vegetarian nutrition in the total nutrition. For that no agitation is necessary; it will happen by itself. On the other hand, the fact of meat nutrition is connected with the development of man into a personality. Meat nutrition enables man "to stand firm on earth," to unfold his personal life. Rudolf Steiner pointed here to the same relationship between nutrition and the life of various cultures that was recognized by Herodotus: "Among our humanity there are those who lead wars against one another, who relate through anger, antipathy, and sensual passions." They draw this force out of animal nutrition. They have, however, also developed "bravery, courage, and boldness." Other cultures, occupied more with spiritual pursuits, customarily obtained their food from plants. But we hear from Rudolf Steiner that with an overemphasis on animal nutrition, man will lose all interest in the spiritual world. In view of the steadily rising meat consumption today, the importance of such a recognition need hardly be emphasized. A few statistics will demonstrate the trend. For West Germany alone the following figures are given for meat consumption:

141

1850 approximately 18 kg per person per year
1870 approximately 28 kg per person per year
1900 approximately 48 kg per person per year
1958 approximately 58 kg per person per year
1970 approximately 69 kg per person per year

In the face of these developments Schipperges came to the conclusion that "in view of the growing avalanche of disease in civilization, only a rapid and vigorous alteration of our life and nutritional habits will bring help."

In another lecture cycle, Rudolf Steiner also emphasized the "specifically earthly" quality of meat nutrition which ties man to the earth.[20] The "light-ness" of the organism mediated by plant nutrition, on the other hand, "lifts it above earth's heaviness." Hearing such weighty statements should we not be rather disappointed when we now also hear from Rudolf Steiner that most persons today are unable to go through with a vegetarian nutrition, because they are unable, due to inheritance, etc., to muster adequate forces to meet the physiological demands?[21]

We must conclude that even in the present time only a relatively small fraction of humanity is capable of fully nourishing itself with plant foods. A large part of the Far East population, because of inheritance, still has the necessary forces, but even it is losing them rapidly because of an inadequate food supply and an increase of western influence. Nevertheless, some statistics are interesting: the daily meat ration of an Indian is 2 gm, that of a Swiss is 194 gm.[22] Another statistic lists the average per capita yearly meat consumption (1960-1961) in the U.S.A. as 85 kg, in West Germany as 60.8 kg, in Switzerland as 59.4 kg, in Italy as 29.6 kg, in Spain as 20.8 kg, and in India as only 730 gm! How do these statistics reflect on the conditions in the West today? Because of the continual over-consumption of meat, the inherited characteristics needed for vegetarian nutrition deteriorate.

At this point we must ask: Should not man be able to gain greater control over his own forces? Should he not be able to free himself from the fetters of inheritance and thereby elevate himself to the possibilities of a plant nutri-tion? It would be regrettable if that were not so. Everyone, who, in the sense of Spiritual Science, is prompted to examine this question, will have to be exceedingly objective before he can arrive at the conclusion that he is presently not yet one of those who serves the progress of humanity through his nutrition.

We will not neglect to remind ourselves of an argument frequently made by modern nutritionists against vegetarianism. Allegedly, the so-called vitamin B 12 cannot be synthesized by plants, but only by man and animal. This substance is, among others, important in hematopoiesis and its de-ficiency can result in a certain kind of anemia, the so-called "pernicious

142

anemia." Accordingly, the inadequate supply of this vitamin (cobalamine) represents a defect in vegetarian diets. "The vitamin B 12 blood level is for that reason very low in vegetarians."[23] Others report that this disease has been found in vegetarians. It is remarkable, however, that Glatzel adds here that "many of the clinically evident symptoms of B 12 deficiency in the sense of a megaloblastic anemia . . . apparently never appear in many vegetarians." Correspondingly significant is A. Ikle's report that 100 gm of parsley contains 60 mg of vitamin B 12 and that the daily requirement during pregnancy is estimated to be 3 mg.[24] Thus it is quite possible that an activation of the organism can result so that the intestinal flora can produce this substance and represent adequate protection from disease. Important, too, is the fact that cobalamine is also found in milk.

Milk and Milk Products

Milk and milk products have long been used in vegetarian kitchens. Despite the fact that milk is an animal product, few vegetarians have been offended by its use. Actually, however, milk represents a very individual product, which cannot simply be labelled as animal substance, although it is produced by animals.

A comparison of blood and milk can clarify its special position. While the blood is formed entirely within the organism and plays its role exclusively in the service of the organism, the situation with milk is different. Certainly milk formation is also dependent on the blood, but it is produced as a creation of the lacteal glands on the periphery of the organism. The typical milk protein, casein, and milk sugar, lactose, are original creations of the milk formation process and cannot be found anywhere else in the organism. Because of this separate formation, milk emancipates itself, as it were, from the blood. It also shows its polar position to the blood in the direction of its formation. While blood, when reaching the body surface, immediately attempts to separate itself from the world by coagulating, milk does not have this possibility. On the contrary, once formed, milk must leave the body. Thus it is totally organized towards an externally directed process while blood is totally organized towards an internally directed process. Milk divests itself of the typical internalizing forces (manifesting itself in the animal realm as soul formation) and orders itself into the pure life forces which characterize the plant organization.

Rudolf Steiner, in the first medical course (1920) emphasized that the blood formation process is placed into the hidden aspects of the human organism, while the milk-process tends more toward the surface. In this sense blood is related to the process of individualization, while milk is closer to the cosmic-extraterrestrial. Consequently, we can group blood with cooked food, and milk with raw foods. Raw milk, however, will have a different quality in nutrition and dietetics than cooked milk, which, through cooking, gains again a kind of "innerness." Actual milk nutrition is thus raw milk.

In 1905 Rudolf Steiner said that "milk expresses the animal process only very weakly. Milk is only half an animal product; it does not permit participation of the astral force in the animal and human nature."[25] There are other indications as well which describe how closely milk is related to the plants. If one looks at mother's milk in this way, on the other hand, and "at the astral which surrounds the plant and for which the plant longs," on the other, then there is, to occult perception, "an extremely close relationship— not a complete equivalence—between the astrality coming from the mother in the milk, and the astrality which approaches the blossom of the plant from the cosmos."[26] Milk leaves an innerness and enters a stream of formative forces which no longer contain the soul element within, but only, as it were, in its environment. That is how milk attains this close relationship to the blossom and fruit formation of the plants. Thus we can see that milk and milk products can justifiably be put side by side with plant nutrition. A lacto-vegetable nutrition is not a mixed nutrition but can be designated entirely as an expanded vegetarian nutrition.

Chapter 10

NUTRITION AND SPIRITUAL LIFE

Historical Aspects

Herodotus' description cited in the last chapter suggests a connection between nutrition and the spiritual life of humanity. At least an indirect effect of nutrition on spiritual life can be seen in the description that the grain-eating cultures far exceed the meat-eating cultures in the arts, sciences, and spiritual development. Bourner, writing about the late Roman period, records that the progressive political decay was accompanied by an increasing indulgence of sensual appetites. This is a phenomenon which is clearly evident in historical development everywhere. On the other hand, the multitude of transmitted diet prescriptions of the old Greek and Oriental schools of philosophy, and especially of the mystery centers, suggests a definite bridge between daily nourishment and its effect on human spiritual life. The forms of nutrition were guided by men of knowledge, by initiates, by those who underwent spiritual schooling. In a certain sense the substance itself played an important role in the achievement of spiritual capacities. And the cultures which were guided by such centers, which were often the external centers of power, received from them their nutritional rules. Whether a people became grain eaters or meat eaters was certainly not a matter of chance. The spiritual guides of those old tribes and cultures knew very well what kind of nutrition was appropriate to the task. Thus it is not a matter of chance that the rice culture was developed in Eastern cultures, that corn was developed in the old American cultures, that the potato originated in the Far West and the soy bean in the Far East.

Today, however, it is evident that the old ties of nutrition to the spiritual life have been lost. We have all the food items which the earth produces at our disposal. Nothing can be withheld from us because it might be inappropriate; at the same time nothing can be given to us simply because it might be for our benefit. In this sense man has left, has overcome, his cultural association. What remains as tradition and continues to exercise an often still powerful compulsion will fully lose its significance in the coming centuries. The "Wiener Küche" will be immersed into the general forms of nutrition as well as the "cuisine francaise." He who is able to read the symptoms will recognize that the ties are already dissolving. Man has become free and wants to choose his own nutrition. But, as we have constantly emphasized, for that he needs a new consciousness.

This development is not only determined by modern techology, although it has been significantly encouraged by its techniques. One could argue the reverse: the spiritual development first made the technological developments possible and then placed it into the service of tasks appropriate to this age. These include the creation of a human world-consciousness, one that is a new nutritional consciousness and one that can lead to spiritually appropriate, individualized forms of nutrition.

We must not neglect, however, the problems which technology brought about in nutrition. When we consider the trend towards "convenience foods," which is spreading rapidly, we will recognize that modern technology has indeed shaped our nutrition. Within the limits of this chapter, however, we will concern ourselves with this problem only insofar as it is related to the connection of the spiritual life with nutrition.

Aspects of Modern Nutritional Science
The Significance of Phosphorus

If we ask what the position of modern nutritional science is with regard to the problem of nutrition and spiritual life, we will discover, surprisingly enough, that mental work does not utilize measurable energy. When we think, we do not utilize calories. This fact is without a doubt of great significance. It means that spiritual activity is independent of metabolism of the body, because no measurable increase can be verified. Metabolic balance does not change with spiritual work, neither in the positive nor in the negative sense. On the other hand, another very significant finding of modern science is that the brain, as the instrument of thinking, has a very intensive metabolic activity. In fact, relatively speaking, it has the highest metabolic rate of all human organs. This means that with inadequate or deficient nutrition the functional capacity of the brain will be diminished.

146

That is a very important finding of the modern science of nutrition. Despite high expectations, however, no intelligence-enhancing foods have been discovered.

Nevertheless, modern nutritional science recognizes that there is indeed a connection between nutrition and spiritual development, although the methods to explore this problem are still inadequate. There appeared, for example, in the *Ernährungsumschau* (Nutritional Review), an essay entitled: "Does Nutrition Influence the Mental Development of Children?" It described studies with results which showed that under certain optimal nutritional conditions, children who received a supplemental diet, when compared to "normally" nourished children, "show at the end of the test period a clearly higher rise in I.Q. than non-supplemented children." (*Ernährungsumschau,* Frankfurt, 8/74)

Let us take, for example, a substance which, in this connection, plays an important role today, namely, phosphorus. Ludwig Büchner, in his successful book of 1885, *Kraft und Stoff,* wrote the following about the chemical composition of the brain: "Among all organs of the body the brain contains the greatest quantity of phosphorus." He reports studies "which have shown that vigorous mental exertion results in the appearance of significant quantities of phosphorus and sulfur-containing alkalis in the urine," and he cites another author who "established that the phosphorus content of the brain in old age and idiocy decreases by almost half and returns to a childhood level." Summarizing, Büchner writes: "These facts establish without doubt that the phosphorus content of the brain has special significance, and they suggest a possible specific relationship between it and mental work." Finally he cited Moleschott's then shocking expression: "Without phosphorus, no thought!"[1]

What does modern physiology have to say about this problem? Everywhere the presence and significance of phosphorus-containing substances in the nervous system is emphasized. There are the lecithins, the cephalins, the sphingomyelins, cerebrosides, gangliosides, etc. The names indicate in many cases their location in the nervous system. They are also, however, found in tissues which are metabolically active. P. Carlson, in his *Lehrbuch der Biochemie* emphasizes that nerve tissue is especially rich in phosphatides and "the fine structure of nerves . . . can only be understood with inclusion of the phosphatides."[2] Among metabolic processes, oxydative phosphorylation is exceedingly important and phosphorus makes its appearance there as a very active substance. Phosphate is essential in the utilization of starch and sugars, and sugar can be absorbed from the intestine only in its presence. Finally, E. A. Schmid, in his book, *Sinnvolle Ernährung-gesundes Leben,* says about phosphorus: "It is especially rich and highly active in the cells and nuclei of the brain," where, in the form of lecithin, "it is absolutely necessary for the intensive cellular respiration necessary to maintain consciousness."[3] It is evident from these reports that modern science considers phosphorus an especially important substance for the structure and function of the nervous system.

In his *Physiologie des Menschen*, Bunge wrote that the phosphorus compounds are most likely among the most essential organic nutrients of man.[4] He emphasized especially the importance of lecithin, found primarily in the brain. In the developmental period of the infant the lecithin content of the brain increases rapidly, because it is used there for the formation of the myelin sheaths of axons. He discovered that the lecithin content of milk is related directly to the relative brain weight. Hence the lecithin content of human milk is highest. Bunge saw in that an indication for the irreplaceability of mother's milk, for the lecithin content of cow milk is 50% less than mother's milk. It is of interest that Büchner, who was a physician, had already written that "all nutrients which contain phosphorus in the form of lecithin are especially suited to replace the loss of substance which occurs during mental work."

What does Spiritual Science have to say about phosphorus? We have already seen that in the organism phosphorus is primarily found in the brain, in the bones, and in combination with protein. As a mineral it is active in the direction of the lifeless, in what is not organized from within, but in what goes into the inorganic. We recall that such substances have a special connection to the Ego-organization, which needs them to unfold its activity by pushing back the living. In this sense it stimulates conscious activity, which can unfold itself on the basis of the mineralizing tendency. That is how we can understand its activity in relation to human spiritual life. That phosphorus "stimulates the conscious activity in man" is stated by Steiner and Wegmann in their book, *Fundamentals of Therapy*. This statement helps to shed light on other observations by Rudolf Steiner. For example, in a lecture to the workers he said: "In our brain we have phosphorus . . . and you know that it is very useful, because without phosphorus one could not use the brain for thinking."[5] This is exactly what Büchner and Moleschott said: "Without phosphorus, no thought!" Actually, however, they wanted to demonstrate the opposite, namely, that "substance or matter does not contain only physical but also spiritual forces." Matter "brings forth" spiritual activity. Spiritual Science, however, must speak of matter in a different way. Rudolf Steiner said that without phosphorus the brain could not "be *used for* thinking." The brain is the instrument which makes possible our becoming conscious of thinking in the physical body. The processes manifested by phosphorus facilitate the unfolding of consciousness. We can see then that although the spiritual appears to be bound to the brain, it is active independent of matter. In this sense the latter is densified spirit; it becomes carrier of the spiritual.

Rudolf Steiner went on in the same lecture to say that "phosphorus is advantageous when it is taken in with nourishment in the right way." In that statement we have a clear indication of the importance of phosphorus-containing nutrition for brain function, for the support of thinking. We will later characterize in detail such "brain nutrition," but here we want only to present fundamental aspects. Nevertheless, we will mention what significance grain nutrition has for the forces of consciousness, especially rice with its high phosphorus content, and hazelnuts, often labelled today as "brain food." Rudolf Steiner said that if one wants to train one's thinking, then one needs above all "a well-constructed, healthy brain-apparatus. Children today seldom receive such a well-constructed brain from their parents and so one needs help in order to strengthen the brain-apparatus; it is especially hazelnuts which yield the substance to build up the brain."[6]

Salt - Silicia - Uric acid - Sugar

The significance of salt for thinking was already mentioned in the last chapter. We salt our food not only so we get a proper taste, but also "so that we are able to think at all." "He who cannot have the effect of salt in the brain will become stupid."[7] We mentioned earlier that salt, as sodium chloride, is the only truly mineral food we have. All other salts we take in via the plant or animal. What is essential in the resistance with which the mineral confronts man is the force with which the human Ego ignites through this resistance.

This is also how other mineral substances act, e.g., quartz (silica). "It forms the physical foundation of the Ego-organization" and through that it unfolds an activity "which is able to form the organs of conscious life."[8] In this sense one can speak of a silicic acid organism in man "upon which are based the sensitiveness of organs underlying the healthy life activity and also their proper relationship inwards, towards the soul and spirit activities." The organism is stimulated in these processes by silica-rich nourishment, such as grains and many roots.

Rudolf Steiner spoke of uric acid in the same way. Generally uric acid, which is a protein breakdown product, is merely considered an excretory product of the kidneys, or a pathological collection in gout. It is, however, also found in the brain in a fine dispersion. "In the uric acid secretion in the brain the Ego-organization is the primary determinant. . . Man can only be the conscious being he is, because of the impregnation of his organs with the inorganic."[9]

Sugar is another substance which, though organic, closely approaches the inorganic and is for that reason also of great significance for conscious processes. This substance, resulting from carbohydrate breakdown, has a very special connection to man. In forming sugar through his digestion, man prepares a substance which can be active in the region of the Ego-organization. "Where there is sugar, the Ego-organization can manifest itself in order to orient the subhuman (vegetable, animal) body qualities towards the human."

Whenever excessive demands are made on the Ego-organization, illness occurs, whether it is in relation to sugar, salt, uric acid, or silica. The excessive consumption of sugar, primarily in the form of refined sugar, makes it impossible for the Ego-organization to place that kind and quantity of sugar into its service.

Man's need for sugar originates from the interaction of sweetness with the Ego. Rudolf Steiner spoke several times of the connection which the taste of sweetness has to the Ego: "Grape sugar is a substance which can be active in the realm of the Ego-organization."[10] "Sugar, consumed directly, is in the Ego-organization. It becomes there the stimulator of the taste of sweetness." Curiously enough, sweetness is perceived on the tip of the tongue, while the organs for bitterness are more near the root of the tongue. Also, we are much less sensitive to sweetness, than to bitterness. This does not mean that the animal is incapable of having a sugar-experience, but it will have a different experience than man.

Man needs a relatively large quantity of glucose for the nourishment of his brain (approximately 110 gm a day) and for that reason it is also very purposeful that mother's milk has, in relation to animal milk, such a high sugar content (more than 7%). The fact that sugar serves as the basis of thinking, for the unfolding of consciousness, says nothing about the quality of thinking. It does, however, increase the state of wakefulness. Notable is a fact which Rudolf Steiner pointed out, that at one time the English consumed far more sugar than the Russians. He further observed that the "Russian farmer will emphasize the Ego as little as possible," while the Englishman already capitalizes the word "I." "The process resulting in digestion from the consumption of larger quantities of sugar has its correlation in the upper man in a stronger independence of the thinking capacity."[11] Here Rudolf Steiner actually indicates a kind of qualitative effect of sugar on thinking. In another lecture he said:

When a person is very independent, and tends strongly towards egotism, then he should eat only small amounts of sugar. . . If someone, however, is without inner and outer security, and always believes he needs support, then he should eat lots of sugar in order to become more independent.

Here we have an entirely new point of view, which uncovers a qualitative relationship.

Now it would be incorrect to believe that by increasing the sugar consumption one would enhance the strength of consciousness. On the contrary, the consequence would most likely be increased egotism. Possibly that is what is happening too much in the West today. The disease consequences would then have to be evaluated more as symptoms of a sort of self-help of the organism, which is somehow trying to deal with the sugar excess. This way of looking at the issue sheds a completely new light on the increasing prevalence of diabetes mellitus in our time.

Rudolf Steiner also spoke of this problem in March 1914 in The Hague.[12] There, too, he emphasized how sugar permeates man "with a kind of natural Egotism," through which a counter-balance can be created, if man strives toward selflessness by spiritual training. The sugar will enable him, "despite all advance into the spiritual worlds, to remain with both legs on the earth." Here again we have a qualitative evaluation of sugar consumption, in this case related to spiritual training. Further we learn that "sugar consumption physically elevates man's personality characteristics," but that it must all be contained within healthy limits. The prevalent sugar consumption, however, has long exceeded the healthy limits. Again we remind ourselves: We need sugar in our nourishment, but we can only use it if we continually dissolve it.

The sugar problem clearly shows that neither a mere chemical approach nor a physiological or psychological approach is entirely adequate in considering all aspects. In the final analysis it becomes evident that the measure of sugar consumption is an individual one.

The Carrot as Root Food

We have discussed sugar because of the indication that all inorganic substances and those tending in that direction develop a special connection to the life of consciousness. In this sense the root formation of the plant is also related to the life of consciousness and the activities of the nerve-sense organism. Root foods will stimulate these functions.

Dr. N. Remer provides an excellent description of the carrot from a botanical-agricultural point of view:

Root and seed formation mutually interpenetrate in this plant. Salt formation in the root mirrors the terrestial influences. The formation of fragrant substances in the seed expresses the relation to warmth and light. . . The cultivated carrot is an especially aromatic form of the mutual interpenetration of above and below.[13]

The view is directed here to the inner dynamics of carrot formation. Under

151

consideration is the polarity óf root and seed-formation; the former is subject to the terrestrial, the latter to cosmic forces. Therewith a fundamental formative principle is indicated which undergoes the most varied metamorphoses in the plant realm. Underlying it is the archetypal formation of the leaf upon which Goethe built his plant studies.

In the carrot the leaves have become inessential; the fruits and seeds, too, are not developed—in contrast to other umbellifera. Everything is concentrated in the root. It not only permeates itself with the aromatic forces coming from above, it also concentrates into itself the color usually found above the ground and called forth by deposition of carotin. Rudolf Steiner characterized the plant root formation as follows: "The root is in the earth and it contains many salts because the salts are in the earth. . . So the root is in special connection with the mineral realm of the earth, with the salts."[14]

There is actually a multitude of salts in the carrot: magnesium, iron, calcium, potassium, phosphorus, arsenic, nickel, cobalt, copper, iodine, and manganese. Furthermore there are considerable quantities of silicic acid (1 - 5%) and much sugar (up to 12 %), both of which have a mineral character. The carotin too lies in the carrot root in crystalline form and thus has a salt character.

What do these salts have in common? They have divested themselves of life, of fluid, of air, and of warmth, i.e., of the imponderables. Thereby salt becomes, as the alchemists expressed it, "selfless." It sacrifices, as it were, its own life, and can therefore open itself to foreign spirituality, to cosmic forces. It becomes a carrier of world-life.

The threefoldness of iron-cobalt-nickel is a telling example. These substances come to the earth with meteors from the cosmos, and, as they enter the atmosphere, they are taken up by air, water, and earth. From there they reach the roots of plants and become part of our food.

The salt formation in the root of the carrot has a very specific connection to man. It is easy to see that corresponding to it is an area in man which is similarly distinguished by a diminution of life forces, a mineral tendency, a salt formative tendency, but also by enhanced formative forces. This is the total nerve-sense organism, everything that developed out of the ectoderm. Rudolf Steiner frequently pointed to this fact and the interaction of this part of the human organization with the plant root. Here the practical consequences of such a dynamic study of nutrition become evident: "The head needs preferably salts." One "needs the root, which is related to the earth, and contains salts, in order to supply the human head."[15]

Thus we recognize that because of its root character, which is endowed with an especially intensive salt-process, the carrot nourishes man's nerve-sense organism. It is supportive because it stimulates a similar salt process in man.

152

A carrot diet will stimulate the nerve-sense function, will support the renunciation of one's own life forces in order to make possible a participation in world events through thought formation and sense organ development. The eye, for example, is a sense organ which pushes back the life forces.

Here we also gain the means to clarify the relationship of the intensive silica process in the carrot to the creative activity in the upper man. There is a similar silica accumulation in the eyes, in the sense organs in general, and in the skin, for "silica carries its effects through the metabolic pathways into those parts of the human organism where the living becomes lifeless."[16] From such insights Rudolf Steiner often suggested the carrot as feed for calves. An animal fed with roots will guide substances to the head in order to enter into the greatest possible sense relation to the cosmic environment. "If the calf feeds on carrots, you have fulfilled the whole process,"[17] for that is what the calf needs in order to choose, through the perceptive forces of the sense organs, the proper feed in the meadow, which is necessary for milk formation.

The human infant also needs the carrot to stimulate the silica organization because his sense organs and his brain are still developing. He needs the proper salt process in order to stimulate the formation of his nerve-sense organization and also of his bones. For that reason carrots are especially important for infants and small children and should be part of the diet at regular intervals. Dr. E. Schneider writes: "Besides the normal infant nutrition, children should get carrot juice or grated carrots when there is deficient tooth formation, inadequate growth, or a need to increase resistance against infections."[18]

The carrot's ability to increase the resistance against infections will depend very much on the quality of the carrot. If it becomes weak, when, for example, it is infested with the carrot fly, then it cannot call forth forces of resistance in the organism. If it is only protected artificially from becoming weak by treatment with poisonous "plant protective substances," then the carrot absorbs these poisons and subjects man to the danger of poisoning. The carrot also becomes weak by fertilization, when excess quantities of water-soluble salts are applied, which the carrot is unable to handle. Such a plant is then much more receptive to taking up poisons; it has less resistance. Consequently, the quality of the carrot plays an important role in its effectiveness in the human organism. A "bio-dynamic" planting must literally be demanded and supported if this magnificent food plant is not to lose its value.

In man the formative forces radiate from their center (the nerve-sense organization) into the remaining organism. Therefore the carrot also encourages and strengthens the activity of such formative forces in the metabolic organs if in that region the life forces are too active. If there is an

153

increase in bacteria or parasites, the carrot can limit their increase by strengthening the salt forces, the silica forces in the upper man. Rudolf Steiner said that when the upper man is weak, worms can easily appear in the intestine, because then the head does not act strongly enough in the whole body. He suggests that when you give carrots for some time, then the head is stimulated by the salt forces to defend against the excessive growth of foreign forms of life in the intestine.

Dr. E. Schneider claims:

> Ascarides can be driven out if one eats ½ - 1 kg of raw grated carrots over 24 hours, with the exclusion of all other food. Pinworms, too, can be removed with certainty by carrots if one eats 1-2 carrots on an empty stomach in the morning and in the evening before bedtime.[19]

From what has been developed here, it should be evident that the carrot can also be useful in severe intestinal diseases. The well-known pediatrician, Professor Glauzmann in Bern, has studied this and gives instructions for the preparation of carrots, which will be passed on here because this food can serve many different dietary purposes:

> 200 grams of carrots are to be well washed, scraped, cut into slices and cooked slowly in ¼ L water with a pinch of salt for 45 minutes. The cooked carrots and the water are then to be pressed through a sieve. A little butter and sugar (honey) may then be added.

This carrot preparation is used primarily for severe intestinal disturbances (e.g., celiac disease). We should add here, however, that Rudolf Steiner remarked that cooked food works up to the head. And, since carrots are especially related to the head, we may say that the cooked carrot will fulfill this function to a greater extent when it is taken directly as food. The raw carrot, however, will serve more specifically for curative purposes. The raw carrot is indicated when specific symptoms have to be treated e.g., dry skin, brittle, dull hair, or brittle finger nails. It is also used to strengthen the resistance in chronic sinus or nose disturbances or to fight against the decreasing smell or taste capacity.

More comprehensive, and more significant for our specific theme is an indication provided by Rudolf Steiner: "If you feel sometimes that you have a weak head, a feeling of emptiness in the brain, that you cannot think very well, then it is good if you add yellow beets for some time to your food." Here he speaks directly of the salt character of the carrot, the process which must take place in our brain in order to use it for the formation of thoughts. When Rudolf Steiner adds the words, "this is most effective of course in children," then we must understand that this is so because the child's brain is still very malleable. Such an indication can be of invaluable help to teachers and physicians.

Certainly the high sugar content of the carrot must also be significant. Professor Gleess writes: "The energy of the neuron comes from sugar metabolism, because the brain appears to live almost exclusively from sugar. . . A good blood supply and adequate sugar supply are prerequisites for brain function."[20]

We have considered the carrot in detail, because it is such an important example of the subject under discussion: Nutrition and Spiritual Life.

Red Beets and Horse Radish

Both red beets and radishes are true root formations, and they are characterized by Rudolf Steiner as follows: "The red beet stimulates thinking very strongly . . . but it does that in such a way that one actually wants to think. He who doesn't like to do this, doesn't like red beets either." The strong salt effect of horse radish is well known and has long been used in dietetics. Rudolf Steiner suggested: "If somebody is not very active in the head, then he will be benefited if he adds horse radish to his meals, because it brings a little movement into the thoughts."[21] In this connection it is remarkable that the beets concentrate certain mustard oils in their roots. The radishes are said to contain a compound which contains sulfur and cyanide, a thiocyanate. In the red beets a color substance has the basic structure of a betacyanide. These are closely related to the alkaloids.[22] We will discuss the cyanides further at another time.

Potatoes and Alcohol

In this section we will discuss some of the foods which inhibit free unfolding and stimulation of consciousness. We have already pointed to protein, which stimulates the growth in life forces, as opposed to the forces of consciousness. "The consumption of proteins should be held within certain limits; otherwise man will be overcome by a perceptive activity of which he should become free," namely, an activity determined by the metabolism. "That is what Pythagoras meant when he taught his students: Don't eat any beans."[23] The legumes have forces which approach animal metabolism and thus give the protein formation an animal character. We can see that the evaluation of a food such as the soy bean, by a true measure of quality, will be at some variance with what is propagated today.

The situation is similar with the potato. As food plant it also has only a limited value; this is true because of the poor digestibility of its starch, which

155

burdens the brain. Rudolf Steiner continually emphasized this point. In the lecture of July 18, 1923, he compared the potato to the radishes and beets: "Whoever eats many potatoes does not get strong thoughts"; he will "be constantly tired and will want to sleep and dream all the time."[24] Here Rudolf Steiner added the important statement: "Therefore it is of great cultural-historical significance what kinds of food men encounter."

To a much stronger extent this inhibiting element is found in alcohol, which can hardly be considered a food, but whose consumption in terms of quantity has in many cases exceeded that of foods. Here we merely point to its inhibiting effect on consciousness. Rudolf Steiner explained, for example, how the formation of alcohol goes beyond the actual plant formative process, that in fermentation something arises which also approaches an animal process, not, however, from the protein side, as in the legumes, but from the sugar side. This is, as such, related to the Ego-organization. Alcohol has, therefore, a special relation to the Ego-forces, one that acts, however, as an opposing force. When alcohol enters the blood stream, it is a foreign body which takes the place of Ego-forces in the blood. "One can actually say that, from a certain point on, it is the alcohol that thinks, feels, and senses, and not man's Ego."[25] Thus it is obvious that he who strives to develop his consciousness "should avoid alcohol in any form, even that contained in sweets." The negative effects of alcohol have already been scientifically demonstrated, "how much more should a person, whose whole striving is directed toward the spiritual, avoid the consumption of a substance which totally excludes a recognition of the spiritual."[26]

Bunge came to a similar realization, not as a fanatic or an ascetic, but from insight and knowledge. He said: "Thus every person with a sense of responsibility should work on the task of the complete removal of all alcoholic beverage, and above all by his own example." He knew that "spiritual exertions are best tolerated if alcohol is avoided."[27] The pharmacologist Möller came to a similar conclusion: "The first functions paralyzed are those which distinguish man from the animal and the child from the adult."[28] Neither are in possession of Ego-forces which make possible a conscious spiritual life.[29]

Coffee and Tea

It is well known that both tea and coffee affect the thought life of man in a certain way. This effect is attributed primarily to caffeine, contained in the coffee bean as well as in the tea leaves. Its effect is pharmacologically well studied and it forms the basis for various "headache powders" available today. The main field of activity of caffeine is the central nervous system, especially the brain. "Caffeine stimulates the function of the cerebral cortex, or to be very exact, it stimulates those processes in the cerebral cortex which are responsible for a smooth-running occurrence of certain mental (also psychological) processes."[30] "Experiments demonstrate that it facilitates the transmission of impulses across synapses, which in turn explains the facilitation of thought connections." In this way "it increases the number of available thought connections, it facilitates the impression of numbers . . ." and also "it elevates the mood. . ." Nevertheless, Möller adds, the effect of caffeine varies for different people. The effect of coffee has even gained fame in literature. In 1587 Abd Al-Qadir composed in Arabian the verse:

"O coffee, you remove all worries, you are desired, by those who study. . ."

About tea, P. Dufour, in 1648, said:

One of the most important advantages of tea is that it has a sobering effect on drunks. It also purifies the brain. The Chinese, who drink so much tea, never spit or blow their noses; their brains are free of all excesses which usually make a situation worse.

It would seem that the effect of coffee and tea is the same, but an analysis of the compounds in which caffeine is contained in tea and coffee shows the difference between the two plants which are also far apart botanically. While roasted coffee contains an average of 1.5% caffeine, the tea leaves contain 1-5%. In addition there is in tea 5-15% tannins, the diuretic theophylline, and the tea oil so important for the aroma. In coffee there is, among other substances, nicotinic acid. Raw coffee is totally without taste and the typical coffee aroma first results from roasting. Gas chromatography has resulted in surprising findings. So far, more than 300 ephemeral aromatic substances have been identified and there are many more unknown components.[31] More and more attention is paid to these roast-substances and one speaks today of an "effective total composition" of coffee and tea. Uniform emphasis is always placed upon their centrally stimulating effect with a transient enhancement of mental functions.

How do these research data relate to the results of Spiritual Science? Rudolf Steiner speaks of the thinking activity, the logical process in thinking, which can be enhanced by certain thought exercises. And then he says that digestion of coffee has an effect similar to that which happens through the soul when logical exercises are done: "If you drink coffee, you enhance in a certain sense a proper logical sequence in thinking."[32] That has so far been well established by modern pharmacological research insofar as it is related to caffeine, but Rudolf Steiner went much further. In a lecture in The Hague

157

he explained in great detail how tea and coffee affect man's various organizations. Coffee affects the etheric body by lifting it temporarily out of the physical body, i.e., the connection is loosened. This condition of loosening the life forces from the physical organization, a kind of pushing back, exists in the realm of the central nervous system as the physiological foundation of thinking. We discussed this earlier in other connections. Coffee thus enhances the condition which represents the physiological precondition for logical thinking. In this sense, "it could be of some benefit, to encourage logical thinking by an occasional cup of coffee."

Tea also, according to Rudolf Steiner, brings about a differentiation between etheric and physical body though, in a certain sense, tea consumption does not take into account the "structure" of the physical body. The result is a stimulation of fantasy, of flighty thinking. While coffee encourages solidity of character, tea consumption encourages a certain care-free, nonchalant way of being. The "total effective composition" of coffee has the same effects but takes a different direction in tea. Both share the relative loosening from the physical body, especially of the brain, but while coffee thereby favors the ordered solid thinking, tea presses the liberated thinking into the fantastic, the unsolid, the fluctuating.

This effect of tea has been described often. In ancient China, for example, the best tea-poem each year received a prize, because the artists felt themselves especially stimulated by tea. Even a verse by Heinrich Heine points in this direction: "They sat and drank at the tea table and spoke much of love. The gentlemen, they were aesthetic, the ladies were of tender kind." This tea-poem originated in a Berlin coffee shop, then a meeting place of literary people. Also in the salon of Rahel Varnhagen, Goethe's "lovely girl," painters, actors, and diplomats met for tea. Eckermann reports: "This evening I was at a big tea party in Goethe's house. I liked the company very much, everyone was relaxed and uninhibited, some stood, some sat, some joked, some laughed. . ." Rudolf Steiner, in a medical lecture, said: Coffee is a good "journalist drink," while tea is an extraordinarily effective "drink for diplomats," who need to become accustomed "to throwing around fragmentary thoughts, which, nevertheless, give the appearance of being witty and intelligent."[33]

We must, however, go still a bit further. In our time, which leans toward excesses, and increasingly abuses coffee consumption, we may ask what influence that abuse could have on man's spiritual life. It is not too far-fetched to think that it could serve as an avoidance of the inner effort of thought training. When one allows several cups of coffee a day to relieve one of inner effort, then, instead of increasing mental activity, one encourages spiritual torpidity. Rudolf Steiner explained this point to physicians in a similar manner: "You should actually make little of such effects because they

158

only make the soul sluggish if you begin to depend on them. . ." More clearly stated, coffee enhances consequential thinking only "in a dependent manner"; it acts like coercion.[34]

Consequential thinking or flighty thinking can both be stimulated or relieved by coffee and tea within limits, but we should learn by now to recognize what we are doing with our soul-spiritual life if we abandon ourselves to such stimulants. Rudolf Steiner adds that just such things are important to know, that these things must be encouraged in another way as a matter of course in a moral life. From that our time is still far removed.

Spiritual Scientific Considerations Freed of Dogmatism and Eccentricity

In still a further and certainly more significant manner, the principle of a "relief" of certain inner activities through outer substances plays an important role in human nutrition in general. We have encountered this principle, or law, several times already, among others, in the issue of plant and animal as food sources. There we had to emphasize that man must mobilize additional forces when eating plants in order to elevate them, through his inner activities, to the human stage. When man eats meat, the animal has already met him halfway. The greater mustering of digestive forces, however, also calls forth a greater measure of strength, which man can then use for higher purposes, as spiritual potencies. Vegetarian nutrition, if it is not a special medical diet, requires greater exertion, but it liberates a greater measure of inner forces. In other words, "certain forces transform themselves from material to spiritual forces." It is important that such forces be utilized. If they "are not utilized, then they may even be detrimental to brain activity."[35] Rudolf Steiner points to something extraordinarily important with these words. We can frequently observe that a one-sided vegetarianism is unable to keep itself free of dangers manifested as abnormalities of the soul life. It provides an excellent soil for fanaticism, dogmatism, narrow-mindedness, and eccentricity. Far more serious and dangerous developments can also be observed, e.g., brutality and boundless egotism.

For that reason Rudolf Steiner advised that a vegetarian must begin a spiritual life at the same time; otherwise it would be better if he continued eating meat. Such advice must be taken seriously, particularly in our time when fashion frequently propagates a tendency towards vegetarianism, especially in connection with old oriental traditions. The old ways of nutrition, as well as the motivation for those ways, have generally been superceded for present-day man. The spiritual life expounded there is a passive soul activity and easily leads to psychological eccentricity and only apparent health. That is why Rudolf Steiner, who, as we mentioned before, became a vegetarian at the same time that he began to disseminate Spiritual Science, had to say in 1905: "Vegetarian life without spiritual striving leads to illness."[36] History also teaches this when we find that a vegetarian way of life is usually a precondition for spiritual training.

Before we turn to the historical aspects of this question, we still have to consider the relation of man's soul life to nutrition. That presupposes, of course, that we have reached an exact understanding of the human soul-being. Yet, we live in a time in which there is hardly a clear differentiation between soul and spirit, in a time in which we have developed a soul science which has difficulty in achieving a clear picture of its object of study.

Chapter 11

NUTRITION AND SOUL LIFE

The Problem

The nutritional science of the 19th century had no other goals than to chemically analyze food substances and to comprehend digestion through physical-chemical laws. In the introduction to his main work, *Die Gesetze des Energieverbrauches bei der Ernährung* (1902), Max Rübner stated this clearly: "The physical manifestations accompanying chemical changes are, as I have proven, so important for biological questions, that they must be considered to be of equal value with the phenomena of matter." It was a scientific conviction at the end of the 19th century that "only an analysis of energy will be able to explain the full picture of the interrelations of substances."[1] It was believed that with the laws of the inorganic world one could comprehend the metabolism of living beings. Given no considerations was the fact that the objects of study, man and animal, have soul and spirit. There was much agitation against the world view of "dualism" when the so-called monism was postulated: "The materialists acknowledge the unity of force and substance, of spirit and body, of God and world." In these words from Moleschott's *Der Kreislauf des Lebens* (1887), the whole inadequacy of the knowledge of that time is mirrored. There is no more talk of the soul, and the spirit is only valued as another appearance of matter. Studies of the central nervous system apparently verified this view; for Moleschott observes, "All animals have in common that without a brain they also have no spirit." One can see from this statement what tremendous dilettantism, concerning the being of soul and spirit, was prevalent. The same was true for

161

the moral properties of man: "The Evil in the individual, just as the whole of mankind, remains a natural phenomenon."[2]

We can recognize Rudolf Steiner's dilemma, since for him the reality of the spiritual world was a matter of direct experience. He was able to justify this experience to himself only by developing an answer to his question through the Goethean scientific method along with the aid of German idealism (Schiller, Fichte, Schelling, Hegel). His question was: "To what extent can it be demonstrated that the spirit is active in human thinking?"[3] His answer appeared in his two fundamental works: *Theory of Knowledge* and *Philosophy of Freedom.* His conclusions there opposed those of Moleschott and others. He wrote: "Actually the sense world is a spiritual world; and the soul lives together with this known spiritual world while it spreads out its consciousness."[4] And, "the impulses which stimulate man to moral deeds" are the manifestation of the spirit world in the experiencing of this spirit world by the soul." The goal of this "Philosophy of Freedom," through which Rudolf Steiner succeeded in overcoming materialism from within, lay in the indication that "the sense world is actually of a spiritual nature and man lives as a soul being, through the true knowledge of the sense world, in a spiritual realm."[5] Therewith the basis of a spiritually appropriate natural science was created, one in which man as a being of body, soul, and spirit could find his proper place. It is precisely this basis that is invaluable for a consideration of the connection of nutrition to the soul life, because it immediately clarifies where we are dealing with soul and where with spiritual qualities.

Results of Modern Behavioral Physiology

The need to clarify that issue is all the more pressing since recently a new branch of science has also entered the field of nutrition: behavioral physiology. This branch of science, which concerns itself with human behavior, has its origin in zoology. Konrad Lorenz, the founder of the comparative study of behavior, sought for parallels to human behavior in his animal psychology experiments. By investigating these parallels he wanted to make a decisive contribution to a new anthropology. As interesting as these experiments are in isolation, and as enriching as they are to our knowledge of details of animal and human behavior, little of their underlying basis can be considered satisfactory.

Lorenz limits his method right from the start. He claims:

The attempt to comprehend soul processes by causal analysis makes a presupposition that is axiomatic for the biologist, just as it has been discarded by metaphysicians: the presupposition is that all "purely" psychological events are at the same time neurophysiological events.[6]

Here the psychological is limited to an expression stimulated solely by neurophysiological events, while actually it is capable of expressing itself through all of man and having in the nervous system only a bodily instrument. The nature of the psychological remains unclear, and no clear distinction of life manifestations from psychological events is possible when we read, for example, that "every psychological event falls under the more general concept of life manifestations."[7] Lorenz writes further that

> causal thinking in man is the most regulated and goal-directed of all organic events on this planet. . . The "freedom" and lack of structure of these achievements is only an apparent freedom, because of the very complex and fine structure and interaction of the participating elements. They are correspondingly disturbed by certain injuries just like any machine function.[8]

This behavioral scientist, as modern as he may want to appear, has obviously obtained his basic education from Moleschott, Feuerbach, Büchner, and the like. This science betrays its own limitations in statements like the following:

> How and why the center for praxis, gnosis, and speech originated in the supramarginal gyrus (of the brain), and how and why the brain of man has enlarged to such an extent and gone through further differentiation, upon which conceptual thinking and the total spiritual future of man are built, about that we know as little as we do about the causes for many far-reaching epigenetic events in evolution.[9]

Adolf Portmann is much more realistic in his book, *Neue Wege der Biologie* (1960), when he writes:

> That science which examines living substance with the methods of physics and chemistry leads further and further away from experience. We should not delude ourselves, even though one may believe it now and then by thinking that in the advance of knowledge towards the nature of substance we will also find an explanation of experience, of the psychological. I will establish right away that that is not my opinion.[10]

This same reservation should be observed in the application of animal behavior studies to man. Glatzel says justifiably:

> The fact that human behavior is affected not only by drives and affects, but also by representation and ideas, is occasionally forgotten, and the temptation to draw conclusions about human behavior without

163

adequate knowledge of the results of sociology, psychology, and psychiatry, appears to be very great for some animal ethnologists.

No matter how we twist and turn the problem, at the end there is always the "Ignoramus" or the "Ignorabimus" of a Dubois Reymond. The Zurich neurologist, Yazargil, in an attempt to explain "the essence of man," writes: "Natural scientific knowledge does not allow us to draw conclusions regarding phenomena which appear as dualisms. To speak of points of contact of somatic and psychic functions is illogical."[11] To that we must say that without an expansion of consciousness it will be impossible to reach a truly useful basis for such a study of behavior. Since the establishment of Spiritual Science that has become possible.

Spiritual Scientific Aspect

If we take, for example, what Rudolf Steiner has to say about human behavior in his work, *Occult Science, an Outline*, we will understand what is meant by such an expansion. There, too, human "behavior" is mentioned, particularly in regard to man's capacity for memory. Anyone who observes how an animal behaves in relation to his experiences "notices the difference between this behavior and man's." He sees that the animal behaves in conjunction with its experiences with an "absence of memory." The animal actually has no memory in the human sense and must therefore behave differently from man in his total soul life. There can only be memory if a being is able to give duration to its experiences. The animal is unable to do this. For that reason, the animal also behaves totally different in regard to nutrition than man. "With the becoming aware of something that has duration, of something that remains permanent despite the changing inner experiences, comes the dawning of a 'feeling for the Ego' which is denied to the animal." The animal "is completely distracted from one impression when a new one comes." Man, however, can carry his consciousness from one impression to another. Thus in the animal, hunger and thirst arise when it becomes conscious of its bodily processes, and then it is driven to satisfy them. In man it is different. While in the animal hunger arises when there is a new occasion for it in the soul, man is led to this experience because during a prior satisfaction a desire has arisen, and the consciousness of this desire has remained, so that not only the present experience of hunger, but the past experience of desire for food impels. In other words, in the presence of the fragrance of a food, as well as in response to a feeling of hunger arising within, man recalls the desire which he experienced earlier in connection with such food. While the animal must respond of necessity to the sensation of hunger, man can develop the freedom to establish his own rules regarding

164

his desire, even if it is merely to observe or think about how much a feeling arises in him or someone else.

In the relationship of the soul to nutrition the instinctual basis must first be considered. In the animal this still plays a far greater role than in man. While the animal is firmly tied to its instincts and follows them sub-consciously, man is now able—at least partially—to separate himself from them, and he will be able to do so even more in the future. In ancient times, however, man still had a certain nutritional as well as a healing instinct. This disappeared as the intellect developed, though in the child instinct is still an important means of choosing food. Our nutrition has in fact developed on the basis of an instinctual relation to food. This instinct is based on a subconscious spiritual connection with the food substances. It is mirrored not only in innumerable moral codes and dietary customs, but also in many myths and fairy tales. It was a wisdom-filled world, which, in the present, pales away, and has often become decadent and misunderstood.

According to Rudolf Steiner, we can study instinct only if we consider it "in connection with the form of the physical body."[12] By looking at the bodies of animals, we can thus learn to recognize the various kinds of instincts as pictures. We can observe, for example, how differently the instinct acts in the lower animals, the ants or bees, in comparison to the higher animals, the cows or the birds.

Through instinct, man in prehistoric times knew how to cook. The drive for nourishment led him to search for the appropriate natural products, and that finding was guided by instinct. Today, when everything is accessible, man has become uncertain within, and so he is frequently confused as to what foods to choose. His instinct tells him less and less what is appropriate for him.

Instinct, Drive, and Craving

Only man can transform instincts, drives, and cravings by organizing his higher capacity for consciousness, his Ego, into the physical, etheric, and astral bodies. What is taken hold of by the Ego will appear as motivation of the will, the goal of all human transformation.

In order to improve the instinct for nutrition, Rudolf Steiner has suggested that, through a light massage, the spleen can be stimulated "to balance out man's instinctual activity." This will result in greater facility in finding food appropriate to that person and establish "healthier relations to what serves and what doesn't serve his organism."[13] It is clear how significant such a measure could be for a general nutritional hygiene today, especially if it were to be taken up by clinics, sanitoriums, and children's homes.

In his *The Education of the Child from the Standpoint of Spiritual Science*, Rudolf Steiner points out that a child will lose his instinctual ability to choose appropriate foods if he cannot establish a proper soul relation to nutrition, i.e., its quality and quantity.[14] This will be lost if he is overfed in infancy. Bunge observed at the end of the last century that bottle-fed babies are much more easily overfed than breast-fed babies. The feeling of satisfaction, of fullness, which is an instinctive regulator of intake in breast-fed babies, does not work as well in bottle-fed babies. That feeling of satisfaction is one of the instincts man has become very uncertain of today. And the early loss of this instinct in the child, by means of wrong nutrition and over-feeding, results from the difficult complex of modern acceleration and all its consequences.[15] Rudolf Steiner pointed out that one of the dangers of over-feeding that also shows up later in life is that man eats too much protein and thereby fills himself one-sidely with life and growth forces. A consequence of such over-feeding is that his instinct for nutrition becomes uncertain. If protein consumption is held within the proper bounds, then he can better maintain his instinct.[16] "Spiritual Science will be able to give indications down to the individual foods which may be required."[17]

At this point we must ask: from what does craving originate? It too arises from within man and we can clearly observe that it is a part of our soul life. On the other hand, we realize that it, as well as other drives, is tied to the physical body. The world of cravings is indeed connected to our "feeling" life, but to that part of soul life which is bound to the body. For this reason, Spiritual Science designates the carrier of all sensations dependent on the physical body as the "sentient" body. However, "Man does not follow his drives, instincts and passions blindly; his thinking brings about the conditions so that he can satisfy them."[18] That is, man is able to elevate himself above dependency on the body in his soul life (and therefore above animality), but at the same time the possibility arises that he can now use his thinking to satisfy his drives and cravings even more effectively. Material culture certainly moves in this direction. The gourmet is an impressive example of how refined thinking is used to satisfy gustatory cravings.

While the world of drives permeates life more as a uniformity, the cravings constantly appear anew in the life of the soul. They arise and they disappear. They are stimulated by the sight of a desirable food, the effect of window displays, the effect of newspaper advertisements, etc.

Through his Ego man can rule these cravings. He can, in the sense of Spiritual Science, let his "intellectual soul" or "consciousness soul" be active.[19] Instead of succumbing to the desire for some chocolate he can recognize that it would not be appropriate to satisfy his need for food with it. He can also fill his consciousness with a thought, a recognition concerning a certain nutrient, and can then correspondingly arrange his nutrition. One can then say that he motivates his need for food. Craving is transformed into a motive of the will when man begins to act with insight with respect to his

166

food. Only then can he liberate himself from the rule of the body. Only then can he enter the path towards Ego-consciousness in nutrition in order to fulfill an increasingly important goal for modern man.

It might be appropriate here to bring up something Rudolf Steiner said in connection with a subject in which we would hardly expect nutrition to come up: a lecture concerning the gospel of St. Mark.[20] As an example of experiences "which can be grasped only with the greatest difficulty of thought," he names daily eating and drinking. "It often takes a rather long time before he who undergoes a spiritual development, also includes, so to speak, these things in his spiritual life. . ." Nevertheless, today, through spiritual knowledge, we can learn at least to form an idea of how "an apple, or any other fruit is related to the whole of the universe." We can then "also spiritualize the most mundane, most material processes." Unfortunately, "in our age only very few are able to think validly about eating."

What Rudolf Steiner intimated in 1911 went through an extraordinary deepening and expansion in the next fourteen years. When he returned from his "Agriculture Course" in Koberwitz in 1924, he said that anthroposophy could be of help in two ways: "in the highest spiritual aspects, and in the very practical." The task is now to recognize "that the spiritual can actually interact with the directly practical activities."[21] That, more than ever, is the command of the day. In the final analysis, everything we are striving to do in this book lies in this direction: to learn to expand our awakened Ego-consciousness in the realm of nutrition. Since Rudolf Steiner's time this demand has become more and more pressing. It is now vital to our existence as is becoming increasingly clear in all facets of our modern civilization.

"Not the Food, but the Soul Nourishes"

Aristotle's expression in modern words might mean: "Normal man doesn't eat to provide himself with the necessary calories, proteins, and vitamins, but because he likes the taste and because he enjoys eating." (Glatzel) The various sense impressions—sight, smell, taste, hearing, and touch—transmit experiences which give man pleasure or displeasure. In the past, when the instinctual forces were still active in man when he was still full of wisdom, they mediated his relationship to foods in an objective manner. He was with them in an unconscious, but strict and much stronger connection. Thereby he was led to the food appropriate for him. He did not have to think about it; he could not think about it; he lived together with nature which gave him his nourishment. His drives, too, were totally in the service of such an innocence-filled interaction. An old atavistic clairvoyance was still active in these instincts, which allowed man to feel protected in a nature experienced as divine. That has continued into the present, in a decadent way, in certain

167

so-called primitive cultures, and has left behind numerous customs and taboos. Such traditions were noticeable in the medicine and dietetics of Hippocrates and Galen.

The dangers for humanity associated with the loss of such instincts were known by some even in the Middle Ages. St. Augustine wrote in his *Confessions*:

> You have taught me to use food and drink like remedies, which I take in, but while I go from the discomfort of need to the rest of satisfaction, greed, with its ropes, lies in wait for me in this transition. . . And while the purpose of eating and drinking is the maintenance of the body, its companion is the dangerous gluttony . . . and often it remains uncertain whether the necessary care of the body still needs further help or whether our craving deceives us and gluttony is served.

This problem has concerned various cultures for millenia. It was considered a moral-religious problem and found expression in ceremonial or cultic fasting and asceticism. In the Christian Middle Ages it reached its high point, when, in association with the festivals of the year, fasting was considered a means for inner purification or an exercise in controlling the lower nature.

Fasting, Curative Fasting, Asceticism

The following statement is attributed to Chrysostomus, 400 A.D.:

> Fasting is food for the soul: it checks the excesses of speech and closes the lips, it bridles carnal appetites and soothes the choleric temperament, it awakens judgment and makes the body pliable, it chases away nightly dreams, heals headaches, and strengthens the eyes.

In a similar manner, Athanasius said in 300 A.D.:

> Do you see how fasting works? It heals diseases, dries out the excessive juices, drives away the bad spirits and wrong thoughts, gives greater clarity to the spirit, purifies the heart, sanctifies the body and finally leads man to the throne of God.

Through fasting, it was believed, the soul would enhance its purifying effect on the body and strengthen the clarity of the spirit, because it could more effectively act as a mediator between these two members of the human

168

being. Such insights resulted in the fasts of Ash Wednesday and Good Friday, as well as the Easter and Whitsun fasts.

The origin of Christian fasting may well lie in old Jewish customs, which followed strict laws and proscriptions. Fasting, generally given as a law to older cultures, was exercised with lesser or greater strictness, depending on man's ability at that time to attain personal insight and judgments.

Such laws for fasting were also prevalent in all oriental religions and mystery centers as a means for strengthening the soul. Subjection to these laws was a necessary requirement for training the soul. It was connected with further means of strengthening soul forces, e.g., concentration and meditation. The abbot Johannes Trithemius von Sponheim (1486) said in a sermon about the well-known Nicolaus v. d. Flue: "Abstinence from food purifies the spirit, decorates the soul with youth, and heals the sinful body. He who values abstinence is wise and he who loves fasting is a strong ruler."[22]

The character of these laws or commandments has slowly changed, depending on the extent to which man could or wanted to take his own education in hand. That resulted, on the one hand, in a rigidification of these rules, which only lived on as tradition, and, on the other, in resistance to them. Protestantism, for example, did away with such commandments or replaced them with inner, voluntary exercises. Increasingly, fasting, used as a bodily means to develop the soul, had less significance and no longer represented a method of spiritual training. Today fasting still retains some of its significance in certain dietary treatments or as a voluntary exercise. This so-called curative fasting, which has gained in popularity in the last few years, should, however, take the whole person, and especially the individuality of the patient, fully into consideration. One fast-day a week, i.e., a so-called juice-fast, may have a beneficial effect for many patients.

Rudolf Steiner, in all his therapeutic suggestions, never suggested fasting. He may well have foreseen the dangers for modern man: one-sidedness, sectarianism, fanaticism, and dogmatism. All that was as far removed from Rudolf Steiner as it could be. In fact, he emphasized to physicians that every special diet makes a person into an unsocial being. He pointed out that in the overcoming of something that one can't tolerate there is an "organ-building force." Steiner's thinking about these questions was highly differentiated. He said, for example, that there was a big difference between the personal selection of a specific diet and selection for the person by a physician. The latter encourages passivity of soul forces and even subjects the individual to some kind of suggestion, undermining soul activity and initiative. The consequence may be that a person will become senile sooner than he would have if he had "continued to actively participate in the choice of his diet until old age."[23]

169

The one-sidedness which asceticism has reached, the disdain of nature through which one seeks access to the spirit, must be relieved and overcome by a new recognition of the spiritual nature of matter. "We must reach the point where we again consider all of nature full of spirit"; otherwise we come under the influence of an asceticism, "the research of which has resulted in materialism. We must get away from disdaining nature."[24]

That does not mean that Rudolf Steiner undervalued asceticism. On the contrary, he said in 1905 that during the time of spiritual striving it is especially important to live in moderation. For moderation "purifies the feelings, awakens capacities, cheers up the spirit, and strengthens memory—the soul is almost relieved of its earthly burden by it and therefore enjoys a higher freedom." To this quotation by an "old wise man" he adds his own observation that much eating interferes with spiritual productivity: "The spirit is never so clear as after long fasting." The greatest saints have lived on fruits, bread, and water, but "no miracle-working saint is known, who activated divine forces while partaking of an opulent meal." In the old times, one still had that living feeling of a connection between microcosm and macrocosm, and it was demanded of every adult member of a community that he make himself more receptive, at definite times, for certain spiritual forces. That was attained by moderation. Whoever acted against these laws was almost always punished with expulsion from the society.

Contemporary Aspects

That is all part of the past. But what is the situation today? We have already said that today there should be freedom, personal insight, and free decision in this area. In a public lecture, Rudolf Steiner dealt with the topic "Asceticism and illness" in a comprehensive manner. Asceticism, a word with Greek origins, means "to exercise oneself," and also "to strengthen oneself." An ascetic exercise of soul forces, in the modern sense, can only mean that "man refines and purifies his thinking, feeling, and willing . . . and strengthens them so that they become victorious over the body." The modern ascetic way is the reverse of the old. Then, the body forces were pushed back through fasting so that the soul could become stronger and open itself to the spiritual. That kind of asceticism, however, estranges man from the world: "A true asceticism leads to the development of a person who becomes progressively more useful to the world."[25]

What is the relationship of a dietary method to this modern concept of asceticism? "It can only be an external help," to give the body "a certain kind of relief," a "support." In this sense, for example, a vegetarian way of life can be of help to the soul's spiritual striving. "The person who develops

170

spiritually with vegetarianism will become stronger, more active, and more resistant to adversity." He will not only be able to compete with any meat eater, but "will far exceed the meat eater in his capacity for work."

At the same time, however, we must remember that 'so long as man desires and craves meat, vegetarianism is of no benefit to him. . .'" Only "if the pleasure of meat consumption has ceased will the proper mood exist, only then will abstinence from meat be of any value in relation to the spiritual worlds." This inner, soul-spiritual asceticism is what is essential in our time, and here it is important to protect oneself from illusions and errors.

It is of course important to be aware of the sources of illusion and error. This brings us back to our discussion of the significance of smell and taste processes in nutrition. The human and animal sense organizations differ significantly from each other. In man we can speak of three sense regions, of an upper, a middle, and a lower region. Smell and taste belong to the middle region. They are related to feeling and hearing; thinking is related to the upper senses. The sense of touch, an inner sense, is more closely related to the will. Our actual soul life is thus first bound to the senses. With our smell and taste we are related to the animal-like soul. As we have mentioned, these senses are frequently highly developed in animals and bring them into a much greater dependency on the environment than is the case with man. Nevertheless, taste sensations also permeate our unconscious, as in the animal, and this is where the parallelism lies: our tasting brings us into a relationship with the inner metabolic process; smelling has a clear connection to the sexual processes; in short, these senses bind our soul, as "sentient soul," to the depths of our bodies, to functions which we share with the animals.

We discover in this way that our connection to the world is a different one, depending upon whether we perceive it with the higher senses or with the lower. We recognize that tasting is an objective event in us. "As it occurs in me, it is a world event." The possibility exists that we might take this kind of sense perception as a standard also for the higher senses, that we might perceive with them just as we do with the lower senses. This will lead to the "immoral" stance we discussed "when the higher senses are subordinated to the character of the lower senses," when we react to other persons as only sweet or sour, as we must do physiologically with our food.

Transformation of Nutritional Habits

There is without a doubt a great gap in man's understanding of the connection between nutrition and soul life. History is full of examples. Higher, wealthy cultures are repeatedly connected with a so-called "refined" gastronomy, which is actually a cruder one, one strongly inclined toward bodily excess. That leads then to various excesses, clever consumption, or boundless gluttony. Our present civilized countries are full of it. This represents an ominous interaction between man's soul life and his nutrition, a certain symptom of decay.

From Roman times we have accounts of how numerous cook books were. Even highly placed persons concerned themselves with gastronomy and wrote books on the subject. Caesar's friend, Martius, wrote about "The Cook," "The Fruit-canner," "The Wine-Master," etc. Most famous was the 10 volume work of the gourmand Apicius on the art of cooking at the time of Tiberius. Of Emperor Vitellius, who was well-known as a glutton, it is reported that he held a festival meal for his brother, during which 2000 fish and 7000 birds were served. It is evident that this sort of luxurious life was accompanied by a decline of morals, which led to the decline of the Roman Empire, although it still took centuries before the edifice collasped completely.[26]

A similar development occurred in the time of the French baroque culture. The new "art" of eating, occasionally calling itself "gastrosophie," was developed at the French court. Again, there were persons in high positions who excelled as resourceful cooks. Louis XIV's master steward, Bechamel Marquis de Nointel, invented the famed sauce named after him, made of cream, onions, ham, and veal. Even of the imperial marshall, Condé, it is reported that he knew as much about the art of cooking as about the art of war. "The French luxury of eating is hardly imaginable today," because the selection of meals and the fineness of preparation depended on their "delicatesse"; to accompany the meals there were select table services, fine table cloths, perfumed and pre-warmed mouth cloths, etc. A dinner given for twenty-two people the night before the French Revolution was said to have nine courses from one kind of meat which was prepared in twenty-two different ways.[27]

Another aspect also deserves our attention: the change in dietary customs is a mirror of the change of the human soul. The soul relationship to food was a completely different one in older times than it is today. Then, the art of cooking was still very close to the art of healing; the views that developed about the healthy or diseased person, as well as about medicines, were also valid for nutrition, for the diet. There was still the concrete experience of "forces," which entered man through his food. In the sense of Hippocratic medicine, these forces were designated according to the qualities moist, dry, warm, and cold. Depending on the qualities of foods, a meal was composed to balance their effects, "to temper them." These measures were not only related to what we today abstractly call "nutritive value," but also to the soul effects of the foods.

Hunger and Thirst

Hunger and thirst are soul states which are first experienced in the body. At first we have no precise consciousness of them. We feel hunger "in the stomach," thirst "in the throat." Brillat-Savarin, in his famous book, *Physiologie du goût* (Physiology of Taste), writes about appetite as the first sensation of need for nourishment—a soul experience. He explains that simultaneously with the announcement of "some languor in the stomach . . . the soul begins to occupy itself with objects appropriate to its needs."[28] The further experiences are described with true French charm:

> In the meantime the digestive apparatus begins to move, the stomach experiences twinges of discomfort, the stomach juices are prepared, like soldiers, only waiting for the command to attack. In only a few more moments, one gets cramp-like attacks, one yawns, one suffers— one is hungry.

Expressed in modern terms: "We speak of hunger as a longing for nourishment, presenting itself subjectively as experience and objectively as a complex of behavior and physical symptoms."[29]

In hunger we experience our need for earth nourishment. Through hunger we regulate our relationship to the earth. Hunger is related to solid nourishment; it announces our need, our willingness and capacity to confront the earth, to take in and overcome the earthly. As long as man is still hungry, e.g., in old age, or when he again hungers after an illness, forces become active to establish anew a firm relationship to the earth body. In this sense hunger, to which we give heed, is the opposite of fasting, asceticism, or even lack of appetite. Satisfaction gives us the earth again. In hunger the soul experiences the longing for earthly existence.

An anecdote about Caesar records the following: When he was notified of the death of a close friend he exclaimed, "What? That man died? But he had sage in his garden." Sage was even then known as an appetite stimulant, and Casear knew that as long as one had an appetite, one did not die.

We have already discussed that our need for food is bound to a strict 24-hour rhythm. The earthly nourishment is used up quickly by the organism, has to be excreted, and the new need for earthly substances and forces again makes itself noticeable. Hunger is thus an experience of the course of the day, the rhythm, which we have characterized for man as the Ego-rhythm. Our Ego, incarnated in an earthly body, creates anew, each day, through hunger, the experience of incarnation, in order to prove itself daily in overcoming the earth, in penetrating matter with the spirit.

In this connection the results of modern physiology are of interest. During

173

prolonged starvation the metabolic organs—stomach, intestines, liver, kidneys, muscles, etc.—atrophy first. The brain, however, remains undamaged for a long time and will only be affected in the case of extreme starvation. In this sense, however, the brain is the most earthly organ and we have discussed earlier how the brain depends on earthly nourishment. In undernutrition this process spreads out over the whole body. "Man becomes almost all head when he is undernourished."[30] The opposite occurs in overnutrition. Then a sort of "brain softening" occurs. Man then "permeates his head with what he should only have in his abdomen."

Thus we see clearly how our relationship to the earth is regulated by hunger. Earthly nourishment, which first supplies the brain with substance and then fills the rest of man with earthly forces, makes possible, through hunger, the Ego's necessary resistance to the solid earth formation. That is why appetite has an individual character through which the relationship of the specific person to the earth is expressed.

Rudolf Steiner goes still further. He asks: What is the organic localization of hunger? He answers: the lung. The lung, through which man, by way of respiration, is connected with the earth from the first to the last breath, actually regulates "deep within man the 'earth formative process.'"[31] This process can be studied, for example, in the metamorphosis of gills to lungs, in the metamorphosis of amphibia or in the lung fish. Simultaneous with lung formation the limbs arise. Another example is the craving for food observed in patients with tuberculosis. The patient attempts to get more earth substance, through an increased appetite, to anchor the Ego more firmly in the body.

In this sense hunger becomes an expression of egotism. "Hunger makes one the enemy of another. Hunger dissolves ties of comradeship, friendship, and love. Hunger destroys the community" (Glatzel). Schenck gives a fitting characterization of the hunger experience in his book, Das Fasten (1938). He describes hunger as "a withdrawal into one's own soul, a progressive coldness of feeling and sluggishness." At the same time, because the brain has no food, concentration and thinking become difficult, if not impossible. In situations of chronic starvation man becomes sleepy, has daydreams, and suffers from hallucinations, a clear symptom of the separation of the soul-spiritual from the body.

Thirst is usually mentioned in the same breath with hunger, but it actually is a unique and different experience. It is not related to the physical, but rather to the life-organization, the etheric body. We have already explained that the etheric body counters the physical body. It lives in levity, in the overcoming of gravity. Nevertheless, this life organization is bound much more to the physical than the soul-spiritual, which separates itself in sleep

174

from the physical. The life-organization permeates the metabolic organization as well as the rhythmic system.

Thirst can be tolerated for a much shorter period than hunger, and it is much more torturing than hunger. If the life forces are not stimulated to be active any more, the body rapidly falls apart. Life ceases and the soul-spiritual separates.

For that reason the regulation of thirst is very subtle and the organism is much more sensitive to fluctuations in the fluid content of the body. A change of even 1% of the water content of intracellular fluid is sufficient to result in a feeling of thirst. If there is an adequate fluid supply, the fluid fluctuation within 24 hours consists of only 0.22%. 2% water loss results in serious disturbances, and 15% loss results in death.

Rudolf Steiner has directed attention to the fundamental significance of body fluid in the actual inner nutritional process, in the region designated today as "intermediary metabolism." "The etheric forces have the main point of attack in man in the liquid constituents."[32] Since nutrition occurs "through an activity which expresses itself in the etheric-liquid and physical-solid," this process can be designated as the actual nutritional process through which life is maintained.

The organ by which thirst is regulated must be sought where there is an important center of fluid metabolism in general, namely, the liver. "For everything related to liquid, we must look for the deeper aspects in the liver system."[33] And so "all thirst is related to the liver system." Here, too, we must realize how intricately liver function is intertwined with man's soul life. Thirst, although initially an unconscious stimulation, is a striving for life forces, for a balance between the fluid-organism, especially the tissue fluids, and the organs, for the proper dissolving force, the activation of chemism, as it expresses itself particularly through the liver. Therefore thirst is also a symptom of liver disease. It can lead to a pathological condition, the effect of which will not only remain in the life-organization, but will also lead to soul-spiritual abnormalities.

From the preceding it should become evident that every experience of hunger and thirst is the beginning of an illness healed by eating and drinking. After every meal an inner satisfaction will arise; this is related to the fact that the digestive organism can be appropriately active. It is concerned with the dissolution of foods and leads, in man, to a soul experience of "inner satisfaction." The "satisfaction" of this activity consists not only in the dissolution of foods, but also in the creative force which is stimulated thereby and which distributes the newly synthesized substances into the various organs.

This all takes place in man's soul, in man's astral body. This is where pathological activity can begin when the inner activity does not proceed in accordance with the organ's demands. Because of a soul-spiritual incapacity, food substances can go into wrong paths, or can be wrongly deposited or dissolved. This can result not only in inner organ disturbances, but in a decomposition in the fluid man. Thus it is especially important to know that an illness takes hold of the whole organism and that a single organ is attacked because "this activity, which I have called astral, directs the substances resulting from that activity to the different organs." In other words, we must look for the origin of inner diseases in the fact "that incorrect substances are dissolved in the liquid man."[34]

The possibility also exists that irregularities may arise in the continuous transition from the liquid to the gaseous, which represent a kind of inner dehydration. The organs cannot then "quench their thirst" properly. The reason for that, as Rudolf Steiner pointed out, lies in the child's first phase of life, i.e., if the infant is not nourished with an appropriate milk and this or that organ remains unsatisfied. An incorrect thirst quenching will disturb the relationship of the fluid organism to the gaseous organism. We have described earlier how the soul activity relates itself to the gaseous man. In this way the healthy activity of the astral body, in relation to the organ forces, can be disturbed and that may result in mental diseases, the organic basis of which are frequently recognized today. "And so one can say that in hunger there is the predisposition to physical disease, and in thirst there is the predisposition to so-called mental disease."[35]

Such a far-reaching perspective shows clearly how intricately the complete nutritional process is intertwined with the soul-spiritual of man. We recognize its significance when we learn that Rudolf Steiner at the end of that lecture said: "Anthroposophy certainly has as one goal to be active hygienically: to properly understand health." In this sense, the influence that wrong nutrition in the first years of life will have on later life becomes evident—not only in relation to the health of the body but also to psychological health.

The Table Prayer

How can we create the proper soul mood to prepare for a meal? This question is especially pertinent if we realize the close relationship between the body and the soul-spiritual. Modern behavioral science has hardly recognized (in fact it has not even noticed) the importance of the "table prayer"—the saying of grace.

Rudolf Steiner supplied a prayer which is valid for persons of all ages and also meets the needs of modern man. This prayer addresses the soul which sprouts within as do the plants outside which provide our nourishment. It

176

points to the relationship of the germinating, sprouting, ripening of this earth food with the soul-spiritual sprouting and ripening process.

Es keimen die Pflanzen in der Erde Nacht.
Es sprossen die Kräuter durch der Luft Gewalt.
Es reifen die Früchte durch der Sonne Macht.

So keimet die Seele in des Herzens Schrein.
So sprosset des Geistes Macht im Lichte der Welt.
So reifet des Menschen Kraft in Gottes Schein.

In the darkness of the earth the seed is awakened.
In the power of the air the leaves are quickened.
In the might of the sun the fruit is ripened.

Thus in the shrine of the heart the soul is awakened,
In the light of the world the spirit is quickened,
In the glory of God man's power is ripened.

One can readily feel the harmonizing force that flows from these words and unites the soul in the right way with earth nourishment. And it will soon be recognized as a matter of fact in a proper nutritional hygiene that such a table prayer should be said when man sits down to eat. Rudolf Steiner allegedly said once that through these words, if spoken in the proper manner, a health-giving element will affect man down into his digestive processes.

Interactions Between Physical Substance and the Soul-Spiritual of Man

We have repeatedly referred to warmth as the mediator between the body and the soul. With that we have addressed a central problem, which, far beyond its significance for nutrition, is a cardinal question of human existence. On the one hand we have established that our total nourishment must be taken hold of by man's inner organization. It is thereby divested of all effects of nature which are foreign to man. He opposes it with his own being, i.e., his physical, life, soul and spirit force, and substance organization, his fourfold individuality. The goal of nutrition is, in this sense, to stimulate the transformation of natural substances and forces into his own individual structure. In doing so he must unfold the force to destroy and dissolve the substances and forces of the outer world, and thus bring them over, at least for moments, into the state of warmth, which he carries within as bearer of his Ego-organization.

In between, however, lies the destruction process through which nourishment must be taken before it can make its appearance again on the other side, as it were, as living, ensouled and spiritualized substance, as the nails and hair which we cut off. There the "end process" takes place. From this a "beginning process" results; as in the dying seed, the sprout unfolds for the future life. In this way our food is "mineralized" and killed off, but it is also lifted up into the warmth-etheric.

In this process there is not only the confrontation with the individual warmth organism, but also a meeting with the warmth-being of the cosmos. In this moment the transformed food substance "is ready to take up into itself the spiritual from world expanses."[36] "And from there, with the help of the warmth etherized earth substance, what this body needs for its formation first enters the body." By hardening anew, it becomes the physical basis for the different organs. In this moment there actually occurs a cosmic fertilization, a touching by cosmic creative forces, from which natural substances themselves originate. These carry, as it were, memories of their origins, and this memory leads them back in man to their world of origin, before they are again densified according to the requirements of the human individuality.

At that moment the law of conservation of matter and energy in man is no longer valid; it is cancelled out. It is the human Ego which destroys natural substance and lifts it to the world creative force, before it can achieve the densification, the way down into its own body—before the physiological individuality forms itself. That is why the spiritual scientists said: "Substance disappears to the zero point. Force disappears to the zero point in our own organism. . ."[37] A world dies in us, and "only because a new one immediately arises again in us do we not notice that substance disappears and is created again. . ."[38]

Everything in us is moving continually, is fluctuating continually, and here it is most evident what we understand by "dynamic nutrition." Without understanding these events, we will be unable to comprehend the nutritional process down to the consequences of nutritional quality and the daily problems of nutrition. We will not understand what man actually needs for his nutrition.

The whole play of forces in nutrition also represents a continuous poisoning, a making sick of the organism, which today is progressively overtaxed. Every over-nourishment or under-nourishment is a poisoning that encourages disease. Every inadequate food quality, every inappropriate process to which food has been subjected before it gets to man, every remnant of poisonous substances, everything that removes food from its archetypal image makes it into a distorted image. The avalanche of "diseases of

178

civilization" is growing uncontrollably. Added to that is the mass production of animal foods with its wide-spread, unconscionable use of various chemicals—estrogens, thyrostatics, arsenicals, and artificial flavors and colors—that result in food alergies, acceleration, and "stress conditioning factors." All of these threaten human existence.[39]

Who will not agree with Ralph Bircher who writes, "When one looks at all that, one wants to shout: Stop! Turn in another direction!"? In fact, an even more fearful question may arise: is it already too late? When we read, for example, that the number of stillborn, deformed babies has increased in the last twenty years by a factor of 12%, and that these damages are primarily attributable to the three hundred various chemicals found in foods, we may be inclined to think that it is. But in the face of this frightening situation we must delve still deeper. We must ask ouselves: How can we attain the forces of consciousness which enter the will as active thoughts so that we can bring about a change? In order to grasp that, we must deepen our understanding of nutrition still further.

The New Image of Man in Earthly and Cosmic Nutrition

Up to now we have said that man with his nutritional processes is the only living being that cancels out the natural law of matter and energy conservation in order to create for himself a path for the new creation of his individual substance. On this path the de-densified substance, elevated to warmth-ether, encounters the forces of the cosmic world.

At this "place" there is also the encounter with the cosmic stream of nutrition, which streams to us out of the world to which we expose the earthly substance, elevated to warmth. These two streams of substance mutually stimulate each other; they call each other forth like inspiration calls forth expiration. This creates a polar tension which calls for equalization.

Rudolf Steiner reports, as a result of his spiritual scientific investigations, that this harmonization of the earthly and cosmic streams of nutrition actually occurs in our rhythmic system: "There heavenly substantiality and activity (the cosmic stream of nutrition) flow in; there earthly substantiality and nutrition flow in."[40] In the respiratory rhythm and the pulse, which are related by a ration of 1:4, we find "the equalization between heaven's soul and earth activity and substantiality." In this sense heart and lung are a center of the nutritional processes. The earth substance streams upwards to the nervous system, for "only the nerve sense system is built up out of earth substance."[41] There it encounters the cosmic stream of substance which moves "down" towards the metabolic-limb organism. The cosmic stream of

179

substance unites with the stream of earth forces in order to permeate us with the forces of will. These forces confront us in the calories. The cosmic world of forces, as such, densifies via the earth substances in the nerve-sense region. This play of forces escapes the analytical methods of natural science because it limits itself to the inorganic world. For just that reason we need an expansion of scientific methods, a dynamic study of nutrition.

Spiritual Science provides us with the possibility of solving the cardinal problem of human existence: the nature of the bridge between the physical and the soul-spiritual world, which otherwise does not seem to exist, and cannot actually be discovered.

For a world picture in which nature exists as a temporary state between an archetypal fog and a heat-death, there is no room for a spiritual world order, which is at the same time a moral world order, if one holds the view that man is no more than a continuation of natural laws. If that were the case, man would also be subject to these laws and there would be neither freedom nor a moral world for man. Energy and matter would continue on in him as they are active in lifeless nature, and he would be destined to increase the world's waste products with his existence.

According to this image of the world, still recognized as "scientific" today, there are no points of contact between the body and the soul-spiritual in man.[42] And so Rudolf Steiner's statement is still correct: "Only if science is inconsistent, will it allow the validity of a moral world order."[43]

But this bridge does exist. We have presented it, at least in thought, through our description, and we need only clarify the existing contours: warmth in us, in conjunction with the world-warmth, fills the abyss between the natural and the moral order. If we awaken in ourselves a true enthusiasm for an ideal, then we experience a vitalization of our warmth-organism. This we can observe in ourselves. When this warmth in us is vitalized by a moral ideal, then it acts upon and affects even our physical body. It takes hold of our gaseous organization, of our fluid organization, and penetrates our physical organization where it creates germs of life. This penetration into the physical body escapes our normal consciousness today. It can only be faintly intimated. To trained supersensible perception, however, it is clearly evident. Rudolf Steiner developed very exact characterizations in his lectures, "The Bridge Between the World Spirituality and the Physical in Man" (Dornach, 17, 18, 19, Dec. 1920). They can, if man makes them his own, be of fundamental significance for our culture today.

What we are able to carry as moral impulses into our physical organization through our active participation in the world-spirituality forms the source of world-creativity in us, the sources of the life processes, down into the chemism which permeates our metabolism. It is this source of warmth which lives in the metabolism and creates the human force of will which is stimulated and ignited by those forces, which, through our daily nourishment, become active in us as apparent "combustion." The result is that at every moment our differentiated warmth-organism is present in all organs, for example, in the muscles, which we are able to move by virtue of these soul-spiritual impulses.

Thus the connection between man and the world "can be comprehended if one follows . . . the physical up to that attenuated state, to that refinement through which the soul can directly interact with this attenuated physical." Through our digestive processes we drive these substances and forces to that "attenuation" and allow them to find the contact points between the physical and the moral-spiritual world order in our warmth organism.

This occurence, however, presupposes the other pole, the opposing pole to metabolism, the nerve-sense organization. It is characterized down into its bodily structure by the fact that it pushes back the life forces, the will stimuli, the warmth, and paralyzes the stream of life. Only then are consciousness and self-consciousness possible in man. And so substance is affected through the formation of consciousness, and it is led to death, even to destruction. We cancel out the constancy of matter and energy because we are able to unfold an Ego-consciousness. That awakens us, allows us to strive for freedom, and inspires our thinking. Where does this destruction and new creation take place? On the one hand, we can say they take place in our brain, in our central nervous system. On the other, we can say we have discovered that destruction and new creation also take place in the metabolic system. There, "down below," it is earth force, coming out of nourishment, which dies and is created anew. It combines itself in this act of creation with the cosmic stream of substance. In the nerve-sense region the earth substance comes to its end and arises anew through revitalization by the cosmic forces which we attain through cosmic nutrition.

Finally, we must say that both "places, " both streams, interpenetrate; fundamentally speaking, "both are one," for have we not discovered a very active metabolism, especially in the brain? We must remember that the brain depends on the stomach. In fact, Rudolf Steiner said that we become men with Ego-consciousness, because we can nourish our brains better than the animal. On the other hand, we have a similar "brain-activity" in the "lower" organs of digestion. We have already mentioned that even modern physiology describes the pancreas as the abdominal brain and that the highest wisdom works in the coeliac plexus, the "solar plexus." Here, too, there is no parallelism, but a dynamic mutual interpenetration based on polarities. The goal of all these processes is the incarnation of the Ego, the creation of man, a self conscious being, able to think, born for freedom, and able to act out of moral impulses, out of love.

181

Chapter 12

COMMUNITY-BUILDING THROUGH THE MEAL

Nutrition as Community-Building Force

A very special community-building force has surrounded nutrition since the earliest times of human evolution. Documents from the most varied cultures provide evidence for that as a historical fact, and today everyone can experience for himself the social significance of taking meals together. In fact, group dining represents one of the most important social events in human life. Brillant-Savarin writes with French esprit:

> After an excellent meal, body and spirit experience a very special sense of well-being. Physically, the face lights up, while the brain refreshes itself; the facial line reddens, the eyes shine, and a gentle warmth permeates all the limbs. Psychologically, the spirit becomes more alert, fantasy more lively. . . In addition, one frequently finds united around the same tables all factors which make society possible: love, friendship, business, speculation, power, protection, ambition, intrigue—that is why a feast brings fruits of all kinds.[1]

Historical Aspects

Like massive pillars encompassing the evolution of humanity, two pictures speak of community-building through the meal. The first, which points into the past, is the picture of Eve, mother of the human race, giving Adam the apple from the tree of paradise. This image points to the descent of man into

183

the sense world, to the permeation of his being with the experience of enjoying the fruits of the earth, to the longing for tasty food. "There his eyes were opened." The second, which looks into the future, is the image of the Last Supper, which shows Christ united with the twelve disciples, who represent all of humanity, passing out bread and wine with the words: This is my body, this is my blood. In both pictures a union is established through the meal, one in which everyone since then participates when he partakes of earthly food.

In ancient times man was aware of this when he took in the archetypal nutrition given by the earth: milk. From the time of the cradle of humanity, when milk "was still the general nourishment taken in from the external environment,"[2] up to our present stage of development in which it flows to us from our mothers, milk has given man a force which unites him to a common humanity. It makes him into "a citizen of the whole solar system."[3]

This statement by the spiritual scientist directs our attention to a significant fact which is almost entirely forgotten today: with every ingestion of food man enters into a soul-spiritual communion with certain earth and cosmic forces, which become active in him, either liberating or binding, elevating or allowing him to sink, depending on what and how he eats. Milk prepares him to be "a human earth creature," but "does not actually tie him to the earth." Milk gives him the strength to fulfill himself with the mission of the earth in a most universal manner; it harmonizes his being with the world. Other foods, however, have very specific properties; "each one has a predominant effect on a specific organ system."[4] Such insights not only prompted the initiates of earlier stages of human evolution to prescribe a certain nutrition to their students, but also made it possible for them to discover laws for the nutrition of the tribes or communities which lived in the mystery centers' sphere of influence.[5] This led to the founding of some communities which had to abstain from meat or intoxicating beverages, and to the establishment of others composed of grain eaters, rice eaters, corn eaters, and tea or coffee drinkers.

The art of grain farming and bread baking reaches back into Atlantean times. As Noah says in one of Albert Steffen's dramas: "Yes, before the flood there were grains with thick, milk-permeated ears, with fragrance of the stars, seven kinds. . ."[6] Demeter initiated Triptolemos into the Eleusian mysteries of grain culture. Herodotus said: "The grain-eating populations far exceed in arts, sciences, number, spirit, and body those populations which live by warring, hunting, fishing, and animal husbandry."[7] As the result of modern Spiritual Science, Rudolf Steiner added that war-like people are more inclined to follow a meat nutrition than peace-loving people, because "animal nutrition enhances the life of the will, which proceeds more unconsciously, which manifests itself more in affects and passions."[8] Yet,

184

originally, the consumption of meat was part of a sacred ritual: the sacrifice. Only later were animals killed merely for regular consumption. In Greece, during the time of the Persian wars, beef was eaten only in public meals related to the sacrifice.

The Community-Building Effect of Certain Substances and Dietary Customs

F. Hausler makes a significant observation from another point of view:

We know well that milk and honey, for example, taste better the more varied the plants are from which they originate, but we do not pay attention any more to their effects on us after the tasting. . . We need only go, however, into countries where nutrition, because of external or internal customs, is closely bound to the rhythms of the year to see that such a nutrition has a far-reaching effect on the soul-life. Without a doubt, that had a totally different significance for the older, nature-bound races than it has for us.[9]

We may remind ourselves here of the community-building capacity of alcohol. It was used in pre-Christian times in the dionysian rituals to bring man completely into the physical plane, to lead him down into experiencing the earthly body. Alcohol cut him off from participating in the spiritual world. For the most advanced segments of humanity at that time, it was a necessary step in consciousness. The human body was prepared in this way for a purely earthly culture. But the segment of humanity achieving earth consciousness was to learn to direct this consciousness toward a higher goal, toward a new striving for the spiritual worlds.

Since then, alcohol has lost its function as a stimulation of earth-consciousness, and its effects are now destructive. This is expressed cogently by a modern pharmacologist, who describes what happens as a result of alcohol consumption: "Those functions are paralyzed which differentiate man from the animal and the adult from the child."[10] Community-building through alcohol now leads back into the childhood stages of humanity, to a descent into sub-humanity.

In earlier times the leaders of humanity knew about the soul-spiritual effects of food. Not only the multitude of laws, but the proscriptions, the abstinence from certain foods, and the periodic fasts, were a living expression of this knowledge. At that time, one still had a living feeling for the interaction of macrocosm and microcosm, so it was required of every adult member of the community that he make himself receptive to certain forces

185

by definite dietary prescriptions. In this way, the Pythagoreans, the Essenes, the Knights of the Grail, the Knights of the Round Table, and the great religious communities of India and the Catholic Church were active up to the Middle Ages.

Not only do the processes intrinsic in foods give impulses to the soul and thus to the whole community which shares the food, but so, too, do the persons themselves, who find themselves together at a common meal, contribute to community-building through their moods and the simultaneity of their physiological and soul-spiritual activities.

When, for example, similar processes are elicited by the stimulation of smell and taste, or even sight and hearing, then these impressions first affect consciousness superficially. The experience of something sweet, for example, stimulates a certain sphere in man. Rudolf Steiner spoke of a mutual correspondence between digestion and thinking; in this relationship "the process which is affected in digestion by consumption of a greater quantity of sugar has, as correlative in the upper man, a stronger independence of thinking."[11] If, for example, a group of people eating together maximize the sugar process by bringing grain starch completely into the sugar state, then independence of thinking will manifest itself in an increased capacity for concentration, greater wakefulness, and greater capacity for individualized thinking. Rudolf Steiner pointed to this phenomenon by citing the significantly higher consumption of sugar by the English when compared to the Russian farmers. Here the national character of a people is being affected by sugar consumption.

A further, far-reaching example, frequently emphasized by Rudolf Steiner is related to potato consumption which has spread and increased enormously in the last few centuries. Steiner explains: "The inner thinking of Europe has been regressing since the moment potato consumption took hold"[12]—now about two hundred years. The potato has effects on man opposite to those of sugar, because "it has no relation to the spiritual." The community of potato eaters, still significant in number today, will elicit completely different physical and psychological processes within themselves, which can even be transmitted to their offspring by inheritance. If parents eat too many potatoes, then, a human germ develops in which the "soul-spiritual is not properly in the physical body."[13] Rudolf Steiner actually drew a parallel between increasing potato consumption in the last centuries and a progressively materialistic way of thinking in the European people.

There are numerous examples to support this contention, but we shall turn now to another interesting fact, that is, that the study of nutrition has, for the last few decades, become a branch of social anthropology. Fréderic Simoons, for example, examined the basis of the most important nutritional customs in relation to cultural and religious beliefs which prohibit various kinds of meats or foods.[14] The prohibition against pork consumption in Jewish cultures makes sense when a modern research finding is considered. This evidence suggests that pork has a detrimental effect on sugar metabolism in the human organism. The Jewish race is, as is well known, very prone to diabetes mellitus. The prohibition against pork consumption may well have been an instinctive protective measure against diabetes—a measure intended to protect the health of a whole race.

The "Bone of Contention Character" of Our Nutrition

We enter a totally different realm if we direct our attention to a phenomenon found in certain Indian tribes: that is, the avoidance of looking at one another while eating. Karl von Steinen, who observed this peculiarity in the Bakairi in 1888, wrote: "There was no such thing as a common meal among these people, not even a family meal." R. Bilz, taking this phenomenon as the starting point in a psychological analysis of community food supply and food choice, wrote: "Eating and drinking are not only nutritive events, but also show their foundation in the so-called higher realms of our humanity."[15] The "bone of contention character" of our nutrition points, in the depths of our souls, to shamefulness, which, as we mentioned before, expresses itself in the image of Adam and Eve. The egotistic character of eating has anti-social effects; everyone wants to enjoy the best piece himself, undisturbed, unobserved. This anti-social drive associated with eating is, without a doubt, active in man's subconscious and must be overcome by the development of higher capacities. It can, however, be intensified and manifest itself as a compulsion, as a phobia, which makes it impossible for the patient to share a meal with others.

It is instructive here to recall what Rudolf Steiner said about the diet question. In his first medical course (1920) he said that dietary questions are very important because they have not only medical significance, but every special diet also "makes an unsocial being out of man." The "more we need something extra for ourselves in nutrition, the more we become unsocial." The significance of the Last Supper is not that Christ gave something extra to each disciple, but that he gave each the same. Bringing about the possibility of being together in eating or in drinking has great social significance.[16] For that reason Rudolf Steiner suggested that every special diet be so structured that the patient will gradually not need it any more and will soon be able to return to the general eating community.

Many other mealtime accessories are connected with the overcoming of the "bone of contention character" of nutrition. For example, the common meal which brings persons of various persuasions together, the service, the table decoration, the table music, all are accoutrements of a higher eating

187

culture, which make use of eye and ear in a higher sense. Also the table conversation and the table prayer are activities which will lead men united for a meal to a new form of community. If Rudolf Steiner himself gave a new table prayer, we can certainly assume that he did so with full consciousness of the community-building force of the human word. This force allows the archetypal image of that society to enter among and be experienced by those united for a meal; this force is the same as that given by Christ at the Last Supper.

The Craving for Enjoyment as Uniting Factor

Under the influence of the materialistic civilization which claims that man is what he eats, the element of community-building through the meal becomes distorted and degraded to the character of an animal drive. The constantly increasing excesses witnessed in all sorts of eating reveal a subhuman, immoral sphere into which a greater part of modern humanity may sink. Much in our civilization reminds us of the conditions in ancient Rome. Not only in worldly meals, but also in so-called "initiation feasts" this Roman decadence became evident. We read about the dishes which the head-priest of Mars, Lentullus, offered his guests on the occasion of his initiation in Varro in 300 A.D.: "Whenever a feast of the priest is in sight, the meat prices increase. On Lentullus' inauguration the appetizers were sea urchins, fresh oysters, clams, song birds with asparagus, etc."[17] Seventy years ago Rudolf Steiner remarked, in reference to the current trend in decadent eating habits, that "one could easily study the change and increase in this respect which took place over a relatively short period of time." It is only necessary to compare a hotel menu from the 1870's with one from today to "see what kind of progress the life of refined consumption, of the cravings for special foods, has undergone."[18]

Collectivization of Nutrition
Problems of Modern Community Food Supply

Through technology a collectivization of nutrition has come about. The family table, for millenia the focal point of human community-building, has been dethroned and its place has been taken by the anonymous spot in the restaurant or the cafeteria. The gigantic kitchens, often central cooking facilities removed from the eating place, have created completely new problems, problems not only of the quality of food, but also of a physiological, psychological, and social nature.

The consequences of this type of collectivization are too numerous to

188

delineate here in great detail, but they must be taken into account because the old forms of home nutrition can certainly not be re-established. Thus we have to attempt to see the possible positive effects of this development, despite their enormous dangers and negative aspects. Man, in our time, is ruthlessly torn by current eating trends from the old community bonds, from the family, and must learn, alone and independently, as a free individuality, to find the way to a new community-building through the meal. To that end, two factors will be increasingly essential. First, man must take the spirit of the time seriously; he must "choose nourishment on the basis of spiritual knowledge." That is a demand made of all those responsible for community nutrition: the kitchen supervisor, the buyers, the producers and processers of foods, the dietary assistants, the industrial physician, and finally the nutritional scientist who, through his research, establishes the criteria for food quality. The farmers and gardeners must become more aware of their responsibilities towards man and the earth. The second demand is made of the consumer himself. Today he cannot merely sit down at a readily prepared table; instead, he must participate in working towards a fundamental knowledge of nutrition and its practical application. All these persons must bind themselves together in new associations. Such a basis will result from the study and practice of Rudolf Steiner's Spiritual Science. Modern man must make the choice.

Chapter 13

THE HISTORY OF HUMAN TRADITION

Introductory Aspects

Spiritual Science's method of approaching the subject of the history of human nutrition is, of necessity, quite different from the usual prevailing method of historical analysis. The latter is based primarily on a knowledge of the physical world and man and thereby consists merely of a temporal arrangement of so-called historical facts. Marx and Engels' materialistic historical analysis shares that basis. According to such a method, man is merely a material object of research as he was claimed to be by the natural science of the 19th century. But the principle that there is a temporal sequence of events is valid only for physical events. Spiritual Science holds that a much more realistic and fruitful study of history makes use of the symptomatologic method: that is, we should "little by little become accustomed to examining history symptomatologically," and in doing so, "consider surface manifestations in such a manner that we allow the inner life of historical progress to work on us."[1]

We do hear that ideas have influences upon history, but these observations remain abstract, because the starting point is always that man's thinking was more or less alike at all times. Allegedly, man has only worked himself out of "primitive" situations, as mirrored, for example, in mythology, into the present soul state.

The method developed by Rudolf Steiner, however, enables man to attain the capacity to rise with full consciousness to higher means of knowledge, to find them again in human development at a more instinctive stage, and to thereby consciously live by including himself in the course of development. In this way it becomes possible to draw information about a certain time period not only from documents, but by placing "oneself as a complete human being into the various periods of time." From such an inner re-experiencing of the soul state of earlier man and cultures, the other facts of history find their rightful place. With this method "we will be able to look back into man's metamorphoses in the various epochs."[2] Through this method it will also be possible to shed light on the development of human nutrition, and thereby achieve something which illuminates not only the past but also the present and the future. "The historian must find in the past the light which shines into the darkness of the future."[3]

Origins of Nutrition

We have indicated in earlier chapters how man today still carries within him past conditions and origins of earth development. This is most impressive and obvious in his metabolism, in the "lower man." Modern medicine, too, has recognized the "internal milieu," the "fluid man," as a decisively important organization in which "an almost unbelievable intensity of exchange" takes place, and one in which, despite this constant movement, "an effective regulatory system prevents any deviation." Here "a control and regulative mechanism . . . whose completeness amazes the observer" is active.[4] Jean Hamburger speaks further of "this sea with countless arms" that corresponds in its composition almost to "that of our oceans." This comparison points not only to the fact that man shares a common element with the environment, but also to the fact that this fluid man points to the past of earth and man. An American scientist puts it this way: "In concentration and composition, the internal milieu is like the waters of that prehistorical day when life made its first conquest of land."[5]

We are led here by modern science to a view of man's past in which man himself still led a life related to the liquid rather than the solid elements of earth. We suggested this idea before, when, in our consideration of digestive events in the intestine, we said that through the liquefication of all foods earlier stages of earth evolution were, as it were, repeated daily. In this sense man contains in himself the early stages of earth evolution.

Rudolf Steiner gave many descriptions of these early stages of man and earth. In the lecture cycle, "World, Earth, and Man,"[6] we read that at a certain stage of earth development man was submerged into the then existing water-earth with the part of his body that later became the metabolic system. He had not developed at that time the later solid formations, the skeleton. With his upper part he extended into a mist of water-steam permeated by warmth. Swimming and floating, he moved through this misty

192

atmosphere, which Rudolf Steiner designated as earth-ocean. In this, the Lemurian Epoch, respiration and nutrition were not what they are today; the substances were different. Respiration and nutrition were to a certain extent connected. They were "a common activity which only separated later." These conditions are still imitated by man today in embryological development. This type of nourishment is described as "a watery, crudely pressed, milk-like substance." Man at that earlier time experienced his first sense-perception; he learned to distinguish warm from cold in his environment by means of an organ which was then a massive formation, but is today only present in a rudimentary form as the pineal gland. This organ closed itself when the other sense organs opened up. At a certain period "it was an organ of fertilization, so that for a certain period of time sense reception and fertilization occurred together."

This archetypal unity of nutrition and respiration, sense activity and fertilization, sheds significant light on the development of nutrition. We can say that in those times nutrition included fertilization, sense perception, and inhalation of cosmic substances and forces. Man was not yet separated into a nerve-sense and a metabolic being. Everything still transpired in the air-liquid and the warmth-permeated atmosphere. The separation of the sexes had not yet taken place.

Nevertheless, man already had an inwardness. In his *Occult Science, an Outline*, Rudolf Steiner remarks that there was a nutrition at that time in the sense that " something taken in from outside was transformed and processed within."[7] Furthermore, a soul body was already integrated into the human body. Thus, in these early stages of man's development, respiration and nutrition were accompanied by feelings, so that "a kind of pleasure arose when substances which were beneficial for the structuring of the human body were taken in from outside." An important element is indicated here, namely, the original nutritional instinct which experiences sympathy for appropriate nourishment and antipathy for inappropriate nourishment. Displeasure results "when harmful substances flow in or even come into the vicinity." In this atmosphere, from which the liquid and the solid later settled down and the air and warmth rose upwards, man lived as in a fine milk-soup, which was somewhat reminiscent of egg-white. The later mineral substances and the elements of which protein consists today were dissolved in it. It was living substance in which such substances reminiscent of today's chemical elements continually arose and disappeared. But everything was "permeated from the cosmos with cosmic ether, which gave life to this substance."[8] Here we have the actual origin of the "inner milieu" of modern man, that fluid which even today is permeated by life-formative-forces.

Thus the archetypal nourishment of man on earth was taken in from the immediate environment just as the lungs take in air today. For man at that time lived more like an etheric-fluid being in the environment to which he was connected, as if with suction tubes "as the embryo is nourished in the body of the mother today." Here Haeckel's law is valid: ontogeny recapitulates phylogeny. These indications are found in a lecture, given by Rudolf Steiner, that is especially relevant to us: "Development of the Forms of Nutrition."[9]

Origin of Milk Nourishment and the Three Phases of Its Development

The old "protein atmosphere" in which Lemurian man moved about, at a time when plant and animal creation had just begun, is actually the origin of milk, which later, when the force of reproduction was separated through the division of the sexes, reorganized itself into the milk glands in mammals. "Earlier, food could be sucked out of the environment. . . Milk consumption is a very old, transformed nutrition. The first nourishment for man was always milk."[10]

In a much later lecture, Rudolf Steiner broached this subject again.[11] He explained that man today receives from his mother's body what in the past he received from the environment. Then "simply everything that man received from the environment was like milk." The old legends also speak of the distant, long-gone land "where milk and honey flow." A remnant of that has been preserved in some plants, like the poppy, the milkweed, and the euphorbia, in which a milky sap permeates the whole plant.

In summary, Rudolf Steiner characterizes three phases of the development of milk nutrition. In the first period milk was taken in externally from the environment. This was replaced by a state during which milk became the general human nourishment. That may well refer to the state of development during which the transition from a completely etheric nourishment to an already earth-like, milky atmosphere occurred. Only then did the present stage, in which mother's milk is taken in, come into being.

This element of the original milk nutrition is hardly to be found in modern analysis. S. Bommer, for example, considers milk only "the second stage" of nutrition, the one that began after man tamed animals and kept herds. Only at that time did he allegedly get his nourishment "partly from the milk and partly from the meat of the herd animals."[12]

Origin of Plant and Animal Nutrition in Lemurian and Atlantean Times

What is the origin of the animal and plant nutrition of man? To answer this question we must keep in mind that the realms of nature in the early stages

194

of the world and human evolution were as little developed into their final stages of formation as was man. The earth, while still in the Lemurian Epoch, was not a solid mineral yet; it was still permeated by a strong inner life and brought forth living and ensouled formations which had a great capacity for transformation. Formation and transformation were then still characteristics of the life of natural beings. The formative forces could take hold of the moldable matter and create forms. A significant remnant of that stage is still evident in the early stages of childhood and much more so in embryological development. To understand the malleable quality of natural development at that time, we need only consider the exceedingly complex formation of the diaphragm with its many forms and transformations, or the fact that the human embryo passes through three organ stages in the development of the kidney before the definitive organ is formed. Even in later life the formative capacity of many organs is retained. The liver is an impressive example. With its life-long high fluid content of about 70%, it retains its embryological formative forces. Likewise, the activity of metamorphosis is very strong and even more evident in the plant realm, even though some limitations were placed upon it when these forces were fixated by the laws of inheritance.

Conditions in those times also enabled the existing animal forms to transform and create new ones continually. "The transformation was naturally a gradual one. The causes for transformation were, for example, a change in habitat or in the way of living."[13] The animals had an "exceptionally rapid adaptability"; the moldable body changed its organs with relative rapidity, so that soon "the offspring of one species looked very little like their ancestors." This is how Rudolf Steiner describes the conditions in Lemurian time when the transformability of plants was even greater than the animals'.

The existing conditions also made it possible, then, for man to take hold of these formative forces, whether it was done to "instinctively bring living beings into such an environment that they took a certain form," or whether "he effected this by breeding." In order to understand this distinction, we must inquire into the significance of breeding and cultivation, the results of which still provide the most important basis for our nutrition today: the cultivation of grains from wild grasses, fruit trees from wild trees, etc. Similarly, we must look into the domestication of animals, the taming of wild horses, cows, pigs, etc. Rudolf Steiner speaks of the highly developed knowledge of breeding animals and plants which man at that time possessed, and he also discusses the fact that man was able to retain that knowledge and apply it in the subsequent epoch of the evolution of man and earth, the "Atlantean period."[14]

Although a certain solidification and mineralization had come about during this time, which progressively limited the free play of formative forces, such improvements continued on the basis of the preceding cultivations. The capabilities for doing this, however, were found only in smaller and smaller groups of people, who, as a prerequisite, had to go through a soul-spiritual training. This brought about the development of capabilities which were later called "magic forces."

This epoch found its spiritual expression in the old myths of the Greeks. It was Plato himself who rescued the knowledge of old Atlantis, brought it into Greece, and developed a picture of that culture. Although this work, unfortunately, exists only as a fragment, Plato's description provides us with an intimation of the abundance of life that existed in Atlantean times. He wrote: "Whatever fragrances nourish the earth—be they of roots, or grass, or woods, or saps, or flowers, or fruits—all these were abundant on the island [Atlantis], as were the vegetables, the fruit trees, and the wild and tame animals."

Ignatius Donelly claims that Greek mythology is "actually a history of the kings of Atlantis," i.e., the Greek gods.[15] Here we enter the realm of the Demeter myth, which makes its most beautiful appearance in a document rediscovered in 1777, "Praise of Demeter." It is thought that this work was written at the turn of the 8th century, B.C. There we encounter Demeter as "goddess with a golden sickle, laden with fruits, her head crowned with a wreath of ears of grain."

Demeter

Bachofen considered the image of Demeter to be the center of the "gynecocratic epoch" in Greek history.[16] Ernst Uehli gives a significant characterization of this mystery culture from the viewpoint of modern Spiritual Science. He writes:

> The fruitfulness of the earth, by virtue of which man has his nourishment and his existence, as well as the force which ripens the harvest, was attributed to the divine earth mother, Demeter, because her activity, her force, could be experienced instinctively.[17]

The mystery center at Eleusis, founded by Demeter, was only an echo of a sunken Atlantis. The Demeter myth actually points to the great Atlantean culture of which Rudolf Steiner writes in his work, *Our Atlantean Forefathers*.[18] He explains: "Outside in nature, forces are active . . . which enter us through nourishment and respiration." What they are outside is ruled by the great Demeter. But "the great Demeter sends the forces into the human soul; there they are assimilated (to put it crudely, through the digestion, which was of spiritual nature) and are transformed into clairvoyant capacities."

Isocrates, a playmate of Plato and great admirer of Socrates, wrote:

196

When the Goddess came to Eleusis she brought us the fruits of the field by virtue of which we were able to make the transition from animal life to human life; then she brought us the initiations which enable those allowed to participate to face with hope the end of life and all of existence.

Thus, in the image of Demeter, we look into a time of human evolution in which the soul-spiritual capacities were still closely bound to the activities of nutrition.

At this time there was also an indication of the "quality" of nutrition. This was the time when man was given the Demeterian creative force to cultivate food plants from the plants covering the virginal earth. Thus we can say: out of the fertilized lap of the earth, seven grains arose: wheat, rye, oats, barley, millet, rice, and corn. Donelly writes:

If we seek the original home of our useful plants we must look to Atlantis. . . We cannot escape the conclusion that the main cereals, wheat, corn, rye, oats, barley, etc., were first planted and cultivated in a time long past.[19]

Here, modern research, because its methods are based only on external findings and documents, is unable to recognize the actual facts. Though modern studies are valuable because they are so detailed, they lead to the temptation of considering them the only valid sources of information. From these sources we learn that it is thought that the first cultivation of grain occurred at least 6000-8000 years ago. But, according to spiritual scientific indications, we must put the time more near 12,000 B.C. According to Plato, Atlantis sank around 8,000 B.C. Whatever the date, we can certainly agree with Walter Adrian when he says: "The research work achieved by the first plant cultivators is on the same level with the greatest discoveries of modern physics and chemistry."[20]

We understand of course that the forces which enabled the cultivation of grains were quite different from those leading to technical discoveries. The Atlanteans were related to nature in such a way that they could use the life and formative forces of the plant for themselves. Rudolf Steiner explained that just as we get warmth out of oil and coal, so the Atlanteans knew how to put the life force of living beings into their technical service. This can be described as follows: A force resides in a grain of cereal. This is the force which enables a seed to develop into a plant. Nature can awaken this force; man today cannot. The Atlanteans, however, knew "what to do in order to transform the force in a pile of grain into technical force. . ." Therefore the plants in Atlantis were cultivated not only for food, but also "to make the forces inherent in them accessible to transportation and industry."[21]

That was also a result, however, of the fact that the grains at that time were still possessed of a different nature. We have already mentioned that from the Lemurian time the plants were permeated by a milky sap, representing a heritage of the sun-origin of plants. Then, as in earlier times, plants were permeated by those archetypal life forces that come to expression in milk. Nourishment actually took place by man sucking the milk sap out of the plants, as the child does from the mother today. The plants which still have sap today are actually remnants of a time when all plants yielded these saps.

The nourishment of that time gave man the force to unfold a dreamlike, clairvoyant consciousness. Only with the complete mineralization of the earth was another consciousness awakened in man. He gradually awoke to the world of senses; he developed an "object consciousness." His nourishment began to be permeated by death forces; grains lost their original fullness of life. Man had to continue on his path of separation from a direct sharing in the life of nature. He had to unfold his individuality by experiencing death within himself in order to allow his Ego to live within himself.

This mighty drama of the evolution of humanity is mirrored accurately in the Demeter myth. It formed the core of the Eleusinian mysteries in ancient times, and it was enacted before modern believers in the *Drama of Eleusis*, Eduard Schuré's reconstructed version of it.[22]

In the initiation ceremonies the neophyte received, after being prepared by a long fast, the draught of barley, consisting of a mixture of roasted barley, water, and mint. It was an "initiation drink" through which the neophyte was transported into the old Atlantean clairvoyant consciousness, i.e., he perceived the Goddess Demeter.

But at the same time there was embodied within the Demeter myth the transformation of this consciousness, the descent to the soul-spiritual darkness of the earth. Demeter's daughter, Persephone, was abducted by Pluto and led to the underworld. The human soul must therefore share its activities between the cosmic and the terrestrial world.

The last and highest act of the Eleusinian mysteries consisted of the revelation of the severed ear of grain. The old connection with the spiritual world was re-established once again, the neophyte was initiated into her secrets, but the ear of grain was already severed from its stream of life. Ego-consciousness strove towards its own full unfolding. Therefore the myth did not end here, but led to the encounter with Triptolemos, the hero of agriculture, the "three time plower."

Otto Neeracher describes this meeting in his book, *Auf Geistespfaden Griechenlands* (On Spiritual Paths of Greece): "Demeter, who in the past brought the spiritual into man through nourishment, as the eternal arche-typal force of soul, becomes spirit in man in a time when bodily life was also spiritual life. Demeter is the helper for a new consciousness."[23] She does this by initiating the king's son into her mysteries and teaching him to plow the earth, to open up the depths of the earth to receive the sun-grain.

"With Triptolemos a similar transformation is given as in the natural event and the initiation process. Triptolemos stood for the autochthonous human being in contact with the matriarchal culture and became the hero of agriculture by putting the masculine plow culture in the place of the digging stick culture taken care of by women." Thereby Triptolemos became the "representative of a new age, the age of Ego-consciousness, which took the place of clairvoyant god-consciousness."[24]

From Hoe to Plow

The problem of the transition from the digging-stick culture to the plow culture has attracted significant attention. Emil Werth reports the results of his decades of study in his book, *Grabstock, Hacke, and Pflug* (*Digging-Stick, Hoe, and Plow*). Men at that time

> knew neither plow nor wagon, nor did they know how to use animals for pulling either. In working the ground with a hoe, the men, or more commonly the women, depended on their own strength. The instru-ment used was primarily the digging-stick, and then the hoe. . . Field work (at least originally) was done by women. . . Characteristic of the hoe-culture is the predominance of tuberous plants . . . then the fruit plants. The most important among the fruit plants is the banana . . . grain-culture is foreign to hoe-culture. .[25]

The time of origin of hoe agriculture is uncertain. Werth thinks it to have begun about 15,000 years ago. That falls into the time of aging Atlantis. In any case there is agreement about the fact that hoe agriculture preceded plow agriculture and that plow culture is distinguished from the former by grain planting. The most significant achievement of plow culture, however, is the breeding of large farm animals.

We can see how important the developmental stages of humanity are here shown to be. These were also the determining factors for nutrition. Hoe agriculture, pointing back to very early times, was carried out primarily by women and did not require the kind of close relationship to the earth necessary to plow farming. The soil was at that time still permeated by virginal life-formative-forces; it hardly needed to be worked. It almost gave of itself what was necessary for nourishment. Man at that time lived almost

199

completely at one with the course of the year. The (tropical) rain seasons, alternating with dry seasons, determined planting and harvest. But "the hoe farmer had always to leave his fields after a few years and prepare new ones by cutting trees and burning the bush." Mirrored in that process is the old nomadic culture found in Lemuria. The hoe farmers were also unaware of the use of manure. Nature alone took care of regeneration and reproduction. The primary plants of that epoch were palms and bananas, fruit trees without wood, which did not yet live in the hardened-mineral element. There were also melons, squash, cucumbers, and other plants characterized by the watery element. Two plants were especially noticeable; these were taro and yams, the typical tuberous growths, the hoe culture plants in a narrower sense.

An essential of the hoe-culture is that it was done mostly by women. What can we conclude from that in view of the significant change from matriarchy to patriarchy, from Demeter to Triptolemus? Bachofen writes: "Using Demeter as an example, the earthly mother becomes the archetypal mother's mortal representative, her priestess and, as hierophant, the one entrusted with the keeping of her mystery."[26]

Here Demeter appears as "the archetypal mother of the human soul and the fruitful forces of nature."[27] The forces active outside in nature enter man through nourishment, through respiration. What these forces are outside in nature is ruled by Demeter. In man, through the forces which Demeter as fruitful goddess brings about in the environment, "clairvoyant capacities are born, represented by Persephone." That is an indication of the transition from the old times when man was still protected in the bosom of natural forces, to the later times, when he not only became more solid, and more isolated, but also an individual. That marked the transition to plow-agriculture, to grain planting, to Tripolemus, to patriarchy.

"The patriarchal family closes itself off into an individual organism; the matriarchal family, however, has the typically general character with which all development begins. . ." In another place we read a significant statement related to our concern:

The life of the bees shows us gynecocracy in its clearest and purest form. It is primarily connected with Demeter, with Persephone, with the image of Demetrian earth soul in its highest purity. . . The purest product of organic nature, in which animal and plant production are so intimately connected, is also the purest food of the mother, used by mankind for ages and to which priestly men, the Pythagoreans, Melchisedek, and John returned again. Honey and milk belong to motherhood, wine to the masculine, dionysian nature principle.[28]

Thus honey joins milk as Demeter's archetypal nutrition. Honey, "an extraordinarily healthy food," has "the force to give man form and solidity."[29] Again that old land, where "milk and honey flow," the archetypal source of health, is indicated. Wine, however, came from a different source.

Grain, given to the coming culture, to Triptolemus, carries, as it were, the forces of milk and honey in a synthesis with itself. It is a nourishment which roots in the earth. Rudolf Steiner emphasized especially this root character, which carries the forces of death, earth, and mineralization up into the seeds, through which at the same time, however, stem and ear open themselves to the cosmic sun forces.

Through Demeter's gift of the grain culture and her initiation of the earth-born Triptolemos into her mysteries, man was deprived of the natural power of clairvoyance. He became a citizen of the earth, he solidified his body as the earth on which he now stands firmly is solidified, but he individualized himself at the same time, he cleared the way for the entry of the Ego-forces into his earth body. He became a farmer and an animal breeder.

In a narrower sense this change brought about the transition of the most advanced segments of humanity from a state of nomadism and semi-nomadism to a stability of existence, to the foundation of a stable home. The "harvesting cultures" then arose and actually

> brought a totally new element into the history of human life on the earth: for the first time a being consciously planned the production of nourishments needed. The nutrition of the carrier of that unique invention was thereby improved and secured as never before in the history of organisms. . . With the cultivation of useful plants, man began to improve his nutritional and life conditions and initiated a development which is designated as the neolithic revolution.[30]

Rudolf Steiner, in his *Akasha-Chronic*, reports that as fore-runners of this development, a small group of people was separated from the population in general at the end of Lemuria, and designated as the fore-fathers of the future Atlantean race. They knew how to prepare the fields and make their fruits useful for life. The "more nomadic existence of earlier times ceased, and stable settlements became more numerous." These were the same groups of people which, when they moved out to establish the various Atlantean races, "took along a highly developed knowledge of the cultivation of animals and plants."

The cultivation of fruit trees, like the various fruit palms such as the banana, and also many vegetable plants, falls into this early time. Among the early domestic animals there were goats, pigs, dogs, and chickens. The use of animals for work was totally unknown. The domestication of cattle and horses falls into the time of the plow-culture, as does the cultivation of the various grains. All that was prepared for at the end of the Lemurian time. The Atlantean culture, then, had the great task of completing these great cultivations and breedings. Humanity began to be divided into those who worked the land and those who raised and bred animals.

In this connection a small point seems worth mentioning, that is, Werth's comment on the place of the guinea fowl in cultural history. One species of guinea fowl, of which twenty-three species inhabit the countries of southern Africa, can still be found in the western African region of Guinea and is the ancestor of the guinea fowls in our local chicken coops. Its history goes back to the prehistorical mythologies. This fact presupposes, according to Werth, that there was a connection at one time between northern and southern Africa, a supposition that is also supported by rock paintings in the Sahara. Of these paintings, Werth says, "Those are rock pictures which I take to be documents from the life of the old legendary land of Atlantis. . . . Evidently at the high point of this culture it had colonial settlements that stretched into the tropical Guinea regions."[31] Here even modern science takes Atlantis into consideration, even though, as we have seen, it views the situation as the reverse: population movements originated from the tropical regions of Africa and went to the West, to Atlantis, and took along their knowledge of animal breeding and farming. What has maintained itself as "Benin-culture" far into later times may more likely represent a remnant of the old Lemurian culture from which movements down to the South of Africa originated. The modern study of cultures has also been unable to establish a connection between the Benin sculptures and the so-called "primitive" Africa. "The German scholar Leo Frobenius postulates that the art of Benin originated from the art of the lost continent Atlantis."[32] As we can see, these relationships appear everywhere, and many point past the threshold of the post-Atlantean cultures to Atlantis, and frequently even further back to old Lemuria.

The "Neolithic Revolution"

Returning once again to Triptolemos, we can see clearly how this mythological figure typified an exceptionally important turning point in the development of human nutrition. "Triptolemos is the representative of a completely new age, the age of Ego-consciousness, which took the place of clairvoyant god-consciousness."[32] We could also say he is the representative of an entirely new consciousness of nutrition, of agronomy, of grain culture, and of animal husbandry.

While the last age of Lemuria brought us up to about 24,000 years B.C., the old Atlantean cultures lasted until about 8,000 B.C. When modern research marks this turning point as being near 3,000 B.C., it is placing it much too late. W. Adrian reports grain fields in the 5th millenium B.C., and notes that the rock paintings, which portray already tamed cattle, are dated much earlier. Thus the fact is established that grain and animal culture experienced a revitalization, a new birth, in the early post-Atlantean period. Zarathustra is known as the creator of that culture. Preceding it was the old Indian culture which began around 8,000 B.C. Rudolf Steiner describes this early post-Atlantean period as an echo of earlier epochs, as a time when man "did not have to touch external nature," when he did not have to butcher, when he took plants for food as they grew wild, without cultivation.[33] However, at the beginning of the 6th and 5th millenium a change took place: "Wild animals were domesticated and man tilled the fields." Rudolf Steiner, too, calls this the great radical turning point, which coincides with the "neolithic revolution" insofar as it actually falls into the mesolithic age, the middle stone age. Then man, as inheritor and descendant of the Atlantean culture, received the arts of agronomy and animal husbandry. In the meantime, the earth had hardened into its mineral form, and the transformations in nature could only be affected by extraordinary magical forces as they were acquired in the mystery centers.

Combined with this stage of nutrition is, on the one hand, the use of domesticated animals to perform work. This change actually made the change from the hoe to the plow possible. On the other hand, the domesticated animals, especially cattle, provided meat for nourishment and thus they supplemented what in earlier times was supplied by hunters and the gatherers of plant foods.

How deeply this "revolution" affected human development becomes evident when we take note of the following: "In the paleolithic age the population density was still approximately one person per 50-100 km^2. The 'neolithic revolution' increased the earth's population by a factor of 100, or according to Ratzel, even by a factor of 1000."[34] Thus the ten-fold increase in population per area in the "industrial revolution is rather modest in comparison. Humanity finally turned to conquering and utilizing the earth at that time, and so the divine law was fulfilled: 'Be fruitful and multiply!' "

Nutrition in Historical Time

Before we bring our discussion into the present, we will present a brief overview of Rudolf Steiner's lecture of 1905, "The Development of the Forms of Nutrition."[35] This lecture begins with the fundamental fact that the so-called laws of nutrition in the various cultures did not arise arbitrarily, but were "born out of knowledge and wisdom." The nutrition of humanity did not depend on chance, but was always guided in earlier times by a higher consciousness, either by the initiates of the mysteries, or still earlier, by spiritual guiding powers which the various peoples and races followed instinctively. Nutrition was always in the service of a definite evolution, the development of certain capacities, or the maintenance of other soul-spiritual forces—always in the service of human evolution as such.

Later, when different segments of humanity were more mature and their own wills began to be active, the various nutritional rules were regulated by laws and proscriptions which came from the spiritual centers of guidance. Doubtless, the various rules and taboos originally instituted grew out of spiritual developments that enhanced or prevented, encouraged or discouraged, certain predispositions. The roots of such eating habits and eating customs, which are still frequently transmitted, are in no way governed by arbitrariness or purely external events. To label them "magic and symbolism" only gives evidence of a lack of understanding.

After the cultures had passed their high points, the usual customs exercised less power, laws and proscriptions became dogma, and the reins of the formerly guided habits of eating slackened, making room for arbitrariness and decadence. This is evident in late Egyptian culture as well as in late Greece and Rome. A further element was contributory here: man was slowly released from the original spiritual guidance, so that he would gradually learn to nourish himself according to his individual needs, so that he would be free in this realm.

That, however, encouraged chaos in nutritional customs and opened the door to all sorts of nonsense in nutrition. Certainly, for a long time, man was still protected by his instincts from the impossible. It is only in the immediate present that we see a progressive loss of instinct; freedom has increased, but with it has arisen the necessity for a new consciousness which can take the place of tradition. This development then led to the origin of the science of nutrition in the 19th century, although this was at first—as we have shown—one-sidely mechanistic-materialistic, necessitating a new spiritualization of the forms of nutrition appropriate to the consciousness of modern man.

Spiritual Scientific Aspects
The Seven States of Nutrition

We designated milk-nutrition as a first early phase in nutritional development when we established that archetypal "milk" had a plant nature. Rudolf Steiner calls it "the old food of the gods, the first form of nutrition." When "man still approached the gods in the physical, he sucked in milk from the environment." The later milk nutrition of mammals is thus "a very old, metamorphosed form of nutrition."

In this lecture, however, Rudolf Steiner points out that prior to the time in which milk was the general nutrition, there was still another form of nutrition. He calls it a "sun-nourishment." To understand what Steiner means by this term, we must refer to his descriptions of earth evolution. Rudolf Steiner characterizes three great developmental stages: first, the old Saturn stage, in which the basis of man's physical body was established; second, the old Sun stage, from whose forces the etheric body was formed; and finally, the old Moon stage, in which man became a soul being. All three developmental stages repeat themselves in the actual Earth stage on a higher level.

We can first speak of an actual nutrition only in the Earth stage of our planet. The preceding stages are still of a purely spiritual character. At the most, in the "old Sun" and "old Moon" stages, spiritual processes preparing for the later nutrition were perceived. In Occult Science, we read of the early "Earth" stage: "Water is also taken in and pushed out: An archetypal process of nutrition begins." A little later: "The taking in of watery parts is experienced by the soul as an addition of forces, as an inner strengthening."[36]

The formation of the plant realm falls into the time of the earth's "Sun development." The upper part of the plant, related primarily to the light and warmth forces, is a pure sun-creation, while the root formation occurred later, as a consequence of the earth's densification. In this sense we can well understand the designation "sun nourishment," in that all fruits and blossoms belong to the sun.

Milk-nutrition is, however, in this sense, "moon nourishment," for the moon forces are the forces of revitalization, of reproduction. Accordingly, "sun nourishment" is a completely archetypal nutrition of man. It is of a "plant nature," but it is not like the plant nourishment we know today. Instead it is much more an etheric nourishment, a transition to a first densification into the fluid element. Hence it is a process going on in man's nourishment today, only in reverse, because in digestion today nourishment is liquified and then taken up into the etheric state.

Even the processes of the first evolutionary stage of the earth, the "old Saturn," are described in Occult Science. These can be designated as "a kind of metabolism" through which "nourishing and excretory processes occur on Saturn." These are, however, purely supersensible processes, which in essence are a "cosmic nutrition."

Thus, in the beginning, there are purely cosmic nutritional processes in man. Only with progressive densification does a coarser nourishment arise. But earthly nutrition does not replace the cosmic nutrition; instead, it is added to it. Just as a part of man's being will always be cosmic, the cosmic nutrition may be modified, but in essence it will persist.

Hence cosmic nutrition is also the archetypal nutrition of man. It is

205

followed by "sun nourishment." Nutrition is modified thereby into a cosmic-etheric nutrition. As the sun evolution progresses from the mineral stage to the plant stage, so nourishment becomes cosmic-etheric. Man nourishes himself on spiritual forces, which later densify into plants, while the "archetypal nutrition" corresponds to the stage of mineral creation.

For that reason, the instrument of cosmic nutrition is the mineral-like sense organization and the skin, which continually die off externally and are in this way also of a "mineral" nature.

The third stage of nutrition corresponds to the "Moon stage." In this "pre-Lemurian time" the general milk-nutrition begins, which man takes from his environment. This kind of nutrition is cosmic-terrestrial. It presages the animal nutrition, which begins in the actual Lemurian time when the mother provides the milk.

We demonstrated earlier that milk may be found in an animal organism, but that it still maintains its plant character. The actual animal element first enters nutrition when man actually consumes meat. Before that happens, however, the fourth stage of nutrition takes place in which man learns to utilize plants, which, in the meantime, have become densified into earth substance. First he is a gatherer, but later he becomes a cultivator of plants which are still oriented towards the cosmos, e.g., palms, bananas, etc. Man eats the fruits ripened in the sun. Only with the progress towards the actual earth stage of evolution, the passage from Lemurian to the Atlantean age, do we find the first instances of agriculture, the transition from hoe to plow, from cosmically oriented to earth nutrition.

To explain what occurred during this epoch, Rudolf Steiner pointed to the deeper contents of the Biblical story of Cain and Abel. Two races confronted each other at the end of the Lemurian age: "the actual sons of the moon, who just raised animals and nourished themselves with the milk of the animals, and a race which originated later and only used plant nutrition. . ." It was the moon race of Abel and the sun race of Cain. As recorded in the legend, Cain nourished himself with grains, with the ears of grain rooted in the earth, but ripened by the sun. Abel, however, still clung to milk, the moon nourishment. His sacrifice was favored by the moon god Jehovah, while Cain's sacrifice was rejected. Cain was before his time, but by becoming the murderer of his brother, he indicated the direction man must now take: he must pass through death. That would only be possible if he took death into his body, on the one hand, with root foods, which escape the cosmic ripening force of the sun by entering the dark of the earth, and on the other hand, with the killed animal. So we have the development of the fifth stage of nutrition in which grain and root nourishment arise and the hunters and animal breeders make their appearance. This is the age of old Atlantis. Rudolf Steiner writes that something hitherto unknown arises in the

206

Atlanteans: "They begin to nourish themselves with foods not taken from life; they nourish themselves with dead foods." But with this stage of nutrition, characterized primarily by meat consumption, we also have an important transition for man: "The transition to egoism was gained." This represents a major step in the development of humanity: the permeation of man's body with the forces of the personality. It is important to realize that this development was achieved specifically with the help of the blood-impregnated animal body. The blood, as a direct expression of animal passion, of soul drives, but also of soul forces, serves, by way of nutrition, in the embodiment of the Ego-permeated soul forces of man. This is the historical role of the animal form of nutrition, which fulfilled its mission in the Atlantean age, because then the human organization was far enough developed to receive the Ego into itself.

About this significant occurrence, Rudolf Steiner wrote the words cited earlier: "Everything which has brought man to his personal interests" is connected with animal nutrition. The people, "who war against each other, and relate through anger, antipathy, and sensual passion," are influenced by "the nutritional connections of man to the animal world." But these are also the people "who develop bravery, courage, and boldness." In this sense it was even necessary for man to use animal nourishment for a certain period of time.

We can now more easily understand one of our earlier concerns: that is, why man's teeth, his intestine, etc., enable him to use both plant and animal nutrition. Both played a purposeful part in man's course of development.

It is appropriate now to turn to a further point made by Rudolf Steiner. He speaks of the fact that man in the past was able to achieve an impregnation with the Ego forces, with the help of plant nutrition, by learning to overcome with his digestion what is under the earth. So "we encounter cultures which used not only food ripened in the sun, but also food ripened under the earth. That food is just as dead as the dead animals." Root nutrition is thus placed here on the same level as animal nutrition, in that both bring forth an element which represents a turning away from extraterrestrial forces. "Everything of the plant which grows under the earth is turned away from the sun, and therefore it corresponds to the blood-permeated body of the animal." This is not saying that the two are the same, but that they have a common property: that they are taken from the world of the devitalized, of the terrestrial. In this sense it is very important to realize that the achievement of earth-consciousness was also possible through a nutrition that was exclusively a plant nutrition. In fact this path was apparently taken by the segment of humanity that was destined to remain open to the spiritual and to nurture it.

It is quite evident what the role of grains was in old Greece. The Roman legionnaire, conquering the world, also did well with his daily portion of barley. This makes clear that plant nourishment can also transmit strength in the physical sense. Certainly the erroneous impression that physical strength is attained only through meat nutrition is spread far and wide, but as we have seen, that kind of nourishment creates egotistic, earth-bound personalities. Even in 1800, W. C. Hufeland writes: "Would the gentlemen, who believe to find strength and health only in meat consumption, only look to the inhabitants of the Swiss Alps who consume primarily bread, milk, and cheese, and what healthy, strong human beings they are!"[37] What has become of them in the meantime is another story.

After Atlantean man was led down to earth through his nutrition, he had to learn to solidify himself still further and to try to take hold of the earth task through his personality. In doing so, he gained a connection to the purely mineral substance, whose representative is cooking salt (sodium chloride). Only now man learned to overcome the mineral even in himself, to re-dissolve it. That was achieved only by the forces of his Ego. Rudolf Steiner describes how later a nourishment was added, which did not even exist before. Man added the purely mineral, as salt, to his nutrition. In the meantime, all of humanity developed the need for salt. We have already seen how civilized man today consumes salt excessively and thereby anchors himself too strongly with his soul-spiritual forces to the body. Disease is the consequence—hypertension, renal disease, heart disease, sclerosis, etc.

Thus we can say that mineral nutrition is the sixth stage of nutrition which humanity has reached in its descent to earth. Alcohol provided another path, but that has since had a far more devastating effect. It first entered human development in the post-Atlantean time. The Bible reports of Noah that he would drink in his vineyards.

Wine and Bread

In preparing alcohol man carries natural processes beyond themselves. Alcohol is produced by a "mineral-chemical process," as Rudolf Steiner called it. In this sense the old wine-makers were the first nutritional chemists.

At first the consumption of wine was "worldly." It served to allow man to experience his own personality while intoxicated. Only in Greek culture was it incorporated into the mysteries. The cult of Dionysos began. "The human body must be prepared for a purely earthly culture. . ." The cult of Dionysos arose so that man could come completely down to the physical plane. That is how Rudolf Steiner describes this development.

While we will concern ourselves with alcohol in greater detail in another work, here we will emphasize its role in the evolution of humanity. In its course of development, humanity was to be removed completely from its old instinctive relationship to the spiritual world, was to turn completely to earth existence. Wine was ideally suited for that purpose. "It cuts man off from the spiritual. He who drinks wine, will not reach the spiritual." Wine, i.e., fermented grape juice, most likely had a specific function and was therefore considered to be of a higher rank, more refined, than all other old alcoholic beverages which were prepared even earlier—the milk-beer, the beverages prepared from grains, palms, bananas, etc. Although all these drinks contain alcohol, a certain differentiation is necessary. At the very least, wine takes the lead among all "mineral-chemical" beverages. It achieves its goal with the greatest intensity and certainty.

Through the preparation of alcohol man has descended most completely to the physical plane. And when he consumes alcohol today, he betakes himself to a subhuman stage, to the animal-like and sub-sensuous level. Alcohol has long fulfilled this function. Its devastating results today speak clearly of that effect. But only isolated "voices in the desert" have recognized the enormous dangers threatening humanity through alcohol. Bunge was one of the first who scientifically established the effects of alcohol, and as a result of his insight and knowledge he became a total abstainer. He said: "I assert that whoever totally abstains from alcoholic beverages is not making any sacrifice; he only gains joy and happiness."[38] In another place he states "that nothing is in the way of a gradual and total abolition of all alcoholic beverages except brutal egotism." It was also Bunge who was among the first to point out that alcohol and meat consumption go together. Vegetarian nutrition, on the other hand, favors moderation in alcohol consumption.

It is known that alcohol also arises (only to evaporate shortly thereafter) in bread-baking. This phenomenon points to an inner relationship: that bread-baking represents a processing of nature similar to wine fermentation. "Bread and wine, in the occult sense, come about when the plant has been killed. Wines come about by killing the plant so that one processes it like a mineral. When baking plant substances, one is doing the same as when killing an animal." Wine preparation and bread-making are thus related to the mineral element in nutrition.

In this way we recognize that the art of bread-making represents a significant step in the development of humanity. In H. E. Jacob's book, *Sechstausend Jahre Brot* (*Six Thousand Years of Bread*), among many other impressive facts, we find that Bethlehem, the birthplace of the son of Mary and Joseph, in English means "house of bread."[39] This motif points to the mighty words of Christ spoken when he passed the bread and wine at the Last Supper: "This is my body, this is my blood."

Significant in this respect is "the marriage at Cana," described in the Gospel of John. In this first "sign" of Christ there is actually an indication of the mission of alcohol and its transformation by Christian consciousness. At this wedding Christ first turned to those who had already separated themselves from the old clairvoyant consciousness, i.e., to those who were already under the influence of alcohol. According to Rudolf Steiner in his lecture cycle about the Gospel of St. John, Christ had to indicate the future of humanity through a kind of Dionysian or wine sacrifice.[40] But Christ also added the words: "My time has not yet come." Water had to be changed into wine, but soon wine would be changed back into water.

In these same lectures we read: "When humanity strives again to find the way back, when the Ego has been developed so far that it can again turn towards the spiritual, the time will have come in which a certain reaction against alcohol arises." The reason is that "many today already feel that something which was once important is not so for eternity."

The consequences of the change in the world-historical significance of alcohol have not been comprehended yet. For most of humanity, the introduction of the communion through Christ still remains, at best, a matter of religious conviction. Modern Spiritual Science, however, has this to say: "If Jesus Christ was the true 'Son of Man,' who descended most deeply," then man had to be shown "how the physical content of human development was connected with his mission." Humanity needed a symbol which "led again from the dead to the living: bread and wine."[41]

We have already attempted to show how bread and wine are "symbols." Both continue the process which changes plant substances to mineral-like substances through the yeast-fermenting in baking and the related process in wine-making. In both, the change of plant substances into sugars is decisive. Starch in the grains is already on the path to sugar, to mineralization. In wine, the already present grape sugar is fermented, and the killed plant is subjected to a chemical-mineral process.

What is the significance of the "Last Supper" given by Christ? Bread and wine stand for the overcoming of the past and also for the development of a future form of nutrition: the overcoming of the animal sacrifice and a view towards a still higher stage of nutrition. In fact, one can even speak of a future "mineral" form of nutrition which already announces itself. "Bread and wine must be given up." That the time of wine is passed has already been shown. But bread, which lets the developing alcohol disappear again, is the great symbol for the overcoming of animal nutrition and the turning towards plant nutrition. Rudolf Steiner said: "Therewith Christ wanted to create a transition from animal to plant nutrition." Thus the significance of the Last Supper is the pronouncement that man can achieve a new consciousness of himself and the world through a form of nutrition which allows him to overcome egotism in the sense we have described.

Future Aspects of Nutrition
Working with Nature as Completed and as Becoming

Today we are in the midst of preparation for a plant nutrition. And for that reason, more and more people appear, who, for various reasons, refuse alcohol and meat and turn to plants for food. This is rarely accompanied by full consciousness, however, so there can be many errors which have damaging effects unless the transition to vegetarian nutrition represents an advance in consciousness at the same time.

The first beginnings of the mineral form of nutrition, still to come in the future, are also found today. Not only with the addition of salt to our food, but also through bread and wine, man unconsciously initiated ways of processing naturally-ripened foods still further. But these are only the very beginnings of a direction of processing food, which Rudolf Steiner designated as "a working with nature as becoming," not only in the sense of a new preparation of remedies, but also as a future perspective of our nutrition.

What does this "chemically working with nature as becoming" mean? We will begin to clarify this issue by first presenting what it does not mean.

Our present day chemical-analytical method, as well as our way of thinking, directs itself to the dismemberment of substance and is certainly not "a working with nature as becoming," but rather with "nature as completed." There we take the finished substance, e.g., milk, and analyze it. In this way we can gain valuable, but by no means exhaustive insights into the substance. We find out what constituents make up the substance and can then develop various products which already play an important role today, e.g., artificial milk and the "astronaut diet." But beyond the mere quantitative aspects we don't find out anything about the qualitative value of the various constituents. An analogy will demonstrate the limitations of current methods. A musician will not compose an expressive melody by a mere addition of notes to certain values. Melody, phrase, and emphasis come about when various values are applied to single tones; they can be short or long, soft or loud; they can be upbeat or downbeat, etc. The shortest tone may in fact be the most important. Nature works similarly in bringing forth its manifestations. It goes through this becoming at every moment anew. We can get a view of "nature as becoming" in our outline of the step-like formation of milk.

Only our modern method of science prevents us from actually comprehending this becoming, because it is static, bound to space, to the physical-chemical laws which only permit the study of terrestrial relationships. As we have seen, this method is inadequate if we want to approach life, much less if we want to reach soul and spiritual realms of activity.

Statements from *Fundamentals of Therapy* can be of help to us:

The effects of substances in the human organism have as little to do with their chemical effects, as the chemical constitution of paints with their use by a painter. . . The essence of the organism lies in activity, not in its substances. The organization is not a connection of substances, but an activity.

Only by separating a substance from its activity, by isolating it chemically, do we get a dead substance.

We must learn to recognize what the state of a substance or process in an organism is, whether it is in the process of becoming or of dying, of metabolism or catabolism. Goethe built his natural science, his study of metamorphosis on this principle:

Observe it in becoming, how little by little, from level to level, the plant forms itself into blossom and fruit. (*Metamorphosis of Plants*)

From such a comprehension of the dynamic, man will be able in the future to continue the steps of nature, and through his own inventiveness he will bring forth new kinds of nourishments. In principle these will be close to bread and wine making, the "mineral-chemical processing" of nature.

Rudolf Steiner also described a method of such a dynamization of substance in two areas. The first concerns the preparation of remedies. The relevant process here is "potentiation." A capacity, which every living organism has, is used to prepare remedies. The potentizing process, as a "working with nature as becoming" has since been described in detail by various students of Rudolf Steiner (W. Cloos, W. Pelikan, A. Leroi, G. Unger).

The second, much more original and varied area is presented by Rudolf Steiner in his *Agricultural Course* (1924). The indications given in that course for the preparation of fertilizers and for feeding animals are built completely upon a dynamic approach and can awaken an understanding of such an approach. For example, a prerequisite for the production of a "good and abundant milk supply" is said to depend on a specific development of the rhythmic activity, which lies between the nerve-system region and the metabolic region. To achieve this, it is necessary to avoid excessive feeding of plants which are related to the nerve-sense activity, such as roots and plants related to the metabolic activity. Instead "one must look to what lies between root and blossom, to everything which unfolds itself in leaves." Rudolf Steiner points to the legumes which have taken the fruit process into the leaves. If a calf is fed with such feed, "the the calf becomes a good milk cow."

Here the concern is with processes, with dynamic plant activities which continue on in the animal, not with substances. Finding food in that way is an example of working with nature as becoming.

212

Such examples could at least indicate how this important principle can serve as a starting point for developing our present nutrition in the future. In fact, Rudolf Steiner mentioned in 1906 that it would be possible "to establish a nutrition laboratory and thereby gain influence over the nutrition of populations."[42] But before this new "mineral principle" of nutrition will unfold, the leading segments of humanity will have to have gone over to plant nutrition. That is in fact the significance of the initiation of the Last Supper by Christ. That is the point in time from which the last earthly forms of nutrition can develop; "then it will be possible that the purely mineral substance can enter nutrition. Man can then create his own nourishment."

This nourishment will certainly have no relation to what comes out of laboratories today. It would be a serious mistake to confuse that future nutrition with what has been achieved in the field of artificial food synthesis today. Rudolf Steiner addressed himself specifically to this issue by pointing out that man "will analyze the foods and make chemical foods," but "he will not recognize that chemical foods are not nourishments in the same sense as natural foods, although they consist of the same substances."[43]

It should be evident by now that such artificial substances, which imitate completed nature and carry no forces of becoming, cannot have the same effects as natural substances. These cannot actually be imitated by the process of analysis and resynthesis. As Goethe says: you only have the parts, the spiritual bond is missing. Thus everything "new" in the field of nutrition today must be overcome in the future, including the "astronaut diet," which consists of a mixture of amino acids, carbohydrates, fatty acids, vitamins, minerals, aromatic substances, etc.—a classic example of the work done with completed nature. Comprehensive studies have already been performed with such "balanced synthesized diets" in mental retardates. Here we record three characteristic results:

1. Enzymatic digestion changes completely. This fully balanced diet powder—it has been said that the world nutrition problem can be solved with it—does not use the processes of the mouth, of salivary formation, of gastric acid, of intestinal activity, of bile activity, of pancreatic secretions. Therein lies the fundamental error, because the unused force will go into wrong directions. The organs will atrophy. Those forces oriented towards the total human organism will be lacking on the one hand, and on the other they will cause diseases.

2. The intestinal flora is starved out.

3. Stool frequency decreased to once in 14 days. This, it was said, was a very practical result for the caretakers of such children.

213

We give this example because it points so clearly to how our thinking, our consciousness, must be transformed in order to prepare the way for a working with "nature as becoming."

The future "mineral" nutrition, to which Rudolf Steiner refers, must approximate more and more the original nutrition, cosmic nutrition. We have described earlier how this "cosmic nutrition" still plays an important role today, how it proceeds in those fine substances such as iron, lead, silica, etc., to enter man from the atmosphere through the skin, the senses, the respiration.

Future nutrition will increasingly approximate this archetypal cosmic nutrition on a new level. The extent to which man will achieve new levels of existence through spiritual development will determine his need for earth nutrition. Pure plant nutrition will bring him a "relief." But this new kind of "cosmic nutrition," which will also be an earth nutrition, must be achieved by man's own forces of consciousness.

In one of his descriptions of this "cosmic nutrition," Rudolf Steiner said:

> If man did not have to live on the earth between birth and death and therefore also do work, he would not have to eat at all, he would be able to take everything out of the cosmos. But if we work with our hands, or if we walk, then we need support through food.[44]

Thus we need earthly nutrition in order to live and work on this earth in our present form. Therefore we embody our Ego and learn to transform ourselves and the world through our individuality. This goal will be achieved more and more if man can go over to a mineral form of nutrition. At the conclusion of his *Occult Science*, Rudolf Steiner develops an image of the future development of world and man, of "the spiritualization which man achieves through his own labor."

When that development has been reached, "there will be no more physical bodies. All of man will be etheric again." At this stage the last form of nutrition will be reached: the etheric cosmic nutrition. Then man and earth will have fulfilled their tasks and will enter new realms of existence.

214

Chapter 14

THE DEVELOPMENT OF NUTRITION
IN THE AGE OF TECHNOLOGY

CONTEMPORARY NUTRITIONAL HYGIENE

The Mechanization of the World Image
in the Mirror of Nutrition

To evaluate the significance of technology in nutrition it is first necessary to become aware of the change in consciousness which man has undergone since the end of the Middle Ages. We have already emphasized that a comprehension of historical developments necessitates, above all, a consideration of the metamorphoses of soul states of man in the various epochs. Here we direct our attention to that significant change in consciousness which occurred in the 14th-15th centuries, the time during which the mechanization of the image of the world originated.

> Among the many changes which scientific thinking underwent in the course of centuries, there is hardly one whose effect was so deep and wide as the origin and development of that way of thinking which is designated as the mechanistic world view.[1]

Some consider it a progressive enlightening of human thinking, but others consider it to have had no less than catastrophic effects on philosophic and scientific thinking and on the structure of society. They are disposed to see, in the ruling of thinking by the mechanistic way of viewing the world, one of the main causes of the spiritual starvation prevalent in the 20th century, despite all technological advance.

215

Closer to our concerns is Mohler's statement: "Mechanization, motorization and automatization . . . influence our way of nutrition more and more."[2] Glatzel is even more concrete:

> For millenia nothing changed in the diets determined by the local agriculture. . . The great change occurred at the beginning of the 19th century. With progressive industrialization, urbanization, and enhancement of the standard of life, decisive changes occur in the Western countries.[3]

Teuteberg and Wiegelmann point to the important fact "that the early industrialization (and the accompanying Age of Enlightenment) had many more effects on nutrition than one tends to assume."[4]

This change of consciousness actually begins much earlier, as Dijksterhuis points out when he writes about Nicolaus of Cusa (De Docta Ignorantia). Through his thought system "a total change of natural scientific thinking could have taken place in the 15th century, if that power of thought, which called these thoughts to life, could have excited the specialists to a renewal." There "the whole Aristotelian-Ptolemaic world system would have been abolished with one blow." In fact, Cusa's contemporaries were unable to do this, but it was actually done by his followers. Cusa provided the foundation: "The Docta Ignorantia of 1440 is an open admission that normal human cognition at that time no longer reached to those distances to which the spiritual had removed itself from man."[5] Shortly thereafter followed Copernicus, Giordano Bruno, Galileo, Kepler, etc. It was the time of the birth of occidental natural science, in which a new developmental stage of man began, in the midst of which we now find ourselves, the time of the unfolding of the "consciousness soul" as human soul force.

Nutrition and Dietetics at the Threshold of the New Age

It was the time of the decline of the medieval medicine of the monasteries, of the famed medical school of Salerno. In their philosophies nutrition and dietetics still had a significant spiritual aspect. The essential factor now began to be the economic life. Homo oeconomicus came to the forefront and burst the traditional chains of old views about nutrition and nutritional customs.

This was accompanied by a well-known change in the consumption and evaluation of meat. The old rule of the Benedictines prohibited meat consumption for all except the weak and the sick. Occasional aberrations by the Cistercians were corrected by the Trappists. The bread of barley and millet was the main food. Later, however, among the knights of the German order, meat consumption and a much greater life of comfort was accepted. Lichtenfels writes in his *History of Nutrition*: "The attempt to keep humanity away from meat consumption forever appeared to become increasingly more difficult, despite coercion, and despite the initial voluntary acceptance of such coercion."[6] And so the drive for meat nutrition established itself more and more in the monasteries. The old dietary rules and ideas increasingly lost their influence.

The appearance of numerous and voluminous cookbooks in the 15th and 16th centuries indicated the beginning of a new consciousness of nutrition. In these books the old ideas about nutrition, stemming from Hippocrates and Galen, found almost no continuation. An exception was Anna Wecker and Sophie Schellhammer's cookbook in which attempts were made once again to make use of old sources and to revitalize the earlier unity of the art of healing and the art of cooking. We can still read in this work of "forces," of a "forceful" meal that indicates a meal full of such "forces." Most likely this referred to the "Archaeus" of Paracelsus, the body of formative forces that, according to Rudolf Steiner, are identical with the "etheric body."

The teaching of the humors, itself a remnant of old clairvoyant perceptions of the etheric, formed the basis of early medicine and nutrition. Originally both were a unity. The four qualities, warm-cold-dry-moist, which we find in Aristotle, formed the basis of a teaching of the elements gained by supersensible perception, which also played an important role in dietetics. In this sense human health was experienced as the properly balanced mixture, as a harmony of the four elements, which was to be reestablished daily by nourishment. Every food had the quality of warm or cold, etc., and had accordingly a specific value, even in the order of the meal. The time of the year, as well as the method of preparation, played an important role, because it was important to find for every food the correct "affinity." Many traditional compositions of meals stem from these long-forgotten ideas.

Rudolf Steiner repeatedly talked about these old teachings and made clear that at their basis lay the direct experience of the etheric body in addition to a conception of the higher members of the human organization. He explained that "these are deep insights which were well understood in the old times, but were then no longer understood. And in the 13th and 14th centuries that understanding disappears completely and a totally new spirit arises."[7]

Remnants of the old teachings were still evident in some of the 19th century literature. In C. W. Hufeland's book, *The Art of Prolonging Human Life* (1800), we read: "Sugar is one of the most cooling substances. After overheating the body, nothing is better than drinking two ounces of sugar

217

dissolved in a glass of water." Huteland also says: "Soup is good protection against dryness and rigidity of the body and is therefore the best food for dry natures and in old age."

These stragglers, however, play a rather insignificant role. Consequently, Teuteberg and Wiedemann's statements appear to be a valid description of the situation:

> Man slid away farther and farther from the traditional dietary rules and therefore also from the philosophically-religiously motivated norms of food consumption. Instead he became an individual who freely chooses his food according to his taste, somewhat subject to income, regional environment, social prestige, and commerical occupation.

Nutrition as a Social Question
The Influence of Technology on Nutrition

Nutrition then became a social question. The feasts at the courts of the nobility reached the pinnacles of gastronomic heights on the one hand, and on the other, the "popular kitchen" originated, and in fact it persists still today. Fundamental to both is man's new consciousness, a consciousness free of the old spiritual ideas which tended to lead more and more to dogmatic confusion. New man began to experience himself as a physical body, and he came to know foods as objects which can be comprehended by measurement, number, and weight. When Santoris, at the University of Padua, in the beginning of the 17th century, learned to measure metabolism with a scale, the rule of physics and chemistry was established in nutrition. It only took men such as Lavoisier, Liebig, Moeschott, and Büchner, to put the new way of thinking into practice.

Liebig, the discoverer of meat extract, was the first food technologist. He industrialized his discovery and even in his lifetime the production of his preparation achieved sizeable proportions.

With the entry of technology and industrialization into nutrition, the foundation was established for a food technology and industry which began with the discovery of canning. The advantages of such a development are incontestable; we have foods on our table today which a few decades ago were practically unobtainable. This situation has, without a doubt, contributed to the progressive abolition of traditional dietary habits and to replacing the old local foods with a "world nutrition." But when Glatzel writes: "Never before in history did mankind have the possibility to provide an adequate nutrition for all," we have to question this claim seriously.

218

Technology may provide for the nutrition of the world population, but the big question is whether the evaluation of nutrition according to the criteria of technical thinking is valid.

We continually read expressions of concern in modern publications regarding the question of food quality in the technological age. A. Aebi presents a clear analysis of the present nutrition situation.[8] He points to three tendencies. The first is that man is relieved of increasingly greater amounts of physical work by the machine and the automobile. Hence correspondingly, man needs less food. However, man is consuming more, not less; the great enemy of health today is excess food consumption. Civilized humanity, intending to arrange its life very "rationally," is not very gifted in developing a necessary inner discipline with regard to eating. The magnificently developed intellect is unable to affect practical life. Our present nutritional situation is a true image of the soul-spiritual chaos within man. The excessive consumption of food in our time is only another aspect of the generalized uninhibitedness, of the loss of all ties, of the inability to establish a new basis of cognition. The rise in sexual excesses is another aspect of this decay.

The second tendency is that the average consumer increasingly turns his favors towards a more concentrated protein nutrition, although it is much more expensive.

The third tendency is the increasing proportion of the production of refined foods, such as flour, fat, and sugar, in order to make them more durable. This enhancement of durability, however, is bought at the expense of substances such as vitamins and minerals. According to Aebi, this last tendency is the most predominant. He, however, provides more questions than answers: "Will these trends increase?. . . We must resign ourselves to live with these foreign substances . . . , which are increasingly added to our foods for various reasons." We can only share Aebi's opinion that the future requires the creation of appropriate guiding ideas which demand a high degree of responsibility.

We will not resign ourselves, however. We have come to the realization that a fundamental transformation and expansion of our image of man and world is an absolute necessity. If we do not want to fall back upon old recipes and decadent traditional teachings, we will find only in modern Spiritual Science, as founded by Rudolf Steiner, the answer to how to meet the demands of a new responsibility and a true guiding idea.

Such a demand is also expressed by R. Heiss and K. Eichner who claim that "the quality of our foods already begins to suffer in agricultural production, but is endangered even more, the more the abiotic, as opposed to the microbiologic decay, dominates in food processing."[9] The three "abiotic" technological procedures are freezing, concentrating and drying, pasteurizing and sterilizing—the great advances of technical civilization in the field

219

of nutrition. In the face of the development of "abiotic" methods, we must ask whether this doesn't represent something like an embodiment of man's cold pole, of his intellectuality, which today looms like a frosty shadow over the human warmth-organization.

Within limits, cold processing still has a natural significance, but the methods used today frequently exceed these limits. In freeze-drying, for example, extreme temperatures and the help of a vacuum are utilized, or numerous, mostly synthetic, substances foreign to the body are added, which alter durability or other properties of the foods. Gases such as CO_2 or nitrogen are used frequently. These definitely have an "abiotic" character, i.e., in their presence life forces are suppressed so far that the desired effects of cessation of growth and ripening, blockage of enzyme activity, etc., are achieved. The same applies to the use of gamma rays in food preservation, a process that is now on the rise.

When these methods are considered by "official" representatives of modern science to embody "a creeping threat to nutritional quality," then such a loss of quality is already admitted. We can see here the direction in which modern food technology is leading. The resulting losses in quality, e.g., aroma, are as much as possible balanced out by the addition of synthetic aromatic substances—lost minerals and vitamins are also replaced with synthetic additives. Thus in Heiss and Eichner's essay we read the curious but understandable statement: "How readily would we accept a few rotten peaches or apricots if only the rest were fully ripe, instead of having to accept the half-raw fruits which taste like raw potatoes." Here human beings speak who are looking for food quality, instead of technicians who are manipulating foods. They go on to say: "A market for such quality products will always be available, even though the products might cost a little more."[10]

Objectification of the Concept of Quality

Such words not only express a true longing for quality, but they also point to an issue which is gaining in popularity: the social component of nutrition. "The food consumer is not only an object with metabolic processes, but also a subject with interpersonal relationships."[11] We must also add that this "subjective" side is also objective! Comprehending this is made difficult by the application of results of animal behavioral studies to human behavior. We can only agree with Teuteberg when he says: "The application of the results of animal behavioral studies to human behavior is severely limited, because man, as is well known, is not merely guided by drives and instincts, but also by reason and ideas." We would like to add: because man is not only an instinctual being bound to his corporeality, but also a being who orien-

220

tates himself according to his spiritual individuality, who can learn to motivate his own activity. And he can only call himself a "human being," insofar as he is able to turn to this spiritual core of his being.

Once again it becomes evident from these indications how only through a new, adequate image of the world and of man are we able to arrive at an "objectification of the concept of quality." In this sense our book is an attempt to accomplish this task. Such a "concept of quality" cannot consist of abstract definitions anymore than we can "define" man or nature. It can only be achieved through a method appropriate to the object of study, in this case a dynamic, living, moving organism. That method will achieve the same exactness as the analytical method for the lifeless world. What matters most is to strengthen thinking in such a way that we overcome the abstract, photographic thinking of modern intellectualism and rise to the living, organic thinking, which Goethe initiated with his study of metamorphosis, and which finds its further development in the modern Spiritual Science established by Rudolf Steiner at the beginning of this century. Through Spiritual Science we will not only get to a "thinking about the ideals" in the abstract sense, but also to "an experience of the spiritual, which gives us the strength to follow the ideals."[12]

Through modern natural science man has developed technology; in fact he was inspired to develop modern technology. It is justified insofar as it is applied to the lifeless. If, however, it also penetrates into the realm of life, as is the case in modern food technology, then it must learn to expand its criteria to include the spiritual and moral side. For that, man must first develop the appropriate standards. Concrete beginnings in the form of suggestions and indications based on modern Spiritual Science are already there. They have found successful application in the preparation of remedies, as well as in nutrition and dietetics. We have pointed out how "bio-dynamic agriculture," as developed by Rudolf Steiner, enters into completely new areas and provides concrete approaches for the enhancement of food quality. This is evident in the great variety of high quality bio-dynamic foods on the market today; they all make a concrete contribution to the struggle for a social concretization of a new hygiene of nutrition.

A contemporary nutritional hygiene will only be established and unfold itself if the ideas indicated here are developed further by human hand and spirit. We can no longer overlook Rudolf Steiner's warning that it can almost be calculated "in how many decades the food products will be so degenerated that they cannot serve for human consumption, even in this century."[13] Since then fifty years have passed and the question of where we stand today is answered from many directions. Whether Rudolf Steiner's answer is heard by our culture before it is too late is one of the questions of the destiny of humanity.

Symptoms of the Contemporary
Nutritional Situation

The consequences of technology on nutrition, or stated more comprehensively, the consequences of technical-intellectual thinking on nutrition can be clearly recognized today: (1) in human health and disease, (2) in social life, (3) in the soul-spiritual life. The "avalanche of diseases of civilization" increases by the day. Even the most conservative scientists cannot escape that fact, and the descriptions are innumerable. Oncologists, cardiologists, rheumatologists, etc., all agree about the significant contribution of nutrition to this avalanche.

Most scientists are in agreement not only about the existence of this increasing loss of health, but also about its causes, the decreasing quality of nutrition, the excessive consumption of food generally and animal protein specifically. This overconsumption, which has become a general phenomenon of modern civilization, combined with the decreasing quality of food, represents symptoms of the inadequate development of human consciousness.

These symptoms also affect infant nutrition today and thus endanger subsequent generations. G. C. Arneil of the Scottish Ministry of Health reports: "More than half of the three month olds were already fed with egg, meat, and fish, only 6% with mother's milk, and most were overfed after only a few weeks."[14] A clever propaganda makes certain that such wrong nutritional patterns will also take hold of the native populations of developing countries.

To counter such patterns, H. G. Schwabe, from the Max-Planck Institute in Germany, asks "everyone, to transform the habits of nutrition," mostly towards plant consumption. In 1958 we hear from the same scientist:

> The view of the scientist, trained for generations to dissect, to analyze, has lost the ability to see great lines and true relationships. The scientist himself is standardized. He has to produce on request planned research in the service of the economic machine. . . Spiritual daring, which once motivated science, and continuous contact with the unknown are hardly tolerated today.[15]

How much nutrition has also become a social question can be shown by many more symptoms. The progressive deterioration of health through nutrition alone represents a massive social problem. From the increase in deformed births because of the increasing number of food additives, to the "diseases of civilization" such as arthritis, diabetes mellitus, cancer, etc., all of

222

which make increasing, unfulfillable demands on the social service institutions, we see the effects of inadequate nutrition.

Of special interest to us is the soul-spiritual aspect. There is much talk about the "temptation" toward excessive meat consumption, of the "animal-protein mentality," and even of a "meat addiction," all of which are soul qualities which affect the contemporary nutritional situation. We have discussed how animal nutrition and animal protein encourage the forces of selfishness and prejudice in man. These soul qualities proliferate more and more today because of the vicious circle encouraged by meat over-consumption, and they thereby also deeply burden the soul-spiritual and the social life. The person, on the other hand, having made himself dependent upon such lower soul qualities like sympathies and antipathies, is increasingly inclined toward meat consumption. He falls into an "addiction-like dependence" on animal nutrition.

In this way the possibilities for soul-spiritual development close themselves off, and the view of "the great connections of all things, which elevates man above the narrow boundaries of personal existence . . ." are darkened.[16] At the same time man overlooks "how much of the human organism's health and disease . . . depends on the nervous system," when he fails to recognize the effect of plant nutrition on this system. Not to be forgotten is what Rudolf Steiner said in his early nutrition lecture: A person "who dares to approach the difficult problem of mastering his sexual passions . . . should consume as little as possible of protein-rich foods."[17] In view of the flooding of our civilization with sexual excess, such an aspect could be of great significance.

While much could be achieved in the field of health by a change in nutrition, this is not so easy to accomplish in the social realm, much less in the soul-spiritual realm. There, a nutritional education, a conscious comprehension of nature from spiritual knowledge, must go hand in hand with self-education, with a meaningful use of the liberated forces for soul-spiritual development. The major statements of Spiritual Science on this issue show how health, social forces, and soul-spiritual striving are inseparably united and how all three are intimately related to nutrition. They are: "Vegetarian life without spiritual striving leads to illness," and "if the vegetarian way of life is not combined with spiritual cognition, it is harmful if a person remains vegetarian." "The vegetarian must at the same time pursue a spiritual way of knowledge."

Ehrenfried Pfeiffer, one of the students of Rudolf Steiner, who distinguished himself in the fields of natural science and agriculture, once asked his teacher:

How is it that, despite your numerous indications, the spiritual impulse, especially the inner path of development, is so little effective in the isolated person. . . How is it that, despite theoretical insight and the will to action, the successful undertaking of the spiritual impulses is so weak?[18]

Rudolf Steiner's answer was remarkable and surprising: "That is a problem of nutrition. Nutrition today does not give man the strength to manifest the spiritual in the physical. The bridge from thinking to willing and acting cannot be built anymore." In this statement we have, in shocking clarity, the expression of the relationship of nutrition to the modern path of spiritual training, the overcoming of the resignation of the intellect and the will in the face of higher knowledge.

The Responsibility of Each Individual

We have spoken of "the bridge," as it is created by warmth and penetrates down into the physiological activities between the two poles of man's organization, thinking and willing, the nerve-sense organization and the metabolism, and how, in these processes, man cancels out the constancy of matter and energy, overcomes the past, and plants the germ for a future. "As man is active, matter is constantly overcome . . . as man develops into pure thinking . . . new matter originates. . ."[19] But we must ask whether the preparation of the bodily organization for the embodiment of man's Ego, which will make him into a free individuality, who can act out of love, may not actually be endangered by our nutrition today. Are the foundations of the bridge crumbling, so that man's life forces, his health, his social forces and his spiritual forces lose their support? In his talk with Ehrenfried Pfeiffer, Rudolf Steiner remarked that "the food plants do not contain the forces any more which they should give to man." But after his *Agricultural Course* in 1924, he spoke of agricultural products in general, whose degeneration could only be avoided by new insights and new knowledge.

In 1966, H. Mohler wrote: "The world nutrition problem will be so acute by 1975 that everything which so moves and frightens us today will appear negligible then."[20] Though we may read Mohler's statement in a totally different way than he originally meant it, his prognosis still approximates the reality of our nutritional situation today. We are now on the threshold of the last quarter of the century, so it will depend more and more on each individual to awaken to this reality.

How can humanity escape this catastrophe? How can it stop this avalanche? Certainly only by starting with the individual himself and his circle, by awakening the spiritual impulses in order to recognize the significance of

224

nutrition, and then, maybe with the help of such a dynamic nutrition, by beginning to strengthen himself and put his knowledge into action.

Such a person will then discover that Feurbach's words, with which we began—"Man is what he eats"—do have a certain truth, though in a transformed way. And he will also experience the reality of Goethe's wise words: "What fruitful is, alone is true."

CONCLUSION

We have attempted in the preceding fourteen chapters to present the foundations of a nutritional hygiene emanating from Rudolf Steiner's Spiritual Science. It is evident how new, how varied, and how multi-layered this is, and how it still cannot be presented exhaustively today. Nevertheless, its fruitfulness in theory and practice has been amply demonstrated.

To us, the most essential suggestion of modern Spiritual Science is expressed in the following words of Rudolf Steiner: "All considerations begin with man; man is the foundation." That requires the true knowledge of man which we can acquire from the presentations of Spiritual Science. Anyone who can grasp them without prejudice will experience a transformation of his thinking, of his soul forces, and these will give him access to a new world of human experience.

We have also presented completely objective developments which demand a new impulse of nutritional hygiene. Rudolf Steiner directed attention to them in his *Agricultural Course* when he remarked that we are confronting "a great transformation of the inner aspects of nature." The old forces of nature and man are in their decline. "We must achieve a new knowledge . . ."; otherwise humanity has no choice but to allow the degeneration of nature and of human life to continue.

Are these words, spoken a half century ago, not of pressing importance today? Again and again we hear "that the future destiny of mankind, maybe even the survival of humanity itself, depends on how rapidly and how effectively these problems can be solved on a world-wide basis." "These problems" refer to population size, food production, and environmental pollution, which "are not isolated, but are dynamically interrelated." We cite here the report of the Club of Rome, "Limits of Growth" (1973), whose authors state: "The behavior of the System tends unequivocally to exceed the limits of growth and therewith to collapse."[1]

If we want to break out of this vicious circle, "we need to break out of our thought forms and liberate ourselves from the domination of a theory which transformed fragmentary data into a system with compulsive character."[2] These words of P. Vogler can also be applied to the modern science of nutrition. It has made enormous progress compared to fifty years ago, but it

227

has, nevertheless, remained very conservative by resting on the calorie teachings and quantitative abstractions. If it could comprehend itself and rise beyond, then its great hour would come. When H. Schipperges cites Goethe's words, "He who cannot rise to the thought that spirit and matter, soul and body, thought and perception, will and movement are the necessary double ingredients of the universe, should long ago have given up thinking," this points to the unmistakable demand that we must break away from the old forms of thought and develop a new thinking which corresponds to reality.[3]

So this book is directed to all physicians, teachers, social workers, and scientists, as well as to the so-called lay population, the parents of our children, the food producers, the consumers, who are destined to work on this problem. Today all should participate in taking health care into their hands with understanding. Rudolf Steiner has offered a new hygienic impulse, for which he called on the physician as continual teacher and helper. To this "living social interaction between the physician and the rest of humanity," this book attempts to make a contribution.

WORKS CITED

INTRODUCTION:

[1] Rudolf Steiner, Lecture, Berlin, 28 February 1911.
[2] Rudolf Steiner, *Agricultural Course*, 1924.
[3] Friedrich Boas, Dynamische Botanik, 3rd ed., München, 1949.
[4] Rudolf Steiner, *Agricultural Course*, 1924.
[5] See also Rudolf Hauschka, *Ernährungslehre*, Frankfurt, 1951; W. Chr. Simonis, *Die Ernährung des Menschen*, Stuttgart, 1960; Werner Loeckle, *Bewusste Ernährung und gesunde Lebensfuhrüng*, Freiburg i. Br., 1970.

CHAPTER 1:

[1] H. Schipperges, "Anthropologien in der Geschichte der Medizin," in *Biologische Anthropologie*, Part II, Stuttgart, 1972.
[2] W. Doerr, "Anthropologie des Krankhaften aus der Sicht des Pathologen," Stuttgart, 1972.
[3] Richard H. Shrylock, *Die Entwicklung der modernen Medizin*, Stuttgart, 1947.
[4] Rudolf Steiner, Lecture, Dornach, 14 October 1917.
[5] Gerhard Schmidt, *Das geistige Vermächtnis von Gustav v. Bunge*, Zürich, 1973.
[6] A. Gigon, *Gedanken zur Ernährung des Menschen*, Basel, 1964.
[7] W. Heitler, "Gilt die Gleichung: Leben = Physik + Chemie?" *Chimia*, 21 (1967) 176.
[8] Rudolf Steiner, *Der Entstehungsmoment der Naturwissenschaft in der Weltgeschichte*, Nine Lectures, Dornach.
[9] Rudolf Steiner, *Occult Science, an Outline*, 1909.
[10] H. Schipperges, "Anthropologien in der Geschichte der Medizin," in *Biologische Anthropologie*, Part II, Stuttgart, 1972.
[11] Rudolf Steiner and Ita Wegmann, *Fundamentals of Therapy*, Dornach, 1925.
[12] Rudolf Steiner, *Geisteswissenschaftliche Gesichtspunkte zur Therapie*, Dornach, 1921.
[13] *Ibid.*

[14]W. Doerr, "Anthropologie des Krankhaften aus der Sicht des Pathologen," Stuttgart, 1972.

[15]Jean Hamburger, *Macht und Ohnmacht der Medizin,* München, 1973.

[16]H. Schaefer and B. Novak, "Anthropologie und Biophysik," in *Biologische Anthropologie,* Part I, Stuttgart, 1972.

[17]Rudolf Steiner, "Ernährungsfragen im Lichte der Geisteswissenschaft," Lecture, Berlin, 17 December 1908.

[18]Rudolf Steiner, *Theosophie,* Dornach, 1924.

[19]Rudolf Steiner, Lecture, Oslo, 29 November 1921.

[20]Rudolf Steiner, "Ernährungsfragen im Lichte der Geisteswissenschaft," Lecture. Berlin, 17 December 1908.

[21]Rudolf Steiner and Ita Wegmann, *Fundamentals of Therapy,* Dornach, 1925.

[22]*Ibid.*

CHAPTER 2:

[1]Magnus Pyke, *Brot für vier Milliarden,* München, 1970.

[2]Konrad Lang and Rudolf Schoen, *Die Ernährung,* Berlin, 1952.

[3]A. Gigon, "Rektoratsrede," Lecture, Basel, 1951.

[4]Gerhard Schmidt, *Das geistige Vermächtnis von Gustav V. Bunge,* Zürich, 1973.

[5]Rudolf Steiner, *Die Philosophie der Freiheit,* Berlin, 1921.

[6]*Ibid.*

[7]Roger J. Williams, in *Der Wendepunkt,* Zürich, 1967.

[8]Rudolf Steiner and Ita Wegmann, *Fundamentals of Therapy,* Dornach, 1925.

[9]Rudolf Steiner, Lecture, Dornach, 14 May 1920, in *Entsprechungen zwischen Mikrokosmos und Makrokosmos.*

[10]Rudolf Steiner, Lecture, Oslo, 29 November 1921.

[11]J. v. Liebig, *Chemische Briefe,* 1858.

[12]Rudolf Steiner, Lecture, Dornach, 23 October 1922.

[13]Gerhard Schmidt, "Zur Problematik der menschlichen Ernährung," in *Anthroposophie und Medizin,* Dornach, 1963.

CHAPTER 3:

[1]Rudolf Steiner, *Geisteswissenschaft und Medizin,* Twenty Lectures, Dornach, 1920.

[2]Rudolf Steiner, Lecture, Dornach, 22 October 1922.

[3]Rudolf Steiner, *Agricultural Course,* 1924.

[4]Rudolf Steiner and Ita Wegmann, *Fundamentals of Therapy,* Dornach, 1925.

[5]*Ibid.*

[6] Rudolf Steiner, *Geisteswissenschaft und Medizin*, Twenty Lectures, Dornach, 1920.

[7] Rudolf Steiner and Ita Wegmann, *Fundamentals of Therapy*, Dornach, 1925.

[8] Rudolf Steiner, *Geisteswissenschaft und Medizin*, Twenty Lectures, Dornach, 1920.

[9] Rudolf Steiner, Lecture, Dornach, 22 October 1922.

[10] Rudolf Steiner, Lecture, Stuttgart, 27 October 1922.

[11] H. Schäfer, *Die Medizin heute*, München, 1963.

[12] Rudolf Steiner and Ita Wegmann, *Fundamentals of Therapy*, Dornach, 1925.

[13] Landois-Rosemann, *Physiologie des Menschen*, München-Berlin, 1950.

[14] *Ibid.*

[15] Rudolf Steiner, Lecture, Dornach, 22 October 1922.

[16] Rudolf Steiner and Ita Wegmann, *Fundamentals of Therapy*, Dornach, 1925.

[17] J. Bohlmann, *Was sagt die Wissenschaft zu unserer täglichen Ernährung?*, Giessen, 1954.

[18] Rudolf Steiner and Ita Wegmann, *Fundamentals of Therapy*, Dornach, 1925.

[19] Rudolf Steiner, *Eine okkulte Physiologie*, Lecture-cycle, Prag, 1911.

[20] *Ibid.*

[21] Rudolf Steiner, *Von Seelenrätseln*, Berlin, 1917.

[22] A. Sollberger, "Biologische Rhythmusforschung," in *Neue Anthropologie*, Vol I, Part I, Stuttgart, 1972.

[23] *Ibid.*

[24] Guenther Wachsmuth, *Erde und Mensch. Ihre Bildekräfte, Rhythmen und Lebenskräfte*, Kreuzlingen, 1952.

[25] Erik Forsgren, *Ueber die Rhythmik der Leberfunktion*, Stockholm, 1935.

[26] W. Menzel, *Menschliche Tag-Nacht-Rhythmik und Schichtarbeit*, Basel, 1962.

[27] A. Sollberger, "Biologische Rhythmusforschung," in *Neue Anthropologie*, Vol. I, Part I, Stuttgart, 1972.

[28] Erik Forsgren, *Ueber die Rhythmik der Leberfunktion*, Stockholm, 1935.

[29] Rudolf Steiner, Lecture, Berlin, 9 December 1909.

[30] W. Menzel, *Menschliche Tag-Nacht-Rhythmik und Schichtarbeit*, Basel, 1962.

[31] Rudolf Steiner, *Heileurhythmischer Kurs*, Dornach, 1921.

[32] Guenther Wachsmuth, *Erde und Mensch*, Kreuzlingen, 1952.

[33] Erik Forsgren, *Ueber die Rhythmik der Leberfunktion*, Stockholm, 1935.

[34] Rudolf Steiner, Lecture, Stuttgart, 27 October 1922.

[35] *Ibid.*

[36] *Ibid.*

[37] *Ibid.*

[38] Rudolf Steiner, *Eine okkulte Physiologie*, Lecture-cycle, Prag, 1911.

[39] *Ibid.*

[40] Rudolf Steiner, Lecture, Stuttgart, 27 October 1922.

[41] Rudolf Steiner, Lecture, Dornach, 22 October 1922.

[42] Rudolf Steiner and Ita Wegmann, *Fundamentals of Therapy*, Chapter 11, Dornach, 1925.

[43] H. Schaefer and B. Novak, "Anthropologie und Biophysik," in *Biologische Anthropologie*, Part I, Stuttgart, 1972.

[44] Rudolf Steiner, "Ernährungsfragen im Lichte der Geisteswissenschaft," Berlin, 17 December 1908.

[45] Rudolf Steiner, Lecture, Stuttgart, 27 October 1922.

[46] L. Ludwig, *Fett und Ernährung*, Hamburg, 1968.

[47] Rudolf Steiner and Ita Wegmann, *Fundamentals of Therapy*, Dornach, 1925.

[48] *Ibid.*

[49] Rudolf Steiner, *Geisteswissenschaft und Medizin*, Dornach, 1920.

[50] Rudolf Steiner, "Weihnachtskurs," in *Meditative Betrachtungen und Anleitungen zur Vertiefung der Heilkunst*, Dornach, 1967.

[51] Rudolf Steiner, Lecture, Stuttgart, 27 October 1922.

[52] Rudolf Steiner, "Die Brücke zwischen der Weltgeistigkeit und dem Physischen des Menschen," Lectures, Dornach, 17, 18, 19 December 1920.

[53] *Ibid.*

[54] Rudolf Steiner and Ita Wegmann, *Fundamentals of Therapy*, Dornach, 1925.

[55] B. Thomas, *Die Nähr-und Ballaststoffe der Getreidemehle in ihrer Bedeutung für die Brotnahrung*, Stuttgart, 1964.

[56] Rudolf Steiner, Lecture, Dornach, 31 July 1924.

[57] Rudolf Steiner, *Geisteswissenschaft und Medizin*, Dornach, 1920.

[58] Rudolf Steiner, Lecture, Stuttgart, 27 October 1922.

[59] Rudolf Steiner, *Geisteswissenschaft und Medizin*, Dornach, 1920.

[60] *Ibid.*

[61] *Ibid.*

[62] T. Baumgärtel, *Klinische Darmbakteriologie*, Stuttgart, 1954.

[63] Escherich, in *Klinische Darmbakteriologie*, Stuttgart, 1954.

[64] T. Baumgärtel, *Klinische Darmbakteriologie*, Stuttgart, 1954.

[65] Rudolf Steiner, *Geisteswissenschaft und Medizin*, Dornach, 1920.

[66] Rudolf Steiner, Lecture, Dornach, 23 January 1924.

[67] Ibid.

[68] Rudolf Steiner and Ita Wegmann, *Fundamentals of Therapy*, Dornach, 1925.

[69] Ludwig Büchner, *Kraft und Stoff*, Darmstadt, 1855.

[70] Hermann Mohler, *Sinn und Unsinn unserer Ernährung*, Aarau und Frankfurt/M, 1972.

[71] E. Fischbach, *Grundriss der Physiologie und physiologischen Chemie*, München, 1940.

[72] Hermann Mohler, *Sinn und Unsinn unserer Ernährung*, Aarau und Frankfurt/M, 1972.

[73] Gerhard Schmidt, *Das geistige Vermächtnis von Gustav v. Bunge*, Zürich, 1973.

[74] Hermann Mohler, *Sinn und Unsinn unserer Ernährung*, Aarau und Frankfurt/M, 1972.

[75] H. Glatzel, *Die Ernährung in der technischen Welt*, Stuttgart, 1970.

[76] Rudolf Steiner, "Ernährungsfragen im Lichte der Geisteswissenschaft," Berlin, 17 December 1908.

[77] A. Gigon, *Gedanken zur Ernährung des Menschen*, Basel, 1964.

[78] Steiner and Wegmann, *Fundamentals of Therapy*, Dornach, 1925.

[79] *Ibid.*

[80] Rudolf Steiner, "Ernährungsfragen im Lichte der Geisteswissenschaft," Berlin, 17 December 1908.

[81] Rudolf Steiner, Lecture, Dornach, 22 October 1922.

[82] Rudolf Steiner, Lecture, Oslo, 29 November 1921.

[83] Rudolf Steiner, *Geisteswissenschaft und Medizin*, Dornach, 1920.

[84] Steiner and Wegmann, *Fundamentals of Therapy*, Dornach, 1925.

[85] Rudolf Steiner, *Occult Science, an Outline*, 1908.

[86] Rudolf Steiner, *Der Entstehungsmoment der Naturwissenschaft in der Weltgeschichte*, Nine Lectures, Dornach.

[87] Rudolf Steiner, Lecture to Workers, Dornach, 23 February 1924.

[88] A. F. Marfeld, *Kybernetik des Gehirns*, Berlin, 1970.

[89] Rudolf Steiner, *Geisteswissenschaft und Medizin*, Dornach, 1920.

[90] A. F. Marfeld, *Kybernetik des Gehirns*, Berlin, 1970.

[91] A. Gigon, *Gedanken zur Ernährung des Menschen*, Basel, 1964.

[92] Rudolf Steiner, *Agricultural Course*, 1924.

[93] Rudolf Steiner, *Heilpädagogischer Kurs*, Lecture, 30 June 1924, Dornach.

[94] Rudolf Steiner, *Initiationserkenntnis*, Lecture-cycle, Penmaenmaur, 19–31 August 1923.

[95] Rudolf Steiner, Lecture, Dornach, 9 February 1924.

[96] F. L. Boschke, *Die Schöpfung ist noch nicht zu Ende*, Düsseldorf-Wien, 1962.

[97] Rudolf Steiner, Lecture, Dornach, 9 February 1924.

[98] Rudolf Steiner, Lecture, Dornach, 31 December 1923.

[99] Rudolf Steiner, Lecture to Workers, Dornach, 7 January 1924.

[100] Rudolf Steiner, *Initiationserkenntnis*, Lecture-cycle, Penmaenmawr, 19–31 August 1923.

[101] Rudolf Steiner, Lecture to Workers, Dornach, 24 September 1924.

[102] Magnus Pyke, *Brot für vier Milliarden*, München, 1970.

[103] Rudolf Steiner, *Heilpädagogischer Kurs*, Lecture, 30 June 1924, Dornach.

CHAPTER 4

[1] H. Rausch: Aufbau und Funktion des Geruchssinnes, in *Ernährungsumschau*, Frankfurt 7/1965.
[2] Rudolf Steiner, Lecture, Dornach, 13 December 1914.
[3] *Aroma-und Geschmacksstoffe in Lebensmitteln*, Zürich, 1967.
[4] *Ibid.*
[5] *Ibid.*
[6] Rudolf Steiner, *Light Course*, Stuttgart, 1919.
[7] Rudolf Steiner, Discussion, 21 August 1923.
[8] Rudolf Steiner, Lecture, Dornach, 14 October 1917.
[9] Rudolf Steiner, Lecture to Workers, Dornach, 8 August 1924.
[10] Rudolf Steiner, Lecture to Workers, Dornach, 16 December, 1922.
[11] Rudolf Steiner, Lecture to Workers, Dornach, 20 December 1922.
[12] Rudolf Steiner, Lecture, 14 December 1914.
[13] Rudolf Steiner, *Geisteswissenschaft und Medizin*, Dornach, 1920.
[14] *Ibid.*
[15] Rudolf Steiner, Lecture, 14 December 1914.
[16] Rudolf Steiner, Lecture, 22 July 1921.

CHAPTER 5

[1] Rudolf Steiner, *Heileurhythmischer Kurs*, Dornach, 1921.
[2] Rudolf Steiner, *Geisteswissenschaft und Medizin*, Dornach, 1920.
[3] Rudolf Steiner, *Heileurhythmischer Kurs*, Dornach, 1921.
[4] Rudolf Steiner, Lecture, Berlin, 9 December 1909.
[5] Guenther Wachsmuth, *Erde und Mensch. Ihre Bildekräfte, Rhythmen und Lebenskräfte*, Kreuzlingen, 1952.
[6] *Ibid.*
[7] Erik Forsgren, *Ueber die Rhythmik der Leberfunktion*, Stockholm, 1935.
[8] A. Sollberger, "Biologische Rhythmusforschung," in *Neue Anthropologie*, Vol. I, Part I, Stuttgart, 1972.
[9] Rudolf Steiner, *Geisteswissenschaftliche Menschenkunde*, Berlin, 1908/9.
[10] Guenther Wachsmuth, *Erde und Mensch*, Kreuzlingen, 1952.
[11] A. Sollberger, "Biologische Rhythmusforschung" in *Neue Anthropologie*, Vol. I, Part I, Stuttgart, 1972.
[12] Rudolf Steiner, *Geisteswissenschaftliche Menschenkunde*, Berlin, 1908/9.
[13] A. Sollberger, "Biologische Rhythmusforschung."
[14] Rudolf Steiner, "Die praktische Ausbildung des Denkens," Lecture, 18 January 1909, Karlsruhe.

CHAPTER 6

[1] Rudolf Steiner, *Wärmelehre*, Stuttgart, 1920.
[2] Rudolf Steiner, Lecture, Dornach, 23 January 1924.
[3] A. Gigon, *Gedanken zur Ernährung des Menschen*, Basel, 1964.
[4] Rudolf Steiner, *Der Mensch als Zusammenklang des schaffenden, bildenden und gestaltenden Weltenwortes*, Lecture-cycle, Dornach, 10 October - 11 November 1923.
[5] Rudolf Steiner, Lecture, Berlin, 26 March 1907.
[6] Rudolf Steiner, Lecture, Dornach, 22 February 1922.
[7] Rudolf Steiner, *Mysteriengestaltungen*, Lecture-cycle, Dornach, 1923.
[8] *Ibid.*
[9] Rudolf Steiner, *Eine okkulte Physiologie*, Lecture-cycle, Prag, 1911.
[10] H. Glatzel, *Verhaltensphysiologie der Ernährung*, Berlin, 1973.
[11] *Ibid.*
[12] Rudolf Steiner, Lecture to Workers, Dornach, 9 August 1922.
[13] Rudolf Steiner, *Wärmelehre*, Stuttgart, 1920.
[14] Rudolf Steiner, Lecture, 10 September 1923.
[15] H. Glatzel, *Die Ernährung in der technischen Welt*, Stuttgart, 1970.
[16] Rudolf Steiner, Lecture to Workers, Dornach, 25 June 1923.
[17] Rudolf Steiner, Lecture to Workers, Dornach, 27 September 1923.
[18] H. Glatzel, *Die Ernährung in der technischen Welt*, Stuttgart, 1970.

CHAPTER 7

[1] Ralph Bircher, *Bircher-Benner, Leben und Lebenswerk*, Zürich/Bad Homburg, v. d. H. 1959.
[2] Rudolf Steiner, *Agricultural Course*, 1924.
[3] Rudolf Steiner, *Occult Physiology*, Lecture-cycle, Prag, 1911.
[4] W. U. Guan, *Kleine Kulturgeschichte der Suppe*, Thayngen, 1957.
[5] J. A. Brillat-Savarin, *Physiologie des Geschmacks*, München, 1962.
[6] Hermann Mohler, *Sinn und Unsinn unserer Ernährung*, Aarau und Frankfurt/M 1972.
[7] A. Ljungquist, *Zur Qualität in der Ernährung*, Dornach, 1955.

CHAPTER 8

[1] Magnus Pyke, *Brot für vier Milliarden*, München, 1970.
[2] Rudolf Steiner, Lecture, Dornach, 13 December 1914.
[3] Rudolf Steiner, Lecture to Doctors, London, 29 August 1924.

[4]F. Lieben, *Geschichte der physiologischen Chemie*, Leipzig-Wien, 1935.

[5]L. Reinhardt, Letter to G. v. Bunge, 4 November 1901, Nachlass Bunge's, Fasc. 84, No. 127.

[6]Dr. John Ranke, *Der Mensch*, Vol. I, cited from a letter in Nachlass G. v. Bunge, Fasc. 86, No. 126.

[7]Gustav v. Bunge, *Physiologie des Menschen*, Vol. II, 1905.

[8]E. K. Dahl, "Der mögliche Einfluss der Salzzufuhr auf die Entwicklung der Hypertonie," in *Essentielle Hypertonie*, Berlin, 1960.

[9]Rudolf Steiner, *Geisteswissenschaft und Medizin*, Dornach, 1920.

[10]*Ibid.*

[11]*Ibid.*

[12]Rudolf Steiner, *Der Mensch als Zusammenklang des schaffenden, bildenden und gestaltenden Weltenwortes*, Lecture-cycle, Dornach, 10 October - 11 November, 1923.

[13]Andreas Hock, ed., *Vergleichende Ernährungslehre des Menschen und seiner Haustiere*, Stuttgart, 1966.

[14]Rudolf Steiner, *Geisteswissenschaft und Medizin*, Dornach, 1920.

[15]Rudolf Steiner, Lecture to Doctors, London, 2 September 1923.

[16]Rudolf Steiner, *Geisteswissenschaft und Medizin*.

[17]Rudolf Steiner, Lecture, Dornach, 22 March 1923.

[18]Rudolf Steiner, *Das Miterleben des Jahreslaufes in vier kosmischen Imaginationen*, Five Lectures, 12 October 1923.

CHAPTER 9

[1]Ralph Bircher, *Bircher-Benner, Leben und Lebenswerk*, Zürich/Bad Homburg v. d. H., 1959.

[2]Hermann Mohler, *Sinn und Unsinn unserer Ernährung*, Aarau and Frankfurt/M, 1972.

[3]Rudolf Steiner, *Geisteswissenschaftliche Gesichtspunkte zur Therapie*, Dornach, 1921.

[4]Rudolf Steiner, "Ernährungsfragen im Lichte der Geisteswissenschaft," Lecture, Berlin, 17 December 1908.

[5]Rudolf Steiner and Ita Wegmann, *Fundamentals of Therapy*, Dornach, 1925.

[6]Rudolf Steiner, "Ernährungsfragen im Lichte der Geisteswissenschaft," Lecture, Berlin, 17 December 1908.

[7]H. Glatzel, *Verhaltensphysiologie der Ernährung*, München-Berlin-Wien, 1973.

[8]B. Thomas, *Die Nähr-und Ballaststoffe der Getreidemehle in ihrer Bedeutung für die Brotnahrung*, Stuttgart, 1964.

[9]Rudolf Steiner, *Geisteswissenschaft und Medizin*, Dornach, 1920.

[10]Rudolf Steiner, Lecture to Workers, Dornach, 2 August 1924.

[11] Rudolf Steiner, Lecture to Workers, Dornach, 31 July 1924.

[12] H. Glatzel, *Die Ernährung in der technischen Welt*, Stuttgart, 1970.

[13] Ralph Bircher, in *Der Wendepunkt*, No. 9/1968, Zürich.

[14] H. Aebi, *Eiweiss: Ernährungsfaktor Nummer 1*, 1971, Bern.

[15] A. Fleisch, *Ernährungsprobleme in Mangelzeiten*, Basel-Stuttgart, 1947.

[16] S. Bommer, *Die Gabe der Demeter*, Krailling bei München, 1960.

[17] H. Glatzel, *Verhaltensphysiologie der Ernährung*, München-Berlin-Wien, 1973.

[18] J. G. Herder, *Ideen zur Philosophie der Geschichte der Menschheit*, 1784–1791, Berlin, 1914.

[19] Rudolf Steiner, "Ernährungsfragen im Lichte der Geisteswissenschaft," Berlin, 17 December 1908.

[20] Rudolf Steiner, *Welche Bedeutung hat die okkulte Entwicklung für die Hüllen des Menschen und sein Selbst?*, Lecture-cycle, The Hague, 20–29 March 1913.

[21] Rudolf Steiner, Lecture to Workers, Dornach, 2 August 1924.

[22] Hermann Mohler, *Sinn und Unsinn unserer Ernährung*, Aarau and Frankfurt/M, 1972.

[23] H. Glatzel, *Die Ernährung in der technischen Welt*, Stuttgart, 1970.

[24] A. Ilke' in *Die Praxis*, Bern, 1 January 1964.

[25] Rudolf Steiner, "Ernährungsfragen im Lichte der Geisteswissenschaft," München, 8 January 1909.

[26] Gerhard Schmidt, "Die Milch als Erdensubstanz" in *Beiträge zur Substanzforschung*, Vol. I, Dornach, 1952.

CHAPTER 10

[1] Ludwig Büchner, *Kraft und Stoff*, Darmstadt, 1885.

[2] P. Carlson, *Lehrbuch der Biochemie*, Stuttgart, 1961.

[3] E. A. Schmid, *Sinnvolle Ernährung-Gesundes Leben*, Zürich, 1953.

[4] Gustav v. Bunge, *Physiologie des Menschen*, Vol II, 1905.

[5] Rudolf Steiner, Lecture to Workers, Dornach, 8 January 1923.

[6] Rudolf Steiner, Summary of Lectures from 1904 to 1905.

[7] Rudolf Steiner, Lecture to Workers, Dornach, 22 September 1923.

[8] Rudolf Steiner and Ita Wegmann, *Fundamentals of Therapy*, Dornach, 1925.

[9] *Ibid.*

[10] *Ibid.*

[11] Rudolf Steiner, Lecture, Berlin, 22 October 1906.

[12] Rudolf Steiner, *Welche Bedeutung hat die okkulte Entwicklung für die Hüllen des Menschen und sein Selbst?*, Lecture-cycle, The Hague, 20–29 March 1913.

[13] N. Remer, "Die Möhre" In *Beiträge zu einer geisteswissenschaftlichen Ernährungshygiene*, No. 17, 1965, Dornach.

[14] Rudolf Steiner, Lecture to Workers, Dornach, 31 July 1924.

[15] *Ibid.*

[16] Rudolf Steiner and Ita Wegmann, *Fundamentals of Therapy*, Dornach, 1925.

[17] Rudolf Steiner, *Agricultural Course*, 1924.

[18] Ernst Schneider, *Nütze die Heilkraft unserer Nahrung*, Hamburg, 1962.

[19] *Ibid.*

[20] P. Gleese, *Wie arbeitet unser Gehirn?*, 1966.

[21] Rudolf Steiner, Lecture to Workers, Dornach, 18 July 1923.

[22] K. Herrmann, *Gemüse und Gemüsedauerwaren*, 1969.

[23] Rudolf Steiner, Lecture, Berlin, 22 October 1906.

[24] Rudolf Steiner, Lecture to Workers, Dornach, 18 July 1923.

[25] Rudolf Steiner, "Ernährungsfragen im Lichte der Geisteswissenschaft," Lecture, Berlin, 17 December 1908.

[26] Rudolf Steiner, Summary of Lectures from 1904–1905.

[27] Gerhard Schmidt, *Das geistige Vermächtnis von Gustav v. Bunge*, Zürich, 1973.

[28] Knud O. Möller, *Rauschgifte und Genussmittel*, Basel, 1951.

[29] Gerhard Schmidt, "Zur Alkoholfrage," in *Anthr.-med. Jahrbuch*, Vol. II, 1951.

[30] Knud O. Möller, *Rauschgifte und Genussmittel*, Basel, 1951.

[31] *Aroma-und Geschmacksstoffe in Lebensmitteln*, Zürich, 1967.

[32] Rudolf Steiner, Lecture, Berlin, 22 October 1906.

[33] Rudolf Steiner, *Geisteswissenschaft und Medizin*, Dornach, 1920.

[34] Rudolf Steiner, Lecture, Berlin, 22 October 1906.

[35] *Ibid.*

[36] Rudolf Steiner, Summary of Lectures from 1904 to 1905.

CHAPTER 11

[1] Max Rübner, *Die Gesetze des Energieverbrauches bei der Ernährung*, Leipzig, 1902.

[2] J. Moleschott, *Der Kreislauf des Lebens*, Giessen, 1887.

[3] Rudolf Steiner, *Mein Lebensgang*, Dornach, 1925.

[4] *Ibid.*

[5] *Ibid.*

[6] Konrad Lorenz, *Vom Weltbild des Verhaltensforschers*, München, 1968.

[7] *Ibid.*

[8] *Ibid.*

[9] *Ibid.*

[10] Adolf Portmann, *Neue Wege der Biologie*, München, 1960.

[11] Gazu Yazargil, in *Das Bild des Menschen*, Engadiner Kollegium, Zürich, 1971.
[12] Rudolf Steiner, *Allgemeine Menschenkunde als Grundlage der Pädagogik*, Lecture-cycle, Stuttgart, 1919.
[13] Rudolf Steiner, *Geisteswissenschaft und Medizin*, Dornach, 1920.
[14] Rudolf Steiner, *Die Erziehung des Kindes vom Gesichtspunkt der Geisteswissenschaft*, 1907.
[15] Gerhard Schmidt, *Das geistige Vermächtnis von Gustav v. Bunge*, Zürich, 1973.
[16] Rudolf Steiner, Lecture-cycle, "Anthroposophie—eine Einführung," Dornach, 1924, Lecture, 27 January 1924.
[17] Rudolf Steiner, *Mein Lebensgang*, Dornach, 1925.
[18] Rudolf Steiner, *Theosophie*, Dornach, 1924.
[19] *Ibid.*
[20] Rudolf Steiner, "Exkurse in das Gebiet des Markus-Evangeliums," Lecture-cycle, Berlin, 1910–11.
[21] Rudolf Steiner, Lecture, Dornach, 20 June 1924.
[22] R. Durrer, *Bruder Klaus*, Sarnen, 1917.
[23] Rudolf Steiner, *Geisteswissenschaft und Medizin*, Twenty Lectures, Dornach, 1920.
[24] *Ibid.*
[25] Rudolf Steiner, "Die Askese und die Krankheit," Lecture, Berlin, 11 November 1909.
[26] P. Carlson, *Lehrbuch der Biochemie*, Stuttgart, 1961.
[27] H. J. Teuteberg and G. Wiegelmann, *Der Wandel der Nahrungsgewohnheiten unter dem Einfluss der Individualisierung*, 1972.
[28] J. A. Brillat-Savarin, *Physiologie des Geschmacks*, München, 1962.
[29] H. Glatzel, *Verhaltensphysiologie der Ernährung*, München-Berlin-Wien, 1978.
[30] Rudolf Steiner, *Geisteswissenschaftliche Gesichtspunkte zur Therapie*, Dornach, 1921.
[31] Rudolf Steiner, *Geisteswissenschaft und Medizin*, Dornach, 1920.
[32] Rudolf Steiner, *Geisteswissenschaftliche Geischtspunkte zur Therapie*, Dornach, 1921.
[33] H. Schäfer, *Die Medizin heute*, München, 1963.
[34] Rudolf Steiner, *Eine Okkulte Physiologie*, Lecture-cycle, Prag, 1911.
[35] Rudolf Steiner, Lecture, Dornach, 1923.
[36] Rudolf Steiner, *Der Mensch als Zusammenklang des schaffenden, bildenden und gestaltenden Weltenwortes*, Lecture-cycle, Dornach, 10 October-11 November 1923.
[37] Rudolf Steiner, *Die Brücke zwischen der Weltgeistigkeit und dem Physischen des Menschen*, Three Lectures, Dornach, 17, 18, 19 December 1920.

[38] *Ibid.*

[39] R. Bircher, "Wo steht die Eiweissfrage heute?" in *Der Wendepunkt*, Zürich, No. 7, 1974.

[40] Rudolf Steiner, Lecture, Dornach, 27 December 1923.

[41] R. Bilz, "Gemeinschaftsverpflegung und Nahrungswahl in physiologischer Sicht," in *Vollwertige Ernährung und Gemeinschaftsverpflegung*, Symposium, Basel, 1961.

[42] Gazu Yazargil, in *Das Bild des Menschen*, Engadiner Kollegium, Zürich, 1971.

[43] Rudolf Steiner, Lecture, Berlin, 9 December 1909.

CHAPTER 12

[1] J. A. Brillat-Savarin, *Physiologie des Geschmacks*, München, 1962.

[2] Rudolf Steiner, Lecture, 4 November 1905.

[3] Rudolf Steiner, *Welche Bedeutung hat die okkulte Entwicklung für die Hullen des Menschen und sein Selbst?*, Lecture-cycle, The Hague, 20–29 March 1913.

[4] Rudolf Steiner, Lecture, Dornach, 6 January 1922.

[5] G. Schmidt and U. Renzenbrink, *Das Getreide als menschengemässe Nahrung*, Vol. I, Dornach, 1967.

[6] Albert Steffen, *Das Todeserlebnis des Manes*, Drama, Dornach, 1934.

[7] S. Bommer, *Die Gabe der Demeter*, Krailling bei München, 1960.

[8] Rudolf Steiner, Lecture-cycle, The Hague, 20-29 March 1913.

[9] Friedrich Häusler, *Die Geburt der Eidgenossenschaft aus der geistigen Urschweiz*, Bern, 1972.

[10] Knud O. Möller, *Rauschgifte und Genussmittel*, Basel, 1951.

[11] Rudolf Steiner, Summary of Lectures from 1904 to 1905.

[12] Rudolf Steiner, Lecture to Workers, Dornach, 22 September 1923.

[13] Ibid.

[14] Magnus Pyke, *Brot für vier Milliarden*, München, 1970.

[15] R. Bilz, "Gemeinschaftsverpflegung und Nahrungswahl in physiologischer Sicht," in *Vollwertige Ernährung und Gemeinschaftsverpflegung*, Symposium, Basel, 1961.

[16] Rudolf Steiner, *Geisteswissenschaft und Medizin*, Dornach, 1920.

[17] S. Bommer, *Die Gabe der Demeter*, Krailling bei München, 1960.

[18] Rudolf Steiner, Lecture, Dornach, 4 January 1915.

CHAPTER 13

[1] Rudolf Steiner, *Westliche und östliche Weltgegensätzlichkeit*, Lecture-cycle, Wien, 1–12 June 1922.

[2] Rudolf Steiner, Lecture, Stuttgart, 21 May 1921.

[3] Friedrich Bäusler, *Weltenwille und Menschenziele in der Geschichte*, Dornach, 1961.
[4] Jean Hamburger, *Macht und Ohnmacht der Medizin*, München, 1973.
[5] Sniveley and Sweeney, *Elektrolyt-und Wasserhaushalt*, München-Berlin, 1958.
[6] Rudolf Steiner, *Welt, Erde, Mensch*, Lecture-cycle, 4–13 August 1908, Stuttgart.
[7] Rudolf Steiner, *Heilpädagogischer Kurs*, Lecture, Dornach, 30 June 1924.
[8] Rudolf Steiner, *Mysteriengestaltungen*, Lecture-cycle, Dornach, 1923.
[9] Rudolf Steiner, Lecture, Berlin, 4 November 1905.
[10] Ibid.
[11] Rudolf Steiner, *Heilpädagogischer Kurs*, Lecture, Dornach, 30 June 1924.
[12] S. Bommer, *Die Gabe der Demeter*, Krailling bei München, 1960.
[13] Rudolf Steiner, *Welt, Erde, Mensch*, Lecture-cycle, 4–13 August 1908, Stuttgart.
[14] Rudolf Steiner, *Aus der Akasha-Chronik*, 1904.
[15] Ignatus Donelly, *Atlantis, die vorsintflutliche Welt*, Esslinger, 1911.
[16] J. J. Bachofen, *Mutterrecht und Urreligion*, Leipzig, 1926.
[17] Ernst Uehli, *Mythos und Kunst der Griechen*, Dornach, 1958.
[18] Rudolf Steiner, *Unsere atlantischen Vorfahren*, 1904.
[19] Ignatus Donelly, *Atlantis*, Esslingen, 1911.
[20] Walter Adrian, *So wurde Brot aus Halm und Glut*, Bielefeld, 1951.
[21] Rudolf Steiner, *Unsere atlantischen Vorfahren*, 1904.
[22] Eduard Schuré, *Das heilige Drama von Eleusis*, put into free rhythm by Rudolf Steiner, Dornach, 1929.
[23] Otto Neermacher, *Auf Geistespfaden Griechenlands*, Basel, 1966.
[24] Ibid.
[25] Emil Werth, *Grabstock, Hacke, und Pflug*, Ludwigsburg, 1954.
[26] J. J. Bachofen, *Mutterrecht und Urreligion*, Leipzig, 1926.
[27] Rudolf Steiner, *Weltenwunder, Seelenprüfungen, Geistesoffenbarungen*, Lecture-cycle, München, August, 1911.
[28] J. J. Bachofen, *Mutterrecht und Urreligion*, Leipzig, 1926.
[29] Rudolf Steiner, *Ueber das Wesen der Bienen*, Lecture-cycle, Dornach, 1923.
[30] F. Schwanitz, *Die Evolution der Kulturpflanzen*, München-Basel-Wien, 1967.
[31] Emil Werth, *Grabstock, Hacke, und Pflug*, Ludwigsburg, 1954.
[32] Basil Davidson, *Afrika-Stämme, Staaten, Königreiche*, 1972.
[33] Rudolf Steiner, *Die Naturwissenschaft und die weltgeschichtliche Entwicklung der Menschheit seit dem Altertum*, Lecture-cycle, May 1921.
[34] F. Schwanitz, *Die Evolution der Kulturpflanzen*, München-Basel-Wien, 1967.
[35] Rudolf Steiner, Lecture, Berlin, 4 November 1905.
[36] Rudolf Steiner, *Geheimwissenschaft im Umriss*, 1909.

[37] Chr. Hufeland, *Die Kunst, das menschliche Leben zu verlängern*, 1800.
[38] Gerhard Schmidt, *Das geistige Vermächtnis von Gustav v. Bunge*, Zürich, 1973.
[39] H. E. Jacob, *Sechstausend Jahre Brot*, Hamburg, 1954.
[40] Rudolf Steiner, *Das Johannes-Evangelium*, Lecture-cycle, Hamburg, May 1908.
[41] *Ibid.*
[42] Rudolf Steiner, Lecture, Berlin, 22 October 1906.
[43] Rudolf Steiner, Lecture, Dornach, 30 September 1919.
[44] Rudolf Steiner, Lecture to Workers, Dornach, 19 January 1924.

CHAPTER 14

[1] E. Z. Dijksterhuis, *Die Mechanisierung des Weltbildes*, Berlin, 1956.
[2] Hermann Mohler, *Sinn und Unsinn unserer Ernährung*, Aarau und Frankfurt/M, 1972.
[3] H. Glatzel, *Die Ernährung in der technischen Welt*, Stuttgart, 1970.
[4] H. J. Teuteberg and G. Wiegelmann, *Der Wandel der Nahrungsgewohnheiten unter dem Einfluss der Individualisierung*, 1972.
[5] Rudolf Steiner, *Der Entstehungsmoment der Naturwissenschaft in der Weltgeschichte*, Nine Lectures, Dornach.
[6] Lichtenfels, *Die Geschichte der Ernährung*, Berlin, 1913.
[7] Rudolf Steiner, *Der Entstehungsmoment der Naturwissenschaft in der Weltgeschichte*, Nine Lectures, Dornach.
[8] H. Aebi, "Veränderte Umwelt: Gewinn und Verlust für unsere Ernährung," in *Ernährungsumschau*, Frankfurt/M, 12/1973.
[9] R. Heiss and K. Eichner, "Ernährung und Umwelt in kosmologischer Sicht," in *Ernährungsumschau*, Frankfurt/M, 2/1974.
[10] *Ibid.*
[11] H. Teuteberg, "Die Einwirkung sozialer und kultureller Faktoren," in *Ernährungsumschau*, Frankfurt/M, 2/1974.
[12] Rudolf Steiner, *Westliche und östliche Welgegensätzlichkeit*, Lecture-cycle, Wien, 1–12 June 1922.
[13] Rudolf Steiner, Lecture, Koberwitz, 20 June 1924.
[14] G. C. Arneil, in *Express*, 10 February 1974.
[15] Gerhard H. Schwabe, *Hochzivilisation in ökologischer Sicht*, 1958.
[16] Rudolf Steiner, Lecture, Berlin, 28 February 1911.
[17] *Ibid.*
[18] Ehrenfried Pfeiffer, "Rudolf Steiners Landwirtschaftlicher Impuls," in *Wir erlebten Rudolf Steiner*, Stuttgart, 1957.

[19]Rudolf Steiner, "Die Brücke zwischen der Weltgeistigkeit und dem Physischen des Menschen," Three Lectures, Dornach, 17, 18, 19 December 1920.

[20]H. Mohler, in *Deutsche Bauernzeitung*, 29 September 1966.

CONCLUSION:

[1]"Die Grenzen des Wachstums," Report of the Club of Rome, Hamburg, 1973.

[2]P. Vogler, "Disziplinärer Methodenkontext und Menschenbild," in *Biologische Anthropologie*, Stuttgart, 1972.

[3]H. Schipperges, "Anthropologien in der Geschichte der Medizin," in *Biologische Anthropologie*, Part II, Stuttgart, 1972.